ROYAL COMMISSION ON ENVIRONMENTAL POLLUTION

CHAIRMAN: SIR TOM BLUNDELL FRS, FMedSci

Twenty-fourth Report

CHEMICALS IN PRODUCTS

SAFEGUARDING THE ENVIRONMENT AND HUMAN HEALTH

Presented to Parliament by Command of Her Majesty
June 2003

Cm 5827   £27.20

Information about the current work of the Royal Commission can be obtained from its website at http://www.rcep.org.uk
or from the Secretariat at Third Floor, 5-8 The Sanctuary, Westminster, London SW1P 3JS

ROYAL COMMISSION ON ENVIRONMENTAL POLLUTION

TWENTY-FOURTH REPORT

To the Queen's Most Excellent Majesty

MAY IT PLEASE YOUR MAJESTY

We, the undersigned Commissioners, having been appointed 'to advise on matters, both national and international, concerning the pollution of the environment; on the adequacy of research in this field; and the future possibilities of danger to the environment';

And to enquire into any such matters referred to us by one of Your Majesty's Secretaries of State or by one of Your Majesty's Ministers, or any other such matters on which we ourselves shall deem it expedient to advise:

HUMBLY SUBMIT TO YOUR MAJESTY THE FOLLOWING REPORT.

'Science is fragmentary, incomplete; it progresses slowly and is never finished; life cannot wait'.

Émile Durkheim, *The Elementary Forms of Religious Life*, 1912

'...it seems to me that if you wait until all the frogs and toads have croaked their last to take some action, you've missed the point...'

One Frog Can Make a Difference – Kermit's Guide to Life in the 90's,
R.P. Riger, Jim Henson Productions Inc. 1993

CONTENTS

Chapter 3

NATIONAL AND INTERNATIONAL APPROACHES TO CHEMICALS REGULATION AND RISK MANAGEMENT

Chapter 4

INFORMING DECISIONS: A BETTER APPROACH TO CHEMICALS MANAGEMENT 99

CHAPTER 5

TOWARDS ENVIRONMENTALLY SUSTAINABLE PRODUCTS   **129**

FIGURES

INFORMATION BOXES

TABLES

Chapter 1

INTRODUCTION

Whereas the regulatory regime for emissions from chemical processes is well established, a coherent approach to regulation of chemical products is needed. What are the objectives and problems facing a new regulatory system?

CAUSE FOR CONCERN

1.1 In recent decades the impact of synthetic chemicals[1] on the environment and human health have been the cause of serious concern. The contribution of the chemicals industry to improvements in life expectancy, human health and living standards for most people in Western-style civilisations is widely acknowledged. Even so, this concern persists.

1.2 There are arguments to the contrary. There is the view that since synthetic chemicals have been in use, and have been present in the environment for many decades, any causes for concern must already have become apparent. But problems with chemicals continue to arise unexpectedly. In our Second Report, *Three Issues in Industrial Pollution*, published in 1972, we discussed the problems produced by the insecticide DDT and by polychlorinated biphenyls (PCBs), and pointed to the need for an early warning system for new substances. The problems with these chemicals and other more recent examples of unexpected adverse effects are summarised in box 1A. In this report we explain why we believe that these are not isolated incidents. Our failure to understand the interactions between synthetic chemicals and the natural environment, and most of all our failure to compile even the most basic information about the behaviour of chemicals in the environment, is a serious matter.

1.3 Societal unease about synthetic chemicals can be attributed to several factors. Accidents at chemical plants, such as those at Flixborough in the UK in 1974, Seveso in Italy in 1976, Bhopal in India in 1984, and Toulouse in France in 2001, all attracted media attention but do not seem to be the main cause of disquiet.[2] Incidents of environmental damage caused by discharges to watercourses and the atmosphere, and by inappropriate management of chemical waste have more impact on public opinion. There is a growing awareness of the environmental effects of synthetic chemicals, and the discovery – as the technological ability to measure trace amounts of chemicals has improved – that synthetic chemicals are widespread in the biosphere, including human tissues. Increasing recognition of actual and potential impacts of chemicals in the environment has damaged the industry's reputation[3] at the same time as public faith in science and safety legislation has declined generally.

1.4 These factors have reinforced each other and contributed to heightened concern about chemicals and doubts about the capacity of regulatory systems to anticipate and prevent unacceptable environmental impacts. Questions continue to arise about the tens of thousands of chemicals presently in use, whether they are regulated adequately, and the extent to which serious effects on the environment may be going unrecognised. As a result

1

of extensive work in academia, public research institutes and industry, much has been learnt about the fate and behaviour of chemicals in the environment and about chemical toxicity. This has undoubtedly led to improved practices and prevented many potentially damaging products reaching the market. However, we are still far from understanding the potential long-term and subtle harm from the burden of chemicals entering the environment. Many synthetic chemicals have not been tested for even the most basic indications of environmental hazard. Current monitoring for effects in the environment is inadequate. When effects are observed, it is difficult to establish statistically significant causal links with particular chemicals and specific organisms; there are problems, for example, in isolating possible impacts on populations of organisms from other factors such as habitat decline.

BOX 1A   UNANTICIPATED EFFECTS OF CHEMICALS IN THE ENVIRONMENT

The impact of the organochlorine pesticide DDT on songbirds was first noted in the 1950s[4] and widely publicised by Rachel Carson.[5] Further studies revealed widespread effects on birds, particularly in raptors.[6] Other organochlorine pesticides have also been linked to declines in populations of mammals as a result of sub-lethal effects.[7]

The presence of PCBs was reported in fish and white-tailed sea eagles in Sweden in 1969. Subsequent investigations into their long-term effects and distribution in the environment revealed widespread adverse effects[8].

In 1974 Rowland and Molina[9] published their hypothesis that chlorofluorocarbons (CFCs) could destroy ozone in the stratosphere. In 1985 the British Antarctic Survey reported the discovery of the ozone hole over Antarctica at altitudes of between 7 and 18 miles.[10]

The widespread contamination of human tissues with trace amounts of organic fluorine compounds derived from commercial products was suggested in 1976.[11] Perfluorooctanyl sulphonate (PFOS), used in a wide variety of consumer goods, is now found in significant amounts in birds, fish and marine mammals across the world.[12]

Tributyltin (TBT), used in marine anti-fouling paints, has been found to have endocrine-disrupting effects on non-target organisms, causing imposex (the development of male sexual structures in females) in organisms such as the dog whelk (*Nucella lapillus*).[13]

Polybrominated diphenyl ethers (PBDEs) are a family of structurally-related chemicals used as flame retardants. They have been used widely to safeguard against domestic fires. However, they have a high potential for uptake and accumulation by organisms and are now widely dispersed in the environment.[14] These compounds have been found in human breast milk[15] as well as in the tissues of several animal species.[16]

1.5   Chemicals are the basic units of the Earth and all living organisms. Even so, they have the capability to disrupt the processes of life or the physical environment. Most successful organisms, including humans, have developed sophisticated mechanisms for degrading or eliminating harmful substances.[17] But these mechanisms, which have evolved over millions of years, cannot be assumed to be successful in coping with the synthetic chemicals that have only been introduced into the environment over the last hundred years or so. Similarly, the chemistries of the atmosphere and of the oceans are resilient but not to the extent that they can continue to absorb this relatively sudden influx of huge amounts of chemicals resulting from human activities without impact.

1.6   Direct effects through interference with the regulatory systems of living organisms, or indirect effects through physical processes such as ozone depletion, may not manifest themselves for many years. In such cases, the adverse consequences of exposure to synthetic chemicals could become increasingly important as people live longer, as our knowledge of the functioning of ecosystems increases, and as improvements in technology increase our awareness of degradation of the physical environment. It remains possible that some chemicals entering the environment will have serious long-term effects – effects that are not being tested for, indeed effects for which tests have not yet been developed. Regulators may not be asking the right questions about the impacts of chemicals on the physical and biological environment, or on human health.

1.7   In this report we address these concerns and propose a new way forward. We cannot fully resolve the uncertainties in our understanding of the fate and effects of chemicals in the environment, but we can envisage a swifter and more comprehensive system of regulating chemicals and keeping track of them, better practices leading to the replacement of hazardous chemicals and chemical processes with less hazardous ones, and a broader debate of the assessment process and its outcomes. We concentrate on the environmental regulation and legislation dealing with synthetic chemicals reaching the market (figure 1-I). We do not consider the manufacture of chemicals, the control of processes and production risks, or emissions from process plant, although the monitoring regimes we propose, primarily to give warnings of the effects of dispersed emissions of chemical products, should also inform the regulation of chemical processes and provide links between regulatory regimes.

THE IMPORTANCE OF CHEMICALS

1.8   Chemicals are widely acknowledged to be important to health and modern lifestyles. For example, pharmaceuticals, disinfectants and food preservatives directly affect human well-being; surface coatings such as paints and varnishes allow our living spaces to be more attractive and hygienic; veterinary medicines and crop protection chemicals play a significant role in food production. A myriad chemicals are also used in the manufacture and maintenance of the items used to provide a high material standard of living – these include plastics, fuels, lubricants, textiles, dyestuffs, flame retardants, detergents, wood preservatives, photographic chemicals, phosphors on television and computer monitor screens, and the chemicals in ink. In our Second Report we argued that placing too high a burden of proof of safety on manufacturers would 'be against the public interest, for it would deprive people of some of the benefits of technology and might even cripple some industries which are very useful and desirable for society' (paragraph 13). Given the slow rate of progress towards a better understanding of chemicals safety over the last 30 years, we are less inclined to that view now, but we are nevertheless alert to the need for a proportionate response to the problems posed by chemicals.

Figure 1-I

Sources of chemicals in the environment

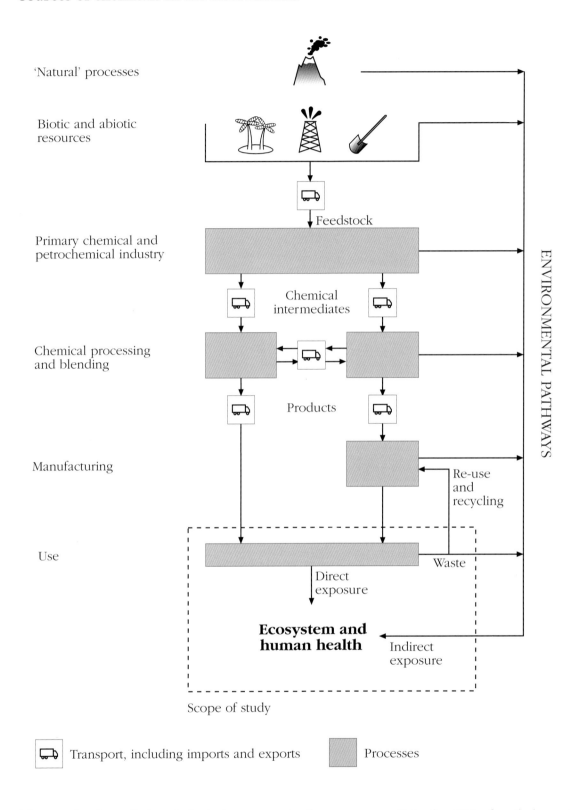

'Natural' processes

Biotic and abiotic resources

Feedstock

Primary chemical and petrochemical industry

Chemical intermediates

Chemical processing and blending

Products

Manufacturing

Re-use and recycling

Use

Waste

Direct exposure

Ecosystem and human health

Indirect exposure

Scope of study

ENVIRONMENTAL PATHWAYS

Transport, including imports and exports   Processes

1.9   The production of chemicals is important to the economy. It is the UK's fourth largest manufacturing sector, representing 7% of the added value in manufacturing and contributing £2.4 billion to the balance of trade (excluding pharmaceuticals). Over £26 billion of chemicals products are manufactured in the UK each year.[18]

1.10 The industry is also important globally. World chemicals industry production exceeds US$1.7 trillion annually, and almost 30% of this production is traded internationally. The UK is a significant player but not among the largest in terms of sales; it contributes about 12% of EU sales, which is approximately equal to those of the US and are about double those of Japan.[19] Based on past trends and drivers, the Organisation for Economic Co-operation and Development (OECD) predicts that demand for chemicals will continue to increase, particularly in developing countries. Globalisation of the industry will also continue, with production in non-OECD countries growing steadily. Industry sources[20] predict that world chemicals output will increase over the next decade by 63% in real terms compared with 1996.

1.11 Between 1979 and 1996, growth in chemicals demand in the developed world, at 2.4% per annum in real terms, was in line with growth in GDP. By contrast, in the same period in the developing world, a growth in chemicals demand of 6.1% per annum exceeded GDP growth by 2% per annum. Similar levels of growth are expected to continue in both types of economy for some time to come.

1.12 The international nature of the chemicals industry arises not just from the number of multinational chemical companies but also from the high volume of international trade in chemicals. This has resulted in a range of international agreements on chemicals safety and on the exchange of information about chemicals but also brings with it some challenges. The need for international consensus has delayed and weakened various chemical safety instruments, and held up the introduction of new and improved testing protocols.[21] Trade rules, particularly those relating to non-tariff barriers to trade, can interact uneasily with countries' rights to control chemicals of concern. Liability issues, which are complicated nationally, become much more difficult to determine across national boundaries.

1.13 The industry is characterised by a complex supply chain between producer and end-user. Very few chemicals are sold directly to retailers. More are sold for formulation into end-user products, either directly or through intermediate formulators, and many are used in the manufacture of finished articles. Supply chain management is difficult. It is not uncommon for producers or importers of chemicals to be unaware of some of the uses to which the chemicals they manufacture are put, or for importers and retailers of products not to know which chemicals their products contain.

REGULATION

1.14 Regulatory regimes are complex and varied. A review of UK chemicals legislation in 1995[22] listed 25 Acts and 50 Regulations overseen by seven government departments. Different safety legislation applies to the production and use of chemicals according to their use as agricultural pesticides, non-agricultural biocides, cosmetics, pharmaceuticals, veterinary medicines, food additives, or in other applications. Exposure through food, through consumer items, through the environment or in the workplace all have their separate regimes. Legislation controlling the discharge of chemicals to the environment is separate and complex – and primarily (but not exclusively) related to the receiving medium.

1.15 The 1991 OECD monograph *Integrated Pollution Prevention and Control* adopted a broad approach to pollution prevention and control, recommending that member countries 'practice integrated pollution prevention and control, taking into account the effects of activities and substances on the environment as a whole and the whole commercial and environmental life cycles of substances when assessing the risks they pose and when developing and implementing controls to limit their release'. In practice, however, regulation (including that in the UK) is still concerned with a narrow application of these concepts, and is applied only to certain processes. It is concerned principally with the prevention and reduction of emissions and effluents from chemicals production.

1.16 In comparison with the regulatory regime for the release of chemicals as emissions from manufacturing processes, regulation of chemical products and their behaviour and effects in the environment is poorly developed, and is not co-ordinated with other regulatory regimes. Society might reasonably expect that adequate assessments have been carried out on chemicals that are on the market, and that appropriate risk management strategies are in place for potentially harmful substances. This is not the case, as discussed in the government's strategy for the sustainable production and use of chemicals,[23] and the European Commission's White Paper on the regulation of chemicals[24]. It has been recognised for more than two decades that a minimum amount of information about likely environmental effects should be available for widely-used chemicals. Despite this, such data are available for only a small proportion of chemicals currently on the market.

1.17 Chemicals legislation addresses the chemicals themselves as manufactured, imported or used, and does not address the problem of products containing chemicals. There are good reasons for this. The complexity of the supply chain (1.13) and the diffuse nature of emissions of chemicals released from products make the management of individual products difficult. Controls on whether or how a chemical may be manufactured or used for a particular purpose are used as a surrogate for addressing the many possible products in which the chemical might be used. Increasingly, however, it has been recognised that chemicals enter the environment in significant quantities through release during the use of products. Examples include phthalates (softeners contained in plastic articles), the brominated flame retardants and zinc in tyres, for which more than 75% of the total emissions to the environment occur during their use.[25]

A NEW APPROACH TO CHEMICALS POLICY

1.18 The current system for managing the risks from chemicals fails to secure public confidence and is overloaded by the massive backlog of chemicals waiting to be assessed. In this report we consider ways of addressing these failures. A more inclusive, precautionary and effective approach is urgently required.

Addressing public concerns

1.19 In our Twenty-first Report, *Setting Environmental Standards*, published in 1998, we proposed a conceptual framework for environmental policy that has important implications for the formulation of policies on chemicals (figure 1-II). The Commission stressed that environmental issues and policy choices of this kind invariably raise questions of values, and that these should be addressed from the outset; expert assessments would continue to be essential, but limits to their certainty, accuracy and objectivity should be recognised.

Figure 1-II

Conceptual framework for environmental policy[26]

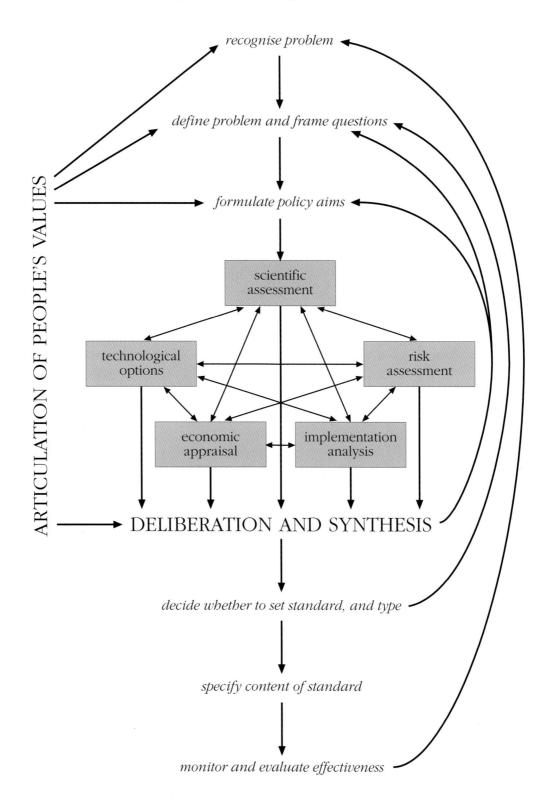

1.20 The framework set out in the Twenty-first Report involved several complementary and inter-related components, including (*inter alia*) scientific evidence, risk assessment and economic appraisal. We recognised that all components would be characterised by uncertainty or indeterminacy, and might be influenced by different interests and beliefs.

1.21 We noted that, in situations of high uncertainty in regulatory science, 'judgements can be swayed, perhaps imperceptibly, by one or another kind of vested interest'.[27] Risk estimates, often presented as the objective outcome of a scientific assessment, may involve important (but often obscure) assumptions and value judgements. Thus perceptions of risk that diverge from expert estimates 'are not necessarily irrational but may well reflect different values from those underlying the expert assessments'.[28] Similarly, the Commission identified divergent perspectives on the practicality and the appropriateness of economic appraisal (particularly cost-benefit analysis) for dealing with many of the issues raised by environmental policies.

1.22 It is essential that uncertainties and different premises are explicit in the policy process and a key recommendation of the Twenty-first Report was that people's values should be integrated into each critical stage of decision-making, including framing the problem under consideration. These principles should be borne in mind when considering the present approaches to assessing and managing the adverse effects of chemicals. We have also sought to apply them in proposing a new approach.

A PRECAUTIONARY APPROACH

1.23 An important concept long advocated by this Commission, and partly incorporated into environmental policy since we first considered the impact of synthetic chemicals on the environment, is that of the precautionary principle. It is encapsulated in Principle 15 of the 1992 Rio Declaration on the Environment and Development:[29]

> 'In order to protect the environment, the precautionary approach shall be widely applied by States according to their capability. Where there are threats of serious or irreversible damage, lack of full scientific certainty shall not be used as a reason for postponing cost-effective measures to prevent environmental degradation.'

1.24 We heard, in evidence for the Twenty-first Report, concerns that the precautionary principle required policy-makers to adopt an approach that errs towards excessive environmental protection; we have received similar evidence during this study. However, the precautionary principle need not conflict with evidence-based decision-making. It clearly does not obviate the desirability of information about chemicals being available to enable decisions to be made with less uncertainty. A precautionary approach to data collection and assessment is already exercised to some extent, in that safety margins are built into existing procedures to allow for uncertainties, for example, in toxicity test methods.

1.25 The precautionary principle is best used in situations where there are judged to be potentially serious or irreversible threats to health or the environment. Under such circumstances the principle holds that action should be taken to reduce or avoid the potential hazards in the absence of actual proof of harm.

1.26 The precautionary principle therefore deals with situations in which, despite the best efforts of science, the data and the safety margins are insufficient to give the necessary level of assurance of adequate risk management. In such situations a precautionary decision is preferable to relying on existing regulatory procedures, which delay action indefinitely as further research becomes available and the chemicals of concern continue to enter the environment. We discuss regulatory systems and the slow progress under the current European system for assessment of existing substances in more detail in chapter 3 and consider possible ways of improving the situation in chapter 4.

TARGETED ASSESSMENT

1.27 The current system is overloaded because of the difficulty of applying a cumbersome and expensive testing and assessment regime to the very large number of chemicals already on the market. Prioritisation schemes, an integral part of most current regulatory regimes, have reduced the number of chemicals under active consideration by a substantial factor, but even so progress is slow.

1.28 In chapter 4 we consider possible ways of speeding up the process, and recommend a new approach to screening chemicals so that a small manageable number of substances can be identified rapidly for further attention and risk management. We explore new ways of assessing the potential for chemicals to cause harm, which also speed up the process of risk assessment and reduce the need for animal testing. In our Second Report we recommended the development of correlations between chemical structure and environmental effects. The use of this sort of information, and computational approaches, have become commonplace in the pharmaceutical industry, which is now able to screen millions of compounds for their potential to exhibit complex physiological effects, rapidly and effectively. In contrast the regulatory systems for other synthetic chemicals have failed to assess the basic properties of a mere thirty thousand or so compounds. We return to this issue in chapter 4 and make recommendations to move ahead now on the basis of the system used by the pharmaceutical industry.

1.29 In this report we recommend that we go beyond assessment of individual chemicals and extend the process to include monitoring of concentrations and effects in the environment, and the use of these monitoring data to target the limited assessment resources onto those chemicals that might already be causing environmental harm. In chapter 3 we point to the huge cost predicted if new EU chemical assessment proposals are implemented, and ask whether a far better use of some of that funding would be to enhance and redirect some relevant environmental monitoring towards understanding the fate and effects of chemicals in the environment.

CHEMICALS MANAGEMENT

1.30 Ultimately, however, we need a more fundamental shift in the way that risks from chemicals are managed. We recommend some ways of doing this in chapter 5. In particular, we envisage a much more prominent role for substitution. The replacement of one chemical with another is commonplace in industry and is normally driven by market forces, for example switching to lower-cost alternatives. In the context of chemicals risk management, substitution has come to mean the replacement of a hazardous substance with another of lower hazard. The term can also helpfully be extended to the replacement of processes that use chemicals with processes that do not; the move towards integrated pest management well exemplifies such a shift (box 5A).

1.31 We have considered possible drivers towards substitution. Linked to the chemicals assessment and management programme that we propose is the opportunity to categorise chemicals according to the hazard they present. This should be used as the basis for economic instruments to provide fiscal incentives for industry to move towards lower-hazard products and processes. Better information flow through the supply chain, better understanding of and access to redress through liability law and greater transparency for the whole process will also drive this trend. Just as importantly, we encourage support for new ideas and technologies to facilitate substitution through the production of more environmentally benign processes and products (green chemistry), new business models (chemical management services) and extended producer responsibility initiatives (chapter 5).

THIS REPORT

1.32 We, like others, are profoundly dissatisfied that after more than a century of chemicals production, and decades of legislation attempting to deliver environmental safety from these chemicals, we still do not have a good understanding of the fate and effects of chemicals in the environment. We do not even have much information from which such an understanding might be derived. We have little faith that either the present regulatory systems or the proposals coming forward to improve them will provide better answers in the future. We believe that only a substantial paradigm shift will allow a start to be made to rectify this situation, and we believe that such a start needs to be made now.

1.33 The objective of this report is to offer a new approach to chemicals assessment and management. It argues for better information about chemicals on the market, more intelligent testing, better use of monitoring, a concerted push for early European legislation and a strong move towards substitution, underpinned by economic instruments and an improved liability regime. It must incorporate full articulation of public values. Furthermore, the chemicals industry must accept the duty of care that was sought through the national chemicals strategy and which many companies have already begun to implement, although it is far from having been realised in practice.

> *Chemical products make an important contribution to quality of life, and are important to the economy. However, public confidence in the industry will not be restored until all chemicals on the market have been assessed for their potential for harm and systems are in place for detecting unforeseen effects on the environment.*

Chapter 2

Evaluating the risks from chemicals

Most of the myriad synthetic chemicals, used in industry and society for many purposes and in many ways, find their way into the environment either as an immediate consequence of their production and use or as a result of the manufacture or disposal of products containing them. What mechanisms exist for controlling the risks from these chemicals?

Introduction

2.1   Some societal mechanism is needed to ensure that the harm caused by synthetic chemicals is contained within acceptable limits. In this chapter we explore the current mechanisms for establishing such limits and managing the risks from chemicals in products within these limits, particularly the regulatory testing regimes that address the direct and indirect adverse effects of chemicals in the environment. We consider the slow rate of progress being made in assessing chemicals, the uncertainties in the science underpinning risk assessment and the lack of transparent mechanisms to incorporate public values into the process, particularly in the light of the loss of public confidence in chemicals regulation that was discussed in chapter 1. We consider what steps might be needed to improve the situation, including the role played by environmental monitoring, leading to our recommendations for action in chapter 4.

Risk assessment

2.2   The current regulatory approach to the management of chemicals is based almost entirely on risk assessment. *Risk assessment* is presented as (a) a structured approach to determining the consequences of an event and the probability of it happening, and (b) a means of informing judgements about the need for, and ways of, managing the consequences of the event.

2.3   The application of risk assessment to environmental hazards has been the subject of much debate (see the Twenty-first Report, *Setting Environmental Standards*), particularly because of concerns about concealed uncertainties and assumptions and the paucity of opportunities to incorporate public values into the process. Although methods of addressing these concerns have been discussed in government guidance on environmental risk assessment and management,[1] the risk management of chemicals seems resistant to their introduction. This is due, at least in part, to a desire by regulators to apply consistent criteria that are understandable and predictable for the international chemicals industry. However, reliance on rigid risk assessment approaches that fail to incorporate public values is likely to be a key factor in the loss of public confidence in the process.

RISKS AND HAZARDS

2.4   Risk assessment methods for chemicals in the environment focus primarily on the intrinsic hazards of the chemical and its potential to reach a vulnerable component of the environment, by considering sources of the chemical, its pathways into and through the environment, and the effects it might have. Each of these factors can, however, be complex and subject to considerable uncertainty.

2.5   The *hazard* posed by a chemical is a consequence of (and usually defined by) a set of inherent properties that render it capable of causing adverse effects to organisms or the environment, depending on the amount of chemical that reaches the target. The *risk* is an expression of the likelihood of harm from a particular hazard being realised, and is a function of both hazard and exposure.[2]

2.6   Risk assessment is the process of identifying and quantifying hazards and exposure. It can be linked to a specific use or occurrence of a chemical or physical agent or, more generally, to the existence of the chemical in commerce. It seeks to take into account the possible harmful effects on the biosphere, the physical environment and on humans of using the chemical in the amount and manner proposed, and ideally should evaluate all likely potential routes of exposure. Quantification requires the establishment of relationships between the dose or concentration of a chemical and the consequential effects in likely vulnerable targets, and estimates of the probable concentrations reaching those targets.

2.7   Risk assessments must be carefully structured and are generally based on four elements: hazard identification; hazard characterisation; exposure assessment; and risk characterisation (box 2A).[3] Each of these is discussed in turn in more detail.

BOX 2A   **THE FOUR ELEMENTS OF CURRENT RISK ASSESSMENT**

Hazard identification The identification of the inherent capacity of a chemical to cause adverse effects, without regard to the likelihood or severity of such effects.

Hazard characterisation Following exposure to a chemical, the quantitative evaluation of the nature of adverse effects, including assessment of toxic potency (the relative toxicity of a chemical) and, where possible, a dose–response assessment.

These first two elements comprise the ***hazard assessment***.

Exposure assessment The quantitative evaluation of the likely exposure of the environment and, via the environment, humans to a chemical.

Risk characterisation The quantitative estimation of the probability that an adverse effect will occur, and of its severity and duration in a given population under defined exposure conditions, based on the three previous elements.

HAZARD IDENTIFICATION

The identification of the inherent capacity of a chemical to cause adverse effects, without regard to the likelihood or severity of such effects.

The nature of chemicals

2.8   To identify the inherent capacity of chemicals to cause adverse effects, it is important to understand their *taxonomy*, that is, how different substances can be distinguished and the characteristics that give rise to their different effects in the environment (box 2B).

2.9   It is conventional and convenient to classify chemicals as either organic or inorganic. Organic chemicals are those that rely on the ability of carbon to bond with itself and with other elements often in long chains and other complex ways to form large molecules. Although organic chemicals are the basis of all biological processes, synthetic organic molecules that do not occur in nature are an important product of the chemicals industry.

2.10   Inorganic chemicals are found in nature mainly as minerals. They too can be synthesised by industry in novel ways, but the main relevant anthropogenic activity is in the extraction and refining of naturally occurring minerals to produce metals and other substances such as salt, sulphur or phosphates. In general, while industry introduces new organic compounds into the environment, its effect on inorganic substances is often to redistribute them, increasing their concentration in specific localities.

2.11   Chemicals with harmful properties can be either simple elements (for example, metals such as lead) or more complex molecules, such as asbestos or organochlorine pesticides. Many structural variations of molecules are possible. Although there is a common perception of difference between natural and synthetic chemicals, chemicals that are identical in all respects behave in the same way regardless of whether their source is natural or synthetic. Chemicals derive the intrinsic properties that define their hazards from their molecular structure, not from their source.

2.12   However, the source of a chemical can determine its molecular structure. For example, natural systems can usually produce or be affected by just one of several stereoisomers (box 2B) because of the very precise spatial fit required between the molecule and the biological system with which it interacts. As a result, certain synthetic pharmaceuticals or pesticides are very stereo-specific; in the case of some synthetic pyrethroid insecticides, one of several possible stereoisomers can be highly potent while others can be almost inactive.

2.13   In contrast, when non-biological production systems produce optical isomers the result is usually a mixture, the proportion of each form varying according to the production method. Such differences can result in chemicals produced by natural systems behaving differently from apparently similar ones produced synthetically (including showing different physiological effects) because of some structural or isotopic difference. However, the perception that there is some distinction between natural and synthetic chemicals goes much further than this.

BOX 2B   **THE NATURE OF CHEMICALS**

The properties of molecules are determined by their composition (the different amounts of elements such as carbon, hydrogen and oxygen they contain, known as the *empirical formula*) and their chemical structure (the way in which the atoms of these elements are linked together, known as the *structural formula)*.

Different structural arrangements are possible, so the same composition (empirical formula) can give rise to many different structural configurations, or *isomers*, each with different properties. This is particularly true of organic chemicals. For example, the empirical formula $C_4H_{10}O$ can represent methyl propyl ether, diethyl ether or butanol, three very different compounds. Furthermore, there are two different possible structures for methyl propyl ether and five for butanol.

butan–1–ol   The 2 forms of butan–2–ol   2-methyl–propan–1–ol   2-methyl–propan–2–ol

diethyl ether   methyl 1–propyl ether   methyl 2–propyl ether

In addition, because the structural arrangements are three-dimensional and the links between the constituent atoms have direction in space, isomers having the same chemical structure can have different spatial configurations (*stereoisomers*). Molecules that are geometrically asymmetric show a particular form of stereoisomerism – such molecules can have forms that are non-identical mirror images, known as *optical isomers*, for example D- and L- glyceraldehyde.

D–glyceraldehyde   L–glyceraldehyde

Furthermore, elements themselves can occur in several different atomic forms or *isotopes* that have different atomic weights. Identical molecules from different sources may differ in the relative amounts of different isotopes they contain. This can affect physico-chemical properties that may be important in the environment such as diffusion rates and reaction rates.

2.14   There is no known scientific reason to suppose that a synthetically-produced molecule will behave in a less benign way than its identical counterpart occurring in nature. However, many synthetic chemicals do not have identical counterparts in nature. While higher organisms have evolved to include mechanisms for the destruction and elimination of many natural toxins (appendix E, box E2), any such ability to deal with synthetic chemicals that are not found in nature is coincidental. No such defence mechanism could have evolved in the short time since the industrial mass production of synthetic chemicals became a prevalent feature of industrial based societies.

2.15   There is evidence, however, that many lower organisms have evolved such mechanisms.[4] Many synthesised chemicals are also sufficiently similar to natural products to mimic their toxic action and, therefore, share aspects of their metabolism and fate in the environment. But other synthetic chemicals do not have this property and it is therefore safer to assume that they are more likely to pose a higher risk to the environment than natural products.

Direct adverse effects of chemicals

2.16   Paracelsus's oft-quoted adage[5] reminds us that any substance is potentially toxic if the dose and duration of exposure are sufficiently high. However, toxicity is not a single concept. There are many ways in which chemicals might disrupt the functioning of an organism, including corrosive or irritant effects, acute and chronic toxicity, effects on the nervous system (neurotoxicity), impairment of the reproduction of cells or organisms (by carcinogens, mutagens or reproductive toxins), or damage to hormone systems, for example, the effects resulting from endocrine-disrupting chemicals (see appendix E, E.38-E.45).

2.17   For each type of toxic effect there are specific tests designed to determine whether or not the effect is evident at varying levels of exposure (dose or concentration). The indicator of the effect is known as the *end-point*. The toxicity end-points tested under current EU regulatory systems for the control of chemicals are listed in appendix D; the methodology of the tests is further described later in this chapter (2.34-2.40 and 2.52-2.56).

2.18   A major source of uncertainty in toxicity testing is the difficulty of including all important end-points. The relatively recent realisation that endocrine disruption is important is a reminder that there may still be end-points that have yet to be recognised, and for which tests have not yet been developed. We discuss, in chapter 4, the sort of research needed to address this important area of uncertainty.

2.19   Toxicity is not solely a characteristic of synthetic chemicals. Some of the most toxic substances known occur naturally in organisms, where they usually form part of a defence mechanism. For example, many plants, including common ones such as clovers, produce hydrogen cyanide when damaged, and a number of Australian plants produce fluoroacetate, a respiratory inhibitor which is highly toxic to sheep, but to which red kangaroos have adapted. Box 2C provides some further examples of toxic chemicals that can be found in foodstuffs.

2.20   Higher organisms have evolved defence mechanisms against many natural chemicals (2.14), but such mechanisms would not necessarily be effective against all synthetic chemicals. Although some synthetic chemicals (such as pesticides) are designed to be toxic, most are not designed to be toxic, but many happen to be so. In particular, compounds containing carbon-halogen bonds, which are rare in nature (fluoroacetate being an unusual example), are commonly produced industrially because of their stability and, sometimes, because of their high toxicity.

BOX 2C   **CHEMICALS THAT CAN BE TOXIC IN THE FOOD MATRIX**

Chemicals may be present in human foodstuffs in a naturally-occurring state within the food matrix, as additives or residues with some purpose in food production, or as contaminants.

Toxic chemicals occurring naturally in the food matrix:
- chemicals found in plants, such as the pyrrolizidine alkaloids which are mutagenic and toxic;
- goitrogens found in the Brassicaceae which interfere with thyroid function in the absence of adequate iodine;
- cyanogenic glycosides, a toxic substance found in cassava;
- a variety of compounds which cause thiamine deficiency; and
- plant phenolics which may cause oral and oesophagal cancer.

Food contaminants known to be toxic:
- products of microbiological contamination, for example mycotoxins (some of which are known human carcinogens) such as aflatoxin produced by moulds growing on groundnuts;
- products of natural or anthropogenic combustion, for example dioxins and polycyclic aromatic hydrocarbons; and
- substances generated during cooking and food processing, for example heterocyclic amines and advanced glycation end products.

Indirect adverse effects of chemicals

2.21   Releases of pollutants can also exert indirect effects on the wider environment by influencing physical systems. In this case, the chemicals concerned may be non-toxic to biological organisms, but through their chemical and physical properties, they may have profound effects on the physical environment upon which life depends.

2.22   Current testing regimes for chemicals are not designed to detect indirect effects. Some, such as eutrophication (2.23), are well understood, to the extent that the chances of discovering in the future that a synthetic chemical is a hitherto unrecognised eutrophicant are small. Other indirect effects, such as those on the atmosphere (2.24-2.28), might be detectable through an extension of the sort of testing programme suitable for chemicals in products (chapter 4).

2.23   *Eutrophication* is an extreme increase in biological productivity in response to an increase in the concentration of nutrients such as nitrates and phosphates. Excess nutrient concentrations in freshwaters, coastal waters or soils, can result in the growth of organisms not usually dominant in that ecosystem. In aquatic ecosystems, eutrophication results in changes in species composition, affecting the delicate balance between aquatic plant species and resulting in a reduction in species biodiversity.[6] Eutrophication in terrestrial ecosystems has resulted in a shift towards vegetation that is more characteristic of nutrient-rich conditions and a decline in plant species associated with nutrient-poor habitats in the UK as a whole.[7] In freshwater, phosphorus is the nutrient of greatest concern as it is naturally in short supply relative to the other major plant nutrients. Nitrogen concentration is the principal concern for other ecosystems.[8] The main source of these nutrients is agriculture, though sewage effluent and nitrogen oxides from car exhausts are also important sources.[9] The nutrients involved are well characterised, and screening tests or an assessment protocol designed for their identification are unnecessary.

2.24   Polluting emissions from a point source to the atmosphere can remain concentrated for a kilometre or more away. Furthermore, some pollutants can be carried thousands of kilometres within days and still remain sufficiently concentrated to take part in reactions that lead to a change in the chemical composition of the near surface region elsewhere. For example, the polar air reaching the UK behind a cold front can contain an array of pollutants that owe their existence to industrial activity in North America and northern Eurasia.

2.25   Chemicals that react very slowly in the atmosphere can be carried to all parts of it and be mixed to produce a much more homogeneous distribution. To impact on stratospheric ozone depletion, for example, any gas emitted from a product has to be extremely persistent so that it can first mix in the lower atmosphere and, over a period of many years, be transported into the equatorial stratosphere and then towards higher latitudes. It must then be able to take part in catalytic reactions that deplete the ozone in these regions. Chlorinated fluorocarbons (CFCs), from aerosols and refrigerants, persist and accumulate in the lower atmosphere and are transferred in time to the polar upper stratosphere, where reaction with sunlight releases chlorine atoms from their normally stable structure. These chlorine atoms react with ozone, drastically reducing the amount present in the stratosphere and consequently the ability of the Earth's protective ozone layer to filter out damaging ultraviolet (UV) radiation from sunlight. The presence of chlorine, bromine or iodine in a molecule is an indication of the physico-chemical properties associated with ozone depletion but laboratory experiments can provide more definitive indications.

2.26   Gaseous emissions from products can influence the enhanced greenhouse effect and so contribute to global warming. Such effects may occur if the substance takes part in reactions to change the levels of a greenhouse gas, such as methane, or if it itself is a greenhouse gas. Given the quantities that are likely to be emitted from any product it is only the latter possibility that is relevant. To impact, as in the example of ozone depletion, the gas must be non-reactive so that it can persist, disperse and accumulate in the atmosphere. It must also have the property of being transparent to solar radiation and opaque to thermal radiation. Such properties can be tested in the laboratory.

2.27   Another example of an indirect adverse effect of chemicals on the atmosphere is the accumulation of oxides of nitrogen and volatile organic compounds (VOCs) from vehicle and industrial emissions, which contributes to the photochemical creation of tropospheric ozone. Ozone is an irritant that can provoke asthma in humans and inhibit photosynthesis and reproduction in plants.

2.28   Testing protocols for atmospheric pollutants suitable for inclusion in the assessment process for chemicals in products are not well developed, although they could be improved, for example, through the routine use of structure activity relationships. A more satisfactory approach to detecting such effects, however, might be through enhanced environmental monitoring and its tighter integration into chemicals regulation. We return to the roles of structure-activity relationships and environmental monitoring in chapter 4.

HAZARD CHARACTERISATION

Following exposure to a chemical, the quantitative evaluation of the nature of adverse effects, including assessment of toxic potency (the relative toxicity of a chemical) and, where possible, a dose-response assessment.

Testing strategies

2.29 In order to quantify risk assessment, some measure is needed that permits prediction of the degree of harm from the estimated exposure. Testing protocols for chemicals are designed with this objective in mind, and those currently in use for the characterisation of the risks from chemicals were described in the Commission's Twenty-first Report. In essence, the aim is to obtain a *dose-response relationship* between the concentration of the pollutant and the effect it produces. In EU countries, for humans, this is normally achieved by using test animals as surrogates for humans. In ecotoxicological testing, a few test species are used as surrogates for all other species that the chemical might reach (2.33).

2.30 Methods for toxicity and ecotoxicity testing have become increasingly standardised. In the EU, the risk assessment method for existing substances is prescribed in European Commission Regulation (EC) 1488/94[10] and implemented in the detailed Technical Guidance Documents on Risk Assessment for New and Existing Substances.[11] Principles of assessment for new substances are laid down in Directive 93/67/EEC[12] and again supported by the detailed Technical Guidance Documents. The European Union System for the Evaluation of Substances (EUSES) has been developed as a software tool to provide decision support in the assessments. Tonnage thresholds for testing and test types are described in further detail in appendix D. OECD and the International Organisation for Standardisation have produced guidelines to address intergovernmental differences in data requirements.

2.31 Different levels of testing are prescribed for new and existing chemicals; the production tonnages of the chemical defining the level. The wide range of concentrations at which different chemicals can exert diverse physiological effects, and the widely divergent behaviours of different chemicals in the environment, leads us to the view that these tonnage levels serve no useful purpose, except that perhaps the very lowest level is useful to define those chemicals that are marketed at levels normally too low to warrant testing. We return to this issue in subsequent chapters.

2.32 Classical toxicology has relied mainly on evidence from controlled exposure of individual organisms or from epidemiological approaches including retrospective case control studies and, more recently, the use of more generic tests on cell lines and computer models. Predicting the toxic effect of a chemical in humans from tests on other animals is made difficult by fundamental differences in the way different organisms respond to chemicals. Despite this, toxicity may manifest in a number of ways that are shared across species, a principle that has been followed in the development of animal toxicity tests that are currently used for regulatory purposes.

2.33   A different approach to hazard characterisation is used to assess toxic effects on non-human species. Ecotoxicology is concerned with the adverse impacts of substances on ecosystems. An ecosystem is an interdependent body of living organisms, usually of diverse species, together with the physical environment in which they live. Within such a system, several communities of interacting organisms may occupy more or less distinguishable physical environments; within these communities populations of species exist. Whereas in assessing effects on humans attention is generally focused on the health of the individual, in ecotoxicology it is populations and communities that are of concern.[13]

Toxicity testing

2.34   Biological systems exhibit great variability in their response to external influences such as exposure to a chemical. Even with a complete and adequate data set based on human tests, as provided for pharmaceutical products, it is impossible to predict the precise influence a chemical will have on each and every member of an exposed human population. Therefore, the aim of most toxicological testing is not to arrive at the best estimate of the magnitude of any risk but rather to determine whether or not there is sufficient reassurance of little or negligible risk under the relevant exposure situation.

2.35   Toxicity tests include assessments of acute toxicity, epithelial (skin) irritation and corrosion, immunological sensitisation, and toxicity expressed only on repeated dosing. Assessments are also made of the ability of chemicals to cause cancers (*carcinogenicity*), to induce permanent transmissible genetic changes (*mutagenicity* or *genotoxicity*), or to cause foetal abnormalities (*teratogenicity*). Other important manifestations of chemical toxicity investigated include damage to the nervous system (*neurotoxicity*), adverse effects on reproduction (*reprotoxicity*), and skin reactions on exposure to light (*phototoxicity*). (See appendix D for a list of toxicity tests required by EU regulations.)

2.36   Toxicity involving any system may manifest within hours or days (acute) or take weeks, months or the organism's lifetime (chronic). Toxicity tests are classified according to:

- the length of dosing – from acute studies lasting up to a few days to chronic studies spanning the lifetime of a test species (18-30 months in rodents);

- the route of administration – ingested, intravenous, oral, dermal, ocular or inhaled; and

- the end-point being studied – which may be death, appearance of a tumour, effects on reproduction or development, allergic sensitisation, or a neurotoxic or behavioural effect.

2.37   Where the end-point of a toxicity test is death, the results are expressed as either the *median lethal concentration* or LC_{50} (the concentration that brings about the death of 50% of the individuals in a test population) or the *median lethal dose* or LD_{50} (the single dose that brings about 50% mortality) within the duration of the test (figure 2-I). On their own, these measures provide only a very rough idea of the relative toxicity of substances and the actual lethal dose will depend heavily on both the target species and the local environmental conditions. LC_{50} and LD_{50} data are rarely, if ever, the sole basis for regulation.

2.38   The results of tests for sub-lethal effects of a substance are expressed as the *median effective concentration* (EC_{50}) or the *median effective dose* (ED_{50}), the concentration or dose which, in a given time under given conditions, causes 50% of the test population to exhibit a particular response or, in some cases, causes a 50% change in a specified response relative to unexposed controls.

Figure 2-I

An example of a concentration or dose response curve showing the relative positions of the median effective concentration (EC$_{50}$) or median lethal concentration (LC$_{50}$), the lowest observed effect concentration (LOEC), the threshold point, and the no observed effect concentration (NOEC).[14]

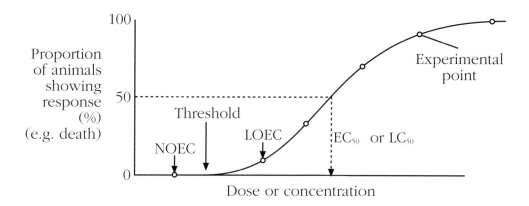

2.39 With the exception of chemicals that have mutagenic or genotoxic effects, it is usually found that there is a level of exposure or threshold below which a chemical will not affect an organism, that is, a dose at which no adverse effect is observed. The *no observed effect concentration* (NOEC) is the greatest concentration or amount of a substance in a bioassay at which the target organisms do not have a response significantly different from the control organism in relation to the critical effect recognised at higher doses,[15] and can therefore be considered to be at or below the threshold point for that organism. The NOEC is not an absolute value; the higher the number of organisms tested and the more sensitive the methods used, the lower the NOEC that will be established. In order to arrive at a regulatory standard, numerical factors (safety factors) are applied to the NOEC in an attempt to allow for the uncertainties involved in the testing process (2.48-2.51).

2.40 It may not be possible to establish a NOEC if a significant effect is observed between the test organisms and the controls at all the concentrations or doses of a chemical used for the testing. In these cases the *lowest observed effect concentration* (LOEC) is substituted for the NOEC. The LOEC is the lowest concentration dose, or amount of a substance in a bioassay, at which the target organisms show a response significantly different to that of the control organisms under the same defined conditions of exposure. However, the LOEC is an artifact of the testing procedure – in effect a limit of detection – and will be an unknown level above the actual threshold level[16] (as opposed to the NOEC, which is at or below the threshold point). Thus the more demanding concept of 'lower safe limits' is neglected and uncertainties may therefore be high.[17]

Uncertainty in toxicity testing

2.41 Reference has already been made to several sources of uncertainty in toxicological methodology. However, there are some fundamental uncertainties which cannot be addressed by refining techniques and which have to be addressed through the use of safety factors (2.48-2.51). These include the errors associated with extrapolating across species, failure to detect very long-term effects, and testing substances individually instead of in the mixtures normally found in the environment. Possibly the most serious source of uncertainty is the impossibility of allowing for all possible effects of a chemical (2.18).

2.42 **Extrapolation across species** There is a degree of uncertainty involved in using animal data to predict the biological activities of compounds in humans. Data from human populations exposed to known levels of a chemical are unlikely to be available (though see 2.131), therefore data from standardised animal experimental systems must be extrapolated to humans. However, there are several problems in extrapolating across species, including:

- extrapolating from relatively small, often homogeneous, groups of laboratory animals to very large and heterogeneous human populations;

- extrapolating from the high doses used to elicit effects in experimental animals to the low doses that more closely reflect human exposure levels;

- extrapolating from non-human species to humans, if no specific information is available. Similar rates of absorption, metabolic pathways, rates of activation or detoxification, rates of elimination and sensitivity at sites of action are assumed in both animals and humans; and

- extrapolating from short to medium-term effects in animals to long-term or lifetime effects in humans.

2.43 The problems surrounding this extrapolation are widely recognised.[18] Species differences in the subsequent fate of a chemical in the body (the time course of uptake, distribution, metabolism and excretion – *toxicokinetics* – which determine the bioavailability of a chemical) arise from differences such as heart rate, cardiac output, fat content and renal and hepatic blood flows. Other limitations for comparability are inter-species differences in breathing rates, organ sizes, basal metabolism, rates of cell turnover, and lifespans.[19] Differences may also occur in the biochemical and physiological mechanisms of action of toxicants on affected target molecules and tissues (*toxicodynamics*). The frequency with which species-specific responses have been documented implies that careful consideration must be given to the nature of the hazards identified and their underlying pathways and mechanisms.[20] Unless detailed toxicokinetic and toxicodynamic information is available on the differences between humans and the key experimental species, there will always be uncertainty when making this extrapolation.

2.44 **Failure to detect very long-term effects** Humans are long-lived and lifespans are increasing. It is difficult to be confident that NOECs based on 90-day toxicity tests are capable of detecting effects resulting from exposure over several decades and through different phases of growth.

2.45 The standard tests to detect long-term effects are repeated dose toxicity tests, except for reproductive, genotoxic or carcinogenic effects, which have separate test protocols. They are based on repeated daily dosing with, or exposure to, a substance for either part of the expected lifespan of the test organism (sub-acute or sub-chronic exposure) or for the whole lifespan (or the major part of the lifespan) in the case of chronic exposure. The establishment of the NOEC is critical to these studies, but even so, there are no test protocols that can reliably mimic a human's lifetime of exposure.

2.46 **Pollutant mixtures** Toxicity tests are usually carried out on a single test chemical, but exposure in the environment is rarely to a single substance. Chemicals in mixtures can act on an organism in different ways:

- independent – the chemicals produce different effects or have different modes of action;

- additive – the chemicals behave in similar ways, so that the effects or responses produced by the chemicals add to each other in a simple way;

- synergistic – the mode of action of one chemical might enhance the effect of another, resulting in an effect greater than the simple sum of their effects when acting alone. One class of synergism is potentiation, where a substance that causes no harm makes the effects of another chemical much worse; and

- antagonistic – the result of a chemical counteracting the adverse effect of another. In other words, the situation where exposure to two chemicals together has less effect than the simple sum of their independent effects.

2.47 Most risk assessments are made on the basis of exposure to a single chemical, which is a pragmatic approach but clearly does not model reality well. As yet, relatively few examples of chemicals acting synergistically at non-toxic or low dose levels have been found,[21,22] although such interactions have been described for mixtures of pesticides in some animal species.[23] Some cases of chemicals acting antagonistically have been observed; for example, the ability of nitrogen dioxide within urban environments to destroy ground-level ozone produced through photochemical oxidation of traffic emissions.

Safety factors

2.48 When assessing risks, it is usual practice to account for these uncertainties by the use of safety (or uncertainty) factors. Current risk assessment procedures incorporate what seem to be large safety margins. These typically include 100-fold uncertainty factors, of which a 10-fold factor accounts for extrapolation from animal data to humans and a further 10-fold factor allows for individual variability in response within the human population (2.125-2.127). Each of these factors can be subsequently subdivided into a kinetic component and a dynamic component. This allows for the introduction of chemical-specific data where available to replace the default (figure 2-II).

2.49 The safety factor of 100 has been used since 1961 following a decision by the Food and Agriculture organization (FAO)/World Health Organization (WHO) Joint Expert Committee on Food Additives (JEFCA) establishing an acceptable daily intake of food additives for the general population using animal data. Although the value of 100 was chosen on a fairly arbitrary basis,[24] subsequent data have provided some validation. For example, analysis of human variability demonstrated that the 10-fold factor was adequate to cover most examples of inter-individual variability in humans.[25]

Figure 2-II

Subdivision of the normal 100-fold default uncertainty factors[26]

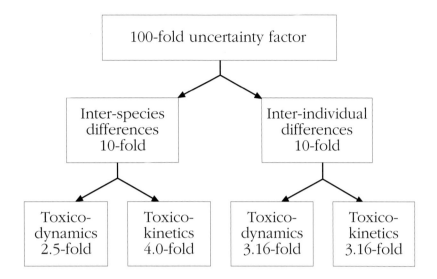

2.50 However, the uncertainty factors are not based on scientific evidence, nor are they accurate predictors of outcomes; they merely attempt to allow for all perceived possibilities and compensate for lack of knowledge.[27] There is considerable debate about the use of safety factors.[28] For example, for effects involving direct interaction with genetic mechanisms (some types of carcinogenicity and germ cell mutagenicity), it is generally assumed that there is a probability of harm at any level of exposure, that is, there is no threshold below which the probability of harm is considered to be negligible. As a result there is no clear consensus on appropriate methodology for dose/concentration-response assessment.[29]

2.51 The International Programme on Chemical Safety (IPCS) framework on chemical-specific adjustment factors,[30] which are factors based on quantitative chemical-specific toxicokinetic or toxicodynamic data, allows increasing knowledge about physiologically-based pharmacokinetic modelling to be incorporated into the assessment process. Detailed guidance has been produced for risk assessors, which describes how to derive these factors to replace the toxicokinetic and toxicodynamic components of inter- and intra-species defaults. Guidance is also given on the type, quality and quantity of data that would be required in order to support replacement of a specific default with a chemical-specific adjustment factor.[31] Factors based on pharmacokinetic modelling, which is further described in chapter 4, can be used to predict tissue concentrations of chemicals in different species under various conditions based on independent anatomical, physiological, and biochemical parameters. Evidence submitted to the Commission by the Department of Health stated that it was generally agreed that it is better to use chemical-specific adjustment factors where such data exist, rather than default uncertainty factors. However, this approach depends on a considerable amount of data being available,[32] which is probably unrealistic for the synthetic chemicals considered in this report.

Ecotoxicity testing

2.52   Ecotoxicity tests may be carried out at levels ranging from the biochemical changes in the cell to the whole organism or ecosystem, usually replicated for this purpose in simplified form in a laboratory. Biochemical tests on cells and tissues are usually simple and of short duration, and may be used for initial screening of substances for toxicity. Tests on ecosystems are of long duration, labour-intensive, often imprecise, and produce results that are usually relevant only to the particular ecosystem studied.

2.53   OECD has produced guidelines for ecotoxicity tests for substances in the aquatic environment. The general approach adopted for regulatory toxicity testing when carrying out assessments for the aquatic environment is to cover three trophic levels in water: algae as primary photosynthetic producer; *Daphnia magna* (the water flea) as primary consumer; and fish as secondary consumer. Amphibians are rarely used and no standard test methods for them have been developed. Nor are there standard test methods for sediment-dwelling organisms, even though many substances with high potential for bioaccumulation tend to migrate towards sediments.[33]

2.54   Test methods for the terrestrial environment are less well developed than for the aquatic environment. The test species most commonly used is the earthworm, for which an OECD guideline is available. Tests using nematodes, slugs, collembola and millipedes have also been developed. Tests of pesticides often use birds, for which OECD test guidelines are available, and bees. In general, ecotoxicity tests have not been developed for small mammals, except for bats in tests of wood preservatives and for the occasional use of wild mammals in the USA.

2.55   Testing for toxicity to mammals thus relies on the standard laboratory tests used for assessing toxicity to humans. Laboratory mammals are not representative of animals in the natural environment. They are usually chosen for their ease of handling in the laboratory, easy reproduction and limited genetic variation. The combined effect of species used and method design has been to improve the precision of testing but reduce its accuracy in reflecting toxicity to heterogeneous wild populations (Appendix E, E.29-E.34).

2.56   Wildlife and vegetation surveys provide a useful source of information for ecotoxicological assessments. These also establish baselines for the state of the natural environment and reveal trends. Concern about endocrine-disrupting chemicals (appendix E, E.38-E.45) arose from field observations, and this led to further investigations both in laboratories and in the field. We note, however, that such information is not routinely used in the risk assessment of synthetic chemicals and we return to this in chapter 4.

Uncertainty in ecotoxicity testing

2.57   The uncertainties in toxicity testing discussed above also apply to ecotoxicity testing. In particular, the available tests use a few test species as surrogates for all vulnerable targets, and current testing protocols do not directly address the possibility of long-term effects.

2.58   **Application factors** In ecotoxicological assessments application factors are used in a similar manner to safety factors in human toxicology to extrapolate from animal toxicity data to the concentration of a substance that would have no harmful effects on the environment. These application factors are empirically derived to extrapolate single species tests to real-life multi-species/population scenarios. For the EU tests, factors are standardised as 10, 50, 100 and 1,000, depending on whether long-term or short-term tests have been carried out and whether these were carried out on algae, *Daphnia magna* or fish. These factors are used to calculate the *predicted no effects concentration* (2.86-2.87) by dividing the lowest short-term *median lethal* (ecotoxcity) *concentration* (L(E)C$_{50}$) or long-term no effects concentration (NOEC) value by the appropriate assessment factor.[34]

2.59   However, application factors may not effectively take into account the issues surrounding inter-species variability, vulnerable threatened species, lifetime exposures or other matters surrounding the complexity of biological systems[35]. They are extrapolation factors that express statistical variability of test results, which are not verified against ecological functionality or structural interactions at population/community or ecosystem levels.[36] However, in environmental impact studies it is increasingly recognised that uncertainties tied to evaluation of ecotoxicological effects may be grossly under-estimated,[37] which indicates that application factors will remain necessary for the foreseeable future until more sophisticated methodologies are available.

2.60   **Chronic toxicity** In ecotoxicological assessments, abbreviated chronic assays, such as the early life stage test in the aquatic environment and a variety of screening tests for mutagenicity and teratogenicity, can be used to assess chronic toxicity. But it is more usual to use a relationship known as the *acute to chronic ratio* to extrapolate between short-term and long-term results. The acute to chronic ratio is determined by dividing the acute LC$_{50}$ by a measure of chronic toxicity such as the *maximum acceptable toxic concentration* , the geometric mean of the no effects and the low effects concentrations. The acute to chronic ratio is then used to extrapolate between different species and different chemicals to give an extremely crude estimate of chronic toxicity.

The need for a better approach

2.61   Protocols for assessing the adverse effects of chemicals, as currently prescribed by regulation, are far from the state of the art. EU testing methodologies at the time of entry of the New Substances Directive (1981) were based, to a large extent, on tests previously developed under OECD's Chemicals Testing Programme (3.70). These in turn were based on compromises by a large number of countries with different levels of scientific expertise and with different political agendas for their chemicals industries. The introduction of the Existing Substances Regulation in 1993 has not advanced the process of assessing the effects of all industrial chemicals to any significant extent.

2.62   The limitations arising from the need to use surrogate species, the consequent use of safety or application factors, the inadequate characterisation of long-term effects, and the use of tests based on single substances, all introduce a significant degree of uncertainty into hazard characterisation. Ways of tackling uncertainties include carrying out sensitivity analyses to determine the consequences of the uncertainties, incorporating transparency into the process to permit broader debate about the significance of the results, and integrating a precautionary approach into the process that would steer decision-making towards chemical safety. None of these potential solutions to uncertainty seem to be a particular feature of current practice, but on the other hand the relatively small number of chemicals that have been comprehensively assessed for toxicity or ecotoxicity suggests that the problem is not only one of uncertainty in the results but also one of getting some results in the first place.

2.63 There is one further problem with these testing regimes, connected not with uncertainty but with the ethical (and to some extent the pragmatic) problems of using higher animals as test organisms. Increasingly, animal testing is unacceptable to many people. It is also expensive and time-consuming, which might be one of the reasons why progress in assessing chemicals has been so slow. It seems at present to be the best approach to answering some questions about toxicity, but it also seems to stand in the way of reasonable progress. Ways of avoiding animal testing must be sought.

2.64 There is clearly a need for a different approach to the characterisation of the hazards from chemicals, which will allow progress in assessing chemicals, will acknowledge inevitable uncertainties, and will help avoid the need for animal testing. We take this further in chapter 4.

EXPOSURE ASSESSMENT

The quantitative evaluation of the likely exposure of the environment, and via the environment, humans to a chemical.

2.65 The potential extent of exposure to a chemical is an important factor in determining adverse effects. Exposure can be a single event, a series of repeated events, or continuous. It can be via a single pathway or from multiple sources. Exposure is difficult to estimate for diffuse sources of pollution and for chemicals that may persist and accumulate in environmental compartments. New chemical substances (those recently placed on the market) will have no relevant measured data.

2.66 Risk assessment, however, requires that some assessment is made of the levels at which a chemical might reach a target, in order to allow a quantitative interpretation of the possible effects. This is achieved through a structured analysis of the sources of the chemical and its pathways through the environment.

Sources of chemicals

2.67 Products have a life cycle, from extraction of raw materials through to disposal or recycling. There will be emissions of the chemical into the environment at each stage of production and processing. Exposure assessment must consider releases from each of the following stages of the life cycle: extraction, production, processing, transport and storage, formulation, use, and disposal. Releases may be accumulative, and all sources have to be considered, including previous releases that may have given rise to elevated background levels of the chemical in certain environmental compartments.[38]

2.68 Data on sources of chemicals are rarely fully available. This has particularly been the case where there is a perceived confidentiality issue, with companies unwilling to reveal where and how their chemicals are used. We return to the question of data availability and confidentiality in chapter 5.

2.69 Some chemicals are intentionally released into the environment in the use phase of their life cycle and other chemicals will find their way into the environment as a consequence of their use, which will result in indirect exposure of individuals mediated via the environment. The environmental pathways by which this exposure occurs and how regulators assess the level of this exposure are described in the following sections.

Pathways through the environment

2.70 Chemicals emitted into the environment are distributed by several kinds of process: *dispersion*, which is due to the turbulent motion of the receiving medium or differential flow through the various pores in a porous material; *molecular diffusion*, which is the result of thermal movements of the molecules themselves; and *transport* in which they are carried by flow of the medium in which they are dispersed. Rates of movement differ greatly in different environmental media; for example molecular diffusion through air is some 100,000 times faster than in solution, while molecular diffusion of material associated with the solid phase may be regarded as negligible for many practical purposes. Pollutants are also transferred between media. For example, emissions to the atmosphere are transported and dispersed, and then directly contact the surface of land or water bodies ('dry deposition') or are washed out by rainfall ('wet deposition').

2.71 Pollutants can also adsorb onto solids, most importantly onto soil particles. Subsequent release from the soil particles may be very slow, will depend on the properties of the soil and pollutant, and can be affected by very local physical or chemical changes in the environment. For instance, heavy metals can be adsorbed onto peat and build up to substantial concentrations.[39] This can occur even in environments seen as 'pristine'. An example is the Lochnagar area of Scotland, where the peat has trapped metals deposited from the atmosphere, so protecting the water in the loch from contamination.[40] However, this leaves the loch vulnerable to pollution if conditions change, such as by acidification of groundwater, so that the metals are desorbed (released from the soil particles) and could then enter the loch water. Pollutants adsorbed onto soil can also be taken up by growing plants, and thus re-enter the food chain.

2.72 A chemical entering a river, through direct release, by transport in groundwater entering the river or by deposition from the atmosphere, may be transported rapidly until changing conditions – for example, higher electrolyte concentrations in an estuary – cause it to be adsorbed onto particulate material. The chemical then accumulates onto sediment, so that it is transported more slowly or effectively immobilised on sediment, which then settles out. Therefore, in the sedimentary environment, a major consideration is the degree to which a chemical will *partition* between the particulate and the aqueous phase. Partition occurs between the vapour, liquid (for example pore water in soils), solid (by sorption) and biota phases. Partition properties have a crucial influence on mobility and availability (to the food chain) of chemicals in the environment, and the relative amounts in each phase depend on the nature of the receiving environment and can differ considerably between different chemicals depending on their molecular properties, with profound effects on behaviour.

2.73 Movement of a chemical through the environment to reach a receptor organism can therefore be very complex. Gaseous emissions can be dispersed and transported rapidly over great distances. However, dispersion and transport may be slow, and can continue for very long periods after emission ceases if the chemical is desorbed slowly from soils and sediments. Exposure prediction therefore requires complex and sometimes detailed mathematical modelling of transport processes to describe all possible environmental pathways and determine how a chemical will be redistributed after release. It is, however, difficult to allow for the variability of the natural environment. Although sophisticated models have been developed to simulate natural heterogeneity (for example in soils), predicting and describing the occurrence of situations that occur rarely but that could be highly significant in relation to pollution, has been problematic. A commonly used approach is outlined in paragraph 2.77.

2.74 The objective of the modelling is to predict the exposure of the receptor organism by respiration, water ingestion, or via the food chain, as the biological effect of any chemical depends not only on its potency and the susceptibility of the affected organism, but also on the dose received. The calculation of dose received through the environment can be complex, but in essence it will be a function of the concentration of the chemical in available form and the duration of the exposure. For example, a chemical that is locked up in sediments is not normally available for biological interaction and chemicals are rarely taken up by direct contact with the solid phase. However, exposure can sometimes be unexpected. An egregious example is the case of mercury in Minamata Bay in Japan[41]: mercury from industrial emissions was assumed to be immobilised in marine sediments, but an unforeseen biological mechanism released it into the food chain with tragic effects on the human population. Recent studies have also shown that snails exposed to cadmium-contaminated soil absorbed 16% of what was previously assumed to be inaccessible cadmium[42].

2.75 Metals are elements and, therefore, not subject to decomposition (although other natural processes alter their distribution between environmental compartments). On the other hand, organic chemicals do degrade but at a rate and to decomposition products which depend on both their chemical structure and on the nature of their local environment such as the presence of oxygen and light. Bioaccumulation occurs if they build up in the cells or tissue compartments of organisms exposed to the pollutant, through high affinity for lipids (fat) or through active transport processes at the cellular level. Bioaccumulation is amplified up the food chain, as persistent pollutants are transferred to the bodies of predators and scavengers. Progressive bioaccumulation can lead to long-term toxic effects, which may only become apparent after years of exposure and are, therefore, difficult to detect and diagnose.

Exposure levels

2.76 Organisms (including humans) are exposed to pollutants via a number of different routes, shown schematically in Figure 2-III. Exposure concentrations should be derived for each environmental compartment potentially exposed. As well as considering a chemical's entire life cycle, its past releases, background concentrations and accumulation (2.67), consideration should also be given as to whether the substance can be degraded (2.75), biotically or abiotically, to give significant degradation products. Exposure levels for human risk assessments should be derived on the basis of both measured data, where available, and model calculations.[43] Human risk assessments consider exposure to chemicals directly via consumer products and occupational exposure (for which measured data are most often available) and indirectly via environmental exposure (2.128-2.132). However, there are instances in which extreme exposure to chemicals may occur through a specific route, for example, the use of household aerosols in confined spaces, where there is absolute lack of knowledge on either exposure or response, a point we revisit in paragraphs 5.37 onwards.

Figure 2-III

Exposure to chemicals: environmental pathways[44]

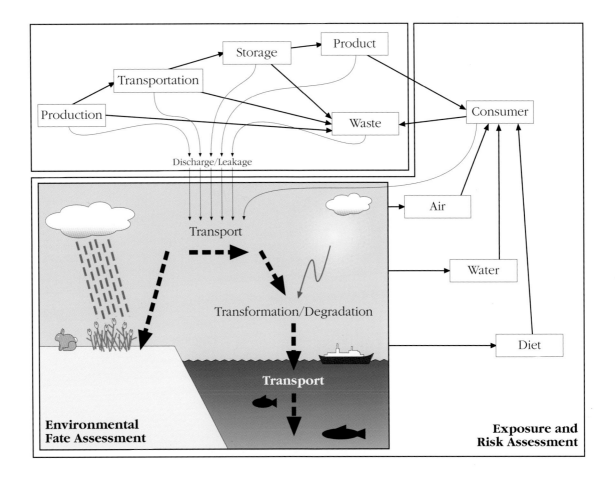

2.77 Although ideally, environmental exposure levels should be obtained from direct measurements of concentration in environmental media and ingested food, environmental exposure of organisms is usually estimated by modelling. For environmental risk assessments the modelling approach known as Mackay modelling[45] is utilised. Transport, dispersion and degradation are considered through a set of environmental compartments, to predict the concentration in each compartment[46]. In principle single releases can be modelled, but the approach is more usually applied to continuous releases. Accumulation of permanent or persistent chemicals, from previous releases and other sources, can be incorporated into the model. Degradation products can also be included. The model calculations depend on physico-chemical parameters describing the propensity of a chemical to degrade, to partition between one medium or compartment to another and to interact with living organisms. EU legislation specifies the necessary parameters and the tests to determine them (these are listed in appendix D).

2.78 One of these parameters is the octanol/water partition coefficient, $K_{o/w}$, which is the ratio of a chemical's concentration in octanol and water phases in direct contact. In effect, octanol is assumed to be representative of lipids (that is, fatty tissue). If $K_{o/w}$ is low (say < 10) the chemical is hydrophilic and migrates to or remains in an aqueous medium (such as blood). On the other hand, if $K_{o/w}$ is high (say > 10,000) the chemical is hydrophobic and partitions predominantly from an aqueous phase into a lipid phase. The parameter $K_{o/w}$ has a general significance, beyond its application in models to describe environmental exposure pathways. It indicates the propensity of a chemical to be taken up from solution in water into the fatty material of living organisms, so that the value of $K_{o/w}$ provides a first indication of how bioaccumulative a chemical is likely to be. Therefore $K_{o/w}$ is an important parameter in screening for potentially bioaccumulative chemicals. For example, a chemical with $K_{o/w} > 10^5$ (that is, log $K_{o/w} > 5$) is likely to be strongly bioaccumulative.

2.79 The basic modelling approach has been developed to describe complex and time-dependent releases and behaviour. Other forms of model describe specific environmental compartments, such as the movement of chemicals in soil pore water, a matter of particular interest in describing the behaviour of pesticides and other agrochemicals. However, there remains uncertainty in the predictions, arising both from the mathematical relationships comprising any model and from the input data and model parameters.

A new approach to exposure assessments

2.80 The European Commission White Paper on chemicals (3.30-3.54) assumes that without exposure there can be no harm and concludes that adequate knowledge about exposure is an absolute requirement for any reliable risk assessment. But information about exposure arising from downstream uses of chemicals is scarce and this shortage of data needs to be addressed.[47] As a result of the lack of appropriate exposure data in the EU, the level of toxicology testing required for chemicals is determined on the basis of tonnage thresholds of production. This is an unsatisfactory basis for determining testing requirements (2.31).

2.81 A recent joint report by the European Environment Agency and the European Science Foundation has suggested that new approaches to exposure assessment be found, to complement conventional approaches.[48] The report recommends the use of integrated exposure assessment, which is a science-based approach that combines the processes of risk estimation for humans, biota, and natural resources in one assessment.[49] This would allow the total exposure of humans and the environment to be considered in risk assessments, rather than separately as at present. Integrated exposure assessments should provide a cumulative summation (over time) of the magnitude of exposure to a toxic chemical in all media, and ideally require a comprehensive model of all exposure pathways and their inter-connections.

2.82 Such assessments should cover a product's life cycle, focus on the intrinsic properties of priority chemicals such as bioaccumulation and persistence, and make intelligent use of 'proxies' for the mixtures and other complexities that have complicated the control of chemicals in the environment.[50] This approach would still require substantial increases in the amount of exposure data needed for both humans and the environment. The proposals we make in chapter 4 for better integration of environmental monitoring will contribute to the further development of integrated exposure assessment as a technique.

RISK CHARACTERISATION

The quantitative estimation of the probability that an adverse effect will occur, and of its severity and duration in a given population under defined exposure conditions.

2.83 The determination of the relationship between actual or predicted exposure of humans to a substance (both directly and via the environment) and the level of exposure at which adverse effects might occur is termed *risk characterisation* under EU legislation.

2.84 To assess risks to human health, the concentrations to which a population may be exposed are compared with those levels at which no toxic effects are expected to occur. This is normally done by comparing the exposure level, obtained from an exposure assessment, with the dose-response assessment making use of the appropriate uncertainty factors.

2.85 The process of risk characterisation of a chemical for environmental risk assessment is based upon comparing the estimates of concentration in different environmental compartments (*predicted environmental concentrations* or PECs) with the concentration or level below which unacceptable effects are not likely to occur, taking application factors into account (*predicted no effects concentration* or PNEC). If the PEC exceeds the PNEC, the relevant environmental compartment is deemed to be at risk. This may trigger risk management action, but first there is usually an attempt to refine the PEC and PNEC by means of more sophisticated testing and modelling.

Calculation of PNEC

2.86 The PNEC is an estimate of the maximum level of a pollutant that would have no effect were it to reach that concentration at a target organism. It is derived from the hazard identification and characterisation components of the risk assessment, that is the toxicity data, incorporating application factors to attempt to allow for uncertainty in toxicological techniques (table 2.1 and box 2D). The information required to derive PNECs in the first instance is obtained from acute toxicity tests on a limited number of species. Further investigations, for example triggered by a PEC:PNEC ratio greater than 1, would include more sophisticated toxicity tests on a broader range of species.

Table 2.1

End-points needed and application factors used to derive a PNEC[51]

End-point	Application factor
L(E)C50 short-term toxicity tests (e.g. plants, earthworms, or micro-organisms)	1,000
NOEC for one long-term toxicity test (e.g. plants)	100
NOEC for additional long-term toxicity tests of two trophic levels	50
NOEC for additional long-term toxicity tests for three species of three trophic levels	10
Field data/data of model ecosystems	case-by-case

2.87 The determination of PNEC is based almost entirely on biological effects. Assessment of a chemical's potential to damage physical components of the environment is limited. For example, for $PNEC_{air}$ the evaluation of abiotic risks to the atmosphere requires only a consideration of whether a chemical might have a potential impact on global warming, ozone depletion in the stratosphere, ozone formation in the troposphere or acidification (formation of acidifying components that can be deposited during precipitation), rather than any actual tests for properties relevant to these effects.

BOX 2D   **CALCULATION OF PNEC FOR DIFFERENT ENVIRONMENTAL COMPARTMENTS**

Aquatic environment

Testing for effects in the aquatic environment is carried out on algae, *Daphnia magna* and fish. The aim is to derive a median lethal concentration (LC_{50}) for short-term tests and a no observed effects concentration (NOEC) for long-term tests (2.37-2.40).

Terrestrial environment

At present, testing is focused on the effects of chemical pollutants on a limited number of soil organisms.[52] There are limited requirements to undertake standard tests for soil functions (if $PEC_{soil}/PNEC_{soil}$ is > 1 on the basis of toxicity data for soil organisms or on the basis of the partition coefficient for the chemical/soil water),[53] but not for functions such as buffering capacity and filtration. Nor are there standard tests required for groundwater, although exposure of soil micro-organisms via pore water and soil are considered. The same assessment factors used for the aquatic environment are applied to the terrestrial assessment.

Atmospheric environment

Toxicological data on animal species other than mammals are not usually available for the air compartment. Hence, only a qualitative assessment of PEC:PNEC can be carried out. Short-term chemical concentrations in air are considered unlikely to cause adverse effects and so long-term chronic toxicity is usually calculated. Tests on invertebrates are rare (there have been some fumigation tests for pesticides on honey bees) and tests on herbaceous species are also usually lacking.

Calculation of PEC

2.88 PEC values are derived from the exposure assessment (2.76-2.79), including, where available, environmental monitoring data. PEC values are derived for both local and regional situations and these may be combined with PNEC values for each of the different compartments leading to a number of PEC:PNEC ratios for each substance.

2.89 Many of the uncertainties inherent in estimating PECs (and PNECs) and in the risk assessment process overall, are the subject of debate or are matters of opinion. There is, however, no specific opportunity within the process for seeking a broader range of views and opinions beyond those of the regulators and their specialist advisors in EU states.

SOCIO-ECONOMIC ANALYSIS

2.90   Risk assessment, as described above, provides information about the potential of a chemical to harm the environment, based on what is known about its intrinsic properties and intended use. In current practice this is seen as an objective, scientific phase, preceding and informing decisions about the acceptability of risk and options for risk management. Though as we have seen, the many uncertainties, assumptions and judgements embodied in the risk assessment process make this distinction somewhat artificial.

2.91   Under the Existing Substances Regulation, a socio-economic assessment is carried out following the risk assessment and preceding the preparation of risk reduction proposals. It is limited in scope and roughly fulfils the function of a regulatory impact assessment.[54] It focuses mainly on the costs to those who use the chemical in their commercial operations, and the revenue lost by the manufacturer, though some consideration of alternatives and the wider consequences of any controls on the chemical are included.

2.92   Drawing on experience in its member countries, OECD has developed a framework for integrating socio-economic analysis in chemical risk management decision-making.[55] It sees socio-economic analysis as a separate process from risk assessment, with the latter being a vital precursor to the effective use of socio-economic analysis. The objective of socio-economic analysis is then one of helping to determine whether a proposed regulation 'is necessary or burdensome'.[56]

2.93   Socio-economic analysis, as represented in the OECD framework, requires 'rigorous analysis of costs and benefits' as well as 'better representation of, and consultation with, different stakeholders' (defined as those affected by the proposed legislation).[57] Although the framework report discusses and advocates a range of techniques, including cost effectiveness and multi-criteria approaches, there is an emphasis on cost-benefit analysis, which 'provides the methodology underlying most of the current guidelines'.[58] It is envisaged that stakeholders would be involved from the early stages of the analysis, and the report notes that a number of countries (Australia, Canada, the Netherlands, the US and the Nordic countries) already place significant emphasis on such involvement.

2.94   The OECD framework for socio-economic analysis differs from the approach advocated in our Twenty-first Report in a number of significant respects. In the light of the Twenty-first Report, and our discussion of current practice in this chapter, it is not clear to us that quantitative risk assessment, conducted prior to and separately from analysis of social and economic implications, can provide the robust and rigorous basis for socio-economic analysis that OECD envisages. Indeed, its framework document acknowledges that 'for all but the most site specific issues, comprehensive assessments of environmental risks and the benefits of reduced chemical exposure are rarely possible'.[59]

2.95   We also take a more circumspect view than OECD of the appropriateness (not just the practicality) of monetary valuation of the environment and of cost-benefit analysis as a basis for making environmental policy choices. OECD acknowledges that monetary valuation may focus the benefit assessment on species, communities and ecosystems that have a recognisable value to people. If concern for the environment is more than purely instrumental, or if people are not generally aware of, and therefore do not give appropriate value to, important environmental functions, then valuation is much more difficult and may be inappropriate.[60]

2.96 Finally, while we endorse OECD's emphasis on early and full involvement of stakeholders, this in itself will not ensure that public values, in relation to risks as well as to social and economic impacts, can properly be taken into account. We make recommendations to address this in chapter 4.

ENVIRONMENTAL MONITORING

2.97 We have explained in this chapter why risk assessment is limited in its potential to predict the fate and effects of chemicals in the environment. In chapter 4 we propose improvements that will both speed up the process and, to some extent, reduce uncertainties. But we have also pointed out that some sources of uncertainty will remain, for example, unforeseen toxicological end-points (2.18) or unexpected natural processes (2.74). Some of this uncertainty could be resolved through better integration of environmental monitoring into the assessment and management of chemicals.

2.98 In a limited way, monitoring is already used to support chemicals risk assessment. The EU handbook on environmental risk assessment recommends that existing monitoring data on the concentration of chemicals in the environment should be compared to the calculated PEC.[61] The Environment Agency undertakes limited targeted monitoring programmes to inform risk assessments carried out under the Existing Substances Regulation to aid decision-making.[62]

2.99 But environmental monitoring is broader than this, and monitoring data can be used to provide a more complete assessment of the ecological effects of toxicants than is possible through risk assessment alone.

2.100 Guidance from the United Nations Environment Programme (UNEP) and the IPCS[63] also argues that because of the limitations of toxicity testing in predicting ecological effects (toxicity tests are carried out under constant laboratory conditions and cannot mimic the complex and fluctuating field environment and the biotic interactions that occur), a comprehensive ecological risk assessment model should be used that incorporates use of monitoring data and better ecotoxicological understanding and ecosystem knowledge. In addition to chemical measurements of environmental toxicants, monitoring should include the assessment of effects of toxicants and pollutants in an ecological context, either by means of their accumulation in organisms other than man, or by looking for abnormal ecological effects at the level of species, community or ecosystem ('ecological monitoring').

2.101 In the next section we discuss monitoring of the fate and effects of chemicals in the environment and monitoring related to health effects in humans (environmental epidemiology). We define what we mean by environmental monitoring and explain the sorts of monitoring currently under way that could be used to support the assessment and management of chemicals. In chapter 4 we will recommend ways of integrating such monitoring into a chemicals assessment and management programme.

MONITORING CHEMICALS IN THE ENVIRONMENT

2.102 Environmental monitoring encompasses a very large and diverse range of activities. We are using the term to include, for example:

- compliance monitoring – for instance, measuring concentrations of chemicals in emissions to ensure that statutory limits are not breached;

- quality monitoring – observing trends in the quality of the environment as indicated by, for example, the chemical and biological quality of rivers, the presence of key pollutants in urban air or trends in populations of key indicator species;

- investigations – monitoring to explain specific phenomena, for example, tracking nutrient concentrations in the sea to improve understanding of algal blooms, or analysing animal and human tissues and biological fluids to investigate mortalities and morbidity;

- research – improving understanding of environmental processes and the way they are affected by human activity; and

- epidemiology – using statistical data to establish correlations between, for example, pollution sources and indicators of human health.

2.103 Monitoring schemes should comprise observational activities in which well-characterised samples are repeatedly collected in a well-defined temporal and spatial framework, and observations made using quality assured techniques.[64] The European Environment Agency and the European Science Foundation[65] recently suggested that an approach for chemical monitoring could be based around three key questions:

- what is the size and nature of the production of chemicals that flow into the environment via products and processes, and what are their principal pathways into the environment?

- how do these chemicals distribute themselves, after initial partitioning into the different parts of the environment (air, water, soil, *etc.*)? and

- where do the flows of chemicals collect and concentrate?

This approach has been described and discussed in some detail for pesticides by the Pesticide in the Environment Working Group[66].

2.104 This implies that the types of monitoring most suited to chemicals management would include collecting data about production and use, and measuring concentrations and loads of chemicals in the environment. However, it is also important to detect and then measure the effects that the chemicals are having on the natural and physical environment, including on human health. This presents a major challenge – detecting chemicals and observing effects do not always lead to reliable identification of causal links between the chemicals and the effects.

2.105 The regulatory regimes for the control of the production and use of general chemicals rely almost entirely on predictive techniques, and particularly risk assessment. The use of monitoring information, if at all, tends to be *post facto* (for example, the recognition that organotin compounds were damaging marine molluscs leading to controls on the marketing and use of certain anti-fouling products) or addressed towards specific concerns (such as the government's Endocrine Disruption in the Marine Environment (EDMAR) programme on endocrine-disrupting chemicals). The regulatory regime for pesticides does include an element of post-release monitoring, such as the monitoring of pesticide residues in food, pesticide levels in drinking water, pesticide-related incidents in humans and wildlife, and levels of pesticide usage. Pesticide approval holders are also legally required to submit immediately any new information on the potentially dangerous effects of a product, or of residues of an active substance contained in a product, on human or animal health, groundwater or the environment. However, the Environment Agency has told us that its monitoring data on the impact of pesticides on the environment, for example on freshwaters, are not included in the regulatory assessments.[67]

2.106 Because risk assessment lacks accuracy, the absence of formal arrangements for follow-up monitoring of chemicals other than pesticides, either to check the accuracy of the predictions from the assessment or to warn of unexpected effects does appear to be an major omission. The Environment Agency's strategy for chemicals[68] appears to be a valuable move to correct this, as it includes the intention to identify emerging problems caused by chemicals through monitoring and observation of environment impacts.

Current environmental monitoring programmes

2.107 The regulatory and other measures relevant to chemicals being introduced throughout Europe are both critical to the protection of the environment (including human health) and expensive to society. Monitoring information is necessary to ensure that risk management programmes are effective and to help identify adjustments in those programmes where necessary. Even chemicals that have been removed from the market may remain in the environment, potentially causing damage, for a long time. For example, DDT, which was withdrawn from the UK market during the 1980s, can still be detected in some landfill discharges.

2.108 Monitoring for regulatory purposes tends to be targeted at particular groups of chemicals (such as pesticides) or environments (for example freshwater). Much other monitoring carried out in the UK is aimed at describing the state of the environment and trends in that state, some of which can contribute to our understanding of the fate and effects of chemicals in the environment. Some of this is co-ordinated internationally and makes data and methodologies from other countries available. The investment in environmental monitoring is large, and has contributed to understanding of the way chemicals behave in the environment and affect its components, providing tools and data to improve that understanding further. But monitoring specifically relevant to chemicals in the environment has been sparse.

2.109 Several institutes and regulatory agencies are responsible for monitoring chemicals and the state of the environment in the UK, including the Food Standards Agency, the Health and Safety Executive, the Environment Agency, the Scottish Environment Protection Agency, the Centre for Environment, Fisheries and Aquaculture Science, the Joint Nature Conservation Council, local councils, the Natural Environment Research Council (incorporating the British Geological Survey, the Centre for Ecology and Hydrology, and the Centre for Atmospheric Science), and the Biotechnology and Biological Sciences Research Council.

2.110 The main monitoring initiatives in the UK can be divided between the four relevant environmental compartments (appendix E):

i.   **Marine monitoring** The UK National Marine Monitoring Programme monitors levels of chemical substances as part of the obligations laid down in various European directives and international agreements, such as the OSPAR Convention (described in chapter 3);

ii. **Freshwater** In England and Wales, the Environment Agency is responsible for monitoring the state of the freshwater environment under the Environment Act (1995). The Scottish Environment Protection Agency and the Environment and Heritage Service in Northern Ireland have similar responsibilities;

iii. **Air** The Air Quality Strategy for the UK sets standards and objectives to be achieved for eight key air pollutants between 2003 and 2008. The EC Air Framework Directive and a number of substance-specific directives include monitoring requirements for air quality. The Department for Food and Rural Affairs (Defra) oversees a national network of air monitoring stations across the UK to meet the above requirements, with additional monitoring carried out by local authorities;

iv. **Terrestrial** The amount of chemical monitoring carried out in the terrestrial environment is comparatively limited. However, the European Commission is attempting to bring current initiatives into an overall framework. The Joint Nature Conservation Committee's National Predatory Bird Monitoring Scheme operated by the Centre for Ecology and Hydrology is the only scheme that monitors the terrestrial environment for chemical levels in biota on a national basis.

2.111 The Joint Nature Conservation Committee, the Centre for Ecology and Hydrology, the British Geological Survey, the Countryside Agencies, some university departments and environmental non-governmental organisations (NGOs) also have monitoring programmes with objectives not necessarily related to chemicals, but which yield information that, if properly integrated and the methodologies standardised, could inform chemicals assessment and management programmes.

Limitations of environmental monitoring

2.112 Monitoring programmes incorporate inherent and methodological uncertainties and limitations. Sampling techniques must be guided by statistical principles or risk, producing enticing but meaningless data. In highly variable systems, for example, in estuaries or mobile animal populations, the intensity of sampling required to provide statistically valid data can prove to be impractically high. Analytical techniques are seldom accurate, leading to wide confidence limits, and limits of detection can be high, resulting in significant concentrations of chemicals being overlooked. Interpretation of the results can be difficult. There is also a sense in which monitoring is always post-release and, therefore, potentially post-damage. Conversely, risk assessment is designed to be predictive. Monitoring is not then a replacement for attempting to predict the potential for a chemical to cause harm. However, there seems to be a clear case for it to be integrated into chemicals assessment and management programmes as an essential adjunct.

2.113 There are also significant limitations in present coverage. Defra (on behalf of the Chemicals Stakeholder Forum) sponsored the collation of information on current monitoring activities in the UK and commissioned consultants Risk and Policy Analysts to compile a database of current activities (excluding various activities relating to emissions and pesticides).[69] Of the 174 monitoring activities included in the database, only five of the monitoring schemes cover more than a single environmental compartment, and the study reported a lack of adequate links between monitoring activities. It also concluded that:

- regulation was a key driver for monitoring chemicals in the environment, such that only regulated chemicals were monitored;

- few of the chemicals in the Existing Substances Regulation priority lists were monitored routinely;

- monitoring activities were generally media-specific and there were only a few examples where chemicals had been measured in more than one medium;

- improved linkages between monitoring activities would provide improved information on the environmental fate of pollutants.

2.114 A study conducted by the US Environmental Protection Agency (US EPA) showed that their environmental monitoring data sources covered only a small proportion of high production industrial chemicals in the USA.[70] The European Environment Agency[71] reported that European coverage of monitoring data for persistent organic pollutants and other organohalogens was rather patchy. Information on degradations, transformations, by-products and exposure to mixtures was also poor, and most monitoring programmes focused on mobile media (water and air), often neglecting soil, sediments and consumer products. A recent report on chemicals in the European environment by the European Environment Agency and the European Science Foundation[72] noted that, in Europe, monitoring was partial, unco-ordinated, sometimes out of date and, on many occasions, irrelevant to current policy needs. Centralised knowledge about different chemical monitoring activities was incomplete and there were very substantial data gaps in information on chemical exposures and impacts, especially concerning vulnerable groups and ecosystems. Soil, food, consumer products, human tissues and biological fluids (such as milk) are often the most relevant monitoring targets yet only a few substances appeared to be routinely monitored in these media,[73] mainly heavy metals, a few persistent organic pollutants and some pesticides. Among OECD countries, Japan appears to be the only country that relies on environmental monitoring data when evaluating risks of industrial chemicals.

2.115 The Commission also heard evidence of considerable wastage in current statutory monitoring programmes.[74] Some of the monitoring requirements in European legislation reflect concerns that are now out of date, leading to expensive monitoring that yields utterly predictable results. Although the example of DDT was offered previously as a chemical that has been phased out but which can still be found in rivers (2.107), its sources are well known, its presence in certain locations is predictable, and its propensity to cause damage is well understood. There is nothing to be gained by regularly measuring its unvarying concentration, at high cost, and yet the legislation requires that this be done. Rationalisation of such EU legislation would enable monitoring effort to be more targeted and risk based.

2.116 At present only a few monitoring schemes in the UK effectively integrate both biological and chemical monitoring.[75] Such monitoring schemes provide data on the status of populations or communities of organisms, in addition to other biological and chemical data that can be used in determining cause and effect. Two examples of schemes that do effectively integrate biological and chemical data are the monitoring of the effects of various chemicals on predatory birds (appendix E) and the impact of anti-foulants on some coastal invertebrates. In chapter 4 we recommend ways of using integrated monitoring techniques of this sort systematically to detect new chemical problems.

Biologically active chemicals in the environment

2.117 Compared to other classes of chemicals, the impacts of pesticides on the environment and human health are comparatively well monitored[76] in order to meet regulatory requirements (2.105). The EC Biocidal Products Directive (table 3.2), requires the monitoring of inputs of non-agricultural biocides into the environment and the collection of data concerning their use, fate and subsequent distribution.[77] Pesticides and biocides are designed to be biologically active and their uses are often widely dispersive. Similar considerations apply to veterinary medicines, though until very recently there has been no regulatory activity to monitor their release into the environment. There are no such regulatory requirements for the monitoring of pharmaceuticals, even though they are often very ecotoxic.

2.118 The Commission has heard evidence that there are particular environmental concerns over the impacts of veterinary medicines on the environment,[78] and examples of chemicals that are suspected of disrupting ecosystems include synthetic pyrethroid sheep dips (box 5B), chemicals used to treat sea lice in fish farming, the antiparasitic chemicals used to treat livestock and the antibiotics added to animal feed as growth promoters.[79] The Environment Agency's Pesticides in the Environment Working Group also recommended that the Veterinary Medicines Directorate should make available data on the volume of sales, use and environmental impact of such products.[80]

2.119 The recognition of xenobiotics as potential endocrine disrupters even at low levels has also highlighted the possibility of biological effects being caused by human pharmaceuticals, veterinary medicines or dietary supplements. As well as lacking monitoring data, human pharmaceuticals, unlike other classes of biologically active chemicals, do not undergo environmental risk assessment. This is in spite of environmental concerns about a wide range of drug groups including beta adrenoreceptor blockers, non-steroidal anti-inflammatories, anti-convulsants, oral contraceptives, lipid-reducing agents, antibiotics, anti-depressants, anti-cancer drugs, and analgesics. Pharmacokinetic data indicate that the human excretory rate of some unchanged drugs exceeds 50%. They are detectable in sewage effluent,[81] and some have been shown to be persistent and bioaccumulative.[82] Recent research shows common drugs can induce sub-lethal and significant ecological effects on freshwater zooplankton. Sulfamethoxazole (an antimicrobial drug), fluoxetine (an anti-depressant), and clofibric acid (a cholesterol-lowering drug) were found to affect significantly normal developmental processes such as growth and sex differentiation in *Daphnia magna* at ambient concentrations.[83]

2.120 The ecological impact of such pharmaceuticals is still uncertain, although their environmental release is substantial. The Scientific Committee on Toxicity, Ecotoxicity and the Environment (SCTEE) (of the EC's Health and Consumer Protection Directorate General) noted that 'some human pharmaceuticals are used in large volumes (> 100 tonnes/year in the EU), have a widespread use and may give rise to acute and chronic ecotoxicological effects in the aquatic environment'.[84] They also noted that a full risk assessment could not be carried out for many pharmaceuticals as information on use, fate and environmental effects was lacking. A study in the UK of risk assessment for environmental effects of pharmaceuticals found that on the basis of worst-case assumptions, PEC:PNEC ratios (2.86) were greater than 1 for 8 of the 60 compounds tested representing the majority of pharmaceutical sales by volume. The highest ratio was found for paracetamol.[85]

2.121 The contraceptive pill ethinyl oestradiol is one of the few pharmaceutical substances that have been widely investigated for effects when present in the environment. High concentrations of this chemical are found in effluent from sources such as urban conurbations. An Environment Agency review of human pharmaceuticals in the environment concluded, however, that ethinyl oestradiol makes a relatively small contribution to endocrine disruption effects in fish when compared with natural hormones from sewage, in spite of its relative potency and persistence in the environment.[86] The review also found that pharmaceuticals were unlikely to cause acute toxic effects in the aquatic environment, but that data on chronic toxicity are lacking and it is therefore difficult to consider long-term effects or effects in combination with other endocrine-disrupting chemicals. The review provided a summary of studies of the levels of pharmaceuticals found in sewage effluent, surface waters and groundwater (both in the UK and worldwide), which showed that some chemicals are detectable in UK surface waters at appreciable concentrations.

2.122 A study by the US Geological Survey has also shown pharmaceutical compounds to be accumulating in streams and waterways in the US. The levels of 15 prescription pharmaceuticals and seven non-prescription pharmaceuticals were measured in 139 streams in 30 US States. This study also noted that measured concentrations of these substances were generally low and rarely exceeded drinking water guidelines or aquatic protection criteria but that guidelines were not in place for many of these contaminants and little was known about the potential effects of mixtures of these compounds.[87]

2.123 We are concerned that these highly active chemicals are not being subject to systematic regulatory monitoring of their fate and effects in the environment. A draft proposal being considered by the European Medicines Evaluation Agency,[88] would introduce mandatory environmental risk assessment on all pharmaceuticals. We strongly support this initiative. The proposals for a more integrated approach to monitoring outlined in chapter 4 would provide the basis for monitoring in support of such assessments.

ENVIRONMENTAL EPIDEMIOLOGY

2.124 Environmental epidemiology is concerned with the impact of environmental contamination on health outcomes. The over-riding aim of environmental epidemiology is to establish causal links between exposures and health effects. Although epidemiology has influenced chemical risk management debates in the past (such as that over asbestos), it is often difficult to establish with certainty whether a chemical is having an adverse impact on human or animal populations (appendix E, E.29-E.37). This is due to the large number of confounding factors (susceptibility, diet, exposure pathways, exposure to degradation products, and delays between exposure and observation of effects) hindering the detection of causal relationships.[89] To show that a causal relationship exists, a number of guideline tests have been developed. These include the consistency of results between different studies, the way in which the results of the different studies fit together (coherence), whether there is a dose-response relationship between the proposed causal factor and the effect, and whether the sequence of events makes sense.[90] However, proof of causality is often very difficult to establish even using such criteria and often relies on expert judgement.

Susceptibility

2.125 There is increasing public concern about the protection of people who are especially sensitive to chemical exposure, and the effects on humans of chronic low-level exposure to chemicals. Susceptible population sub-groups are usually assumed to include children, pregnant women, people with pre-existing health conditions, the elderly and certain ethnic groups.[91]

2.126 The concept of susceptibility can be defined in a number of ways in different scientific and policy settings, ranging from easily identifiable sets of sub-population traits to individual genetic variability. Scientific literature tends to define susceptibility in terms of individual variability, particularly genetic susceptibility. The susceptibility of individuals within a population to a particular chemical varies widely and is dependent on many genetic and environmental factors, including the state of nutrition or presence of disease.[92] At all levels, from uptake to excretion, the molecules in the human body that interact with specific chemicals are subject to genetic variation. In particular it is believed that the genetic variation in certain enzymes, especially those in the liver and at epithelial surfaces, responsible for metabolising chemicals (the phase II enzymes, see appendix E, box E2) usually determines the extent of endogenous protection against chemicals that might cause genetic damage in humans.[93]

2.127 Studies looking at human health have to contend with a multitude of potential confounding influences, not least to do with the heterogeneity of the lifestyle and mobility of the individuals in a population. Variation in susceptibility is often unknown, but is increasingly important in risk assessment.[94] Another example of such complexity is multiple chemical sensitivity (MCS) syndrome (box 2E). Although risk assessment approaches have considered susceptibility to varying extents, it has not been considered comprehensively or effectively. Inter-disciplinary views of susceptibility tend to incorporate several concepts, including physiological state, risk, variability, probability, exposure that exceeds the population norm, adverse health outcomes following exposure, and dose response. All these factors influencing susceptibility need to be considered to understand the risk posed by chemicals, but considerable research is required to understand their inter-relationships.[95] It should also be noted that epidemiological studies will not usually identify an effect to which only a small percentage of the population is susceptible.[96]

Exposure data

2.128 For human risk assessments it is recommended that all available good quality monitoring data be used in the exposure assessment. However, data on human exposure to chemicals are limited, and the most reliable data tend to be on occupational exposure (2.137). Difficulties can occur in establishing levels of human exposure to toxic chemicals as it can occur through a number of routes, with diet and exposure via consumer products being two significant pathways.

2.129 In the United States, routine monitoring of human exposure to chemicals is carried out by the Centers for Disease Control and Prevention. The main output has been the *National Report on Human Exposure to Environmental Chemicals*, part of a wider National Health and Nutritional Examination Survey (NHANES). The report aims to determine which chemicals get into the population and at what levels, as well as to determine the prevalence of levels of chemicals at above known toxicity levels, establish reference ranges to determine whether particular individuals, groups or susceptible members of the population have higher exposure, assess the success of chemical controls, and set priorities for research on human health effects.[97]

BOX 2E	**MULTIPLE CHEMICAL SENSITIVITY (MCS) SYNDROME**

Multiple chemical sensitivity (MCS), or idiopathic environmental intolerance (IEI), is an acquired disorder with multiple recurrent symptoms associated with environmental chemicals in low concentrations that are otherwise well tolerated by the majority of people. A similar syndrome has been described with chronic exposure to pesticides, for example organophosphate sheep dips.

At present there is considerable debate as to whether such syndromes represent externalisation (somatisation) of psychological or psychiatric distress, or a true physical disorder for which no unifying symptoms can be provided. It has been suggested that MCS leads to neurone damage in the brain, but positron emission tomography (PET) has so far not detected functional brain changes.[98] Formal psychometric testing has shown that MCS subjects score higher than controls on scales of chemical odour intolerance and anxiety sensitivity.[99]

A detailed assessment of 264 consecutive cases of MCS revealed that a psychiatric disorder (39%), somatic condition (19%), or a combination of the two provided sufficient explanation of the symptoms.[100] Toxic chemicals were regarded as the most probable cause in only five cases.

One interesting hypothesis is that in certain individuals there is an over-sensitivity of the vomeronasal organ (a tubular organ in the nose) leading to systemic effects.[101] The capsaicin (extract of hot pepper) inhalation test has been shown to reflect the degree of airway sensitivity to chemicals[102] and reinforces the view[103] that further studies are needed on provocation testing to find positive criteria for MCS.

2.130 The report represents the start of an ongoing assessment of the exposure of the US population to environmental chemicals using *biomonitoring*. Biomonitoring uses the assessment of human exposure to chemicals by measuring the chemicals or their metabolites (breakdown products) in human specimens such as blood or urine. Blood and urine levels of 116 environmental chemicals, including 13 heavy metals, seven phthalate esters, six organophosphate pesticides, four organophosphate pesticide metabolites, nine organochlorine pesticides, three carbamate pesticides, five herbicides, and four biocides, were measured in a sample of individuals as part of NHANES.

2.131 The US EPA has also carried out National Human Exposure Assessment Survey (NHEXAS) Phase I pilot surveys to investigate the multiple pathways and media distribution of exposures to several classes of chemicals. The surveys were designed to test the feasibility of conducting a national survey to estimate the status of human exposure to potentially high-risk chemicals. NHEXAS also aims to measure 'total exposure', the levels of chemicals participants absorb through the air they breathe, the food, drinking water, and other beverages they consume, and via the soil and dust in their home environments; chemical levels in the blood and urine of participants were also determined. Phase II of NHEXAS will be a national study conducted on the basis of the Phase I results, and Phase III will follow up by studying selected sub-populations.[104]

2.132 In the UK, the Food Standards Agency funds several monitoring activities in relation to dietary exposure to chemicals in food. The most widely monitored chemicals in foods are PCBs, dioxins and metals (most commonly tin but also arsenic, cadmium, lead, mercury and zinc). Monitoring activities for food are designed either to reflect the national diet or to focus on food produced in certain localities. The most frequent food analysed for PCBs and dioxins is cows' milk. Recent surveys have included dioxins and PCBs in fish oil supplements, and tin in canned fruit and vegetables. There are also a number of monitoring activities focused on chemicals that migrate from packaging materials into food.[105] Other UK-based assessments of human exposure to chemicals include the SUREmilk Project (box 2F).

BOX 2F   **THE SUREMILK PROJECT** [106]

The SUREmilk Project (SUrveillance of REsidues in human milk) has been jointly funded by four government agencies – the Food Standards Agency, the Department of Health, Defra, and the Health and Safety Executive – and is being carried out by the University of Leeds in co-operation with the Central Science Laboratory. The project aims to explore the feasibility of collecting, storing and managing a regional archive of breast milk samples, and to pilot such methods prior to the establishment of a national archive.

A structured set of milk samples collected from three cohorts of women, is being analysed for five main contaminant groups: organochlorine pesticide residues; phthalates; heavy metals; PCBs; and dioxins and furans. The aim is to identify the range of variation in levels of these chemicals in breast milk, and account for how and why these contaminants appear in breast milk (for example, through diet, home environment or occupation). The results, together with information on the dietary exposure of other population groups to any chemicals detected, will inform decisions by regulatory bodies on the need for strategies to reduce their use, emissions and dietary exposure.

The end-point for such work will be to derive realistic estimates of risk to infants from consuming measurable levels of contaminants, and to put them in the context of the measurable health gains of breast feeding. The information will be made available to the public in an accessible way.

Linking effects to exposure

2.133 Although national morbidity statistics are collated, human health is not monitored on a routine basis in the UK. There have been some studies of people's health in circumstances where they might be expected to be exposed to chemicals, of chemicals and disease, and of chemical levels (such as asbestos) in human tissues. But establishing cause-effect relationships has proved difficult, for instance due to multiple chemical sensitivity as described in box 2E. Thus, while there is increasing information on health effects, for example, drug prescribing and cancer registers collected on a geographical basis by the Health Service, this has not been aligned with environmental monitoring. There is also a considerable body of material on chemicals in the human diet.

2.134 Another approach has been adopted by the Small Area Health Statistics Unit (SAHSU), which was established in 1987 to investigate the incidence of disease around point sources of pollution in occupational and 'high' concentration exposure settings and to advise government. SAHSU was established in response to considerable scientific and public interest in the distribution of diseases across small areas that arose following the identification of a 'cluster' of childhood leukaemia cases near the Sellafield nuclear plant in 1983. SAHSU incorporates national cause-specific data on deaths (from 1981), cancers from the national cancer registry (from 1974), hospital admissions (from 1992) and congenital malformations (from 1983), using the postcode of residence to locate cases to within 100 m.

2.135 SAHSU is an important resource in this country for carrying out environmental epidemiological studies. There are, however, some problems in applying the principles of small area health statistics. Although this methodology is excellent for establishing and localising occupational or point-source causes of illness, some pollutants influencing human health are not derived from point sources. Where exposure is via multiple routes or exposure is influenced by meteorological (air) or geological (earth) factors to create plumes that are non-concentric from the source, new methodology is needed to develop more realistic models of exposure. Complex interactions between environmental factors at different times during human developmental stages also present severe problems for applying the SASHU approach. Obtaining statistically significant signals in the analysis of effects on health by chemicals is often difficult against typically variable backgrounds unless the health signal is profound, for example in the case of mesothelioma and asbestos exposure.

2.136 Causality can only be assessed on probabilistic (probable or most likely) and not deterministic (predictable or known) criteria, that is, potential cause and effect relationships are weak and often subjective. Hence, the results of statistical association with an environmental measure in epidemiological studies must always be interpreted with caution and complemented with other approaches including laboratory studies. In addition the accurate assessment of exposure is crucial in strengthening the value of population-based epidemiology (2.128-2.132). As stated in the Commission's Twenty-first Report,[107] when evaluating such studies, potential sources of bias must be taken into account, the principal ones being selection, misclassification and confounding, and where association is found between an exposure and effect it must be assessed against standard criteria (such as the Bradford Hill criteria) to determine whether the association is causal.

2.137 At present, however, exposure assessments are often conducted within different legislative and regulatory frameworks (chapter 3), with different sets of information and at different levels of accuracy. Susceptible population groups, such as the elderly, with varying resilience to chemicals are rarely taken into account (2.125-2.127). The monitoring of some chemicals with known biological activity (2.117-2.123) and other chemicals of concern is inadequate, with significant gaps in the data on exposure via soil, consumer products and biological tissues.[108]

2.138 Although useful data on human exposure are sometimes available, they are not generally included in quantitative risk assessments. Some researchers have proposed a more extensive use of human data, since real-life exposures reflect the actual situation. Epidemiology has thus far only provided a useful input to decision-making where the results have been relatively clear-cut. This has happened specifically in the case of occupational exposures to harmful substances, where an unusual disease such as mesothelioma can be attributed to a specific environmental cause, in this case asbestos, and in the cases of easily measured indicators, such as IQ and blood lead levels in children.

2.139 Despite the current limitations, epidemiology has the potential to contribute to the risk management of chemicals if the appropriate methodologies are employed and the necessary exposure data are available.[109] Epidemiological data can provide a sense of perspective in relation to the actual degree of risk posed by chemicals to the public in the larger context of public health priorities. In chapter 4 we propose a wider role for epidemiological data in the risk management of chemicals.

COST OF MONITORING

2.140 Environmental monitoring is costly. For example, the Environment Agency spends about £20 million per annum on its environmental monitoring programmes.[110] New environmental monitoring programmes, or even the redirection of existing ones, must be clearly justified if they are to receive funding either from government or from industry.

2.141 On the other hand, the cost of risk assessment is not small either. The testing requirements alone for the base set assessment of a single new chemical cost around €20,000, and a full level 2 data set costs around €300,000.[111] It has been estimated that implementing forthcoming EU legislation (REACH, discussed in chapter 3) for all 30,000 chemicals on the European market would cost around €4 billion.[112]

2.142 In this chapter we have shown that risk assessment on its own is not effective, and that the monitoring that could enhance our understanding of the fate and effects of chemicals in the environment is not being carried out effectively. In chapter 4 we recommend ways of making better use of monitoring in a chemicals assessment and management programme. To a large extent our proposals rely on existing monitoring but this will need to be augmented and redirected to some degree. However, our proposals will also reduce considerably the cost of assessing chemicals, and therefore the main challenge will not necessarily be to find new money but rather to re-assign funds between the bodies devoted to risk assessment and those devoted to monitoring.

IS THE CURRENT ASSESSMENT SYSTEM WORKING?

2.143 It is clear that a substantial effort has been expended over many years to develop the chemicals assessment procedures described above. But despite the resources and time spent on testing and assessing chemicals there are still many unknowns about the possible impacts of chemicals on the environment. More than 20 years after the introduction of the new chemicals scheme in Europe and almost 10 years after the Existing Substances Regulation, the proportion of chemicals on the market that has been properly tested and assessed still remains extremely small.

2.144 Chemical risk assessments, due to the uncertainties and information gaps in available ecotoxicological knowledge, rely too heavily on simple models, embodying a number of flaws and assumptions that limit their efficiency. As with human toxicity testing, to counter this problem the risk assessment process usually incorporates a number of safety factors, application factors, acute to chronic ratios and other attempts to inject a degree of precaution into the process. Claims that this process is scientific must be doubted – the basis for using these factors is often a political or regulatory decision, and subjective interpretation can dominate the risk assessment. The problem is not one of subjectivity *per se*; it is unacknowledged subjectivity in what is often represented as an 'objective' risk assessment process.

2.145 Chemical risk assessment is already a very expensive process. But even given access to unlimited funds we could not hope to perfect it. Current risk assessment procedures follow the law of diminishing returns, in that additional effort will not increase our ability to protect the health of the environment by a proportionate amount.

2.146 A key consideration is whether risk assessment should always be a prerequisite to a decision on whether or not a chemical should be marketed. History teaches us that the no effect levels used in risk assessments are time-dependent properties – our lack of understanding of how chemicals interact with biological systems leads us to regular revisions of the threat posed. However, despite giving lip service to the precautionary principle, regulatory authorities continue to insist that control must be on the basis of known risk, regardless of other indications of concern. This is in spite of the fact that problems continue to occur due to unforeseen risks and the inability of the system to pick up on problems in the making and react quickly.

2.147 The challenge posed by evaluation of existing chemicals in the coming decades, and the rapid changes in technology available that could be applied to these problems indicate that a more robust approach will be required in the future. This approach will need to combine precaution with an evidence-based approach, and provide decision-makers with timely advice.

2.148 To speed up the assessment of the environmental risk of all industrial chemicals to a time-scale far shorter than either that of the current regime or of that which might flow from forthcoming EU legislation (REACH, see chapter 3), we propose a faster and more transparent screening process, moving towards a better understanding of environmental processes, and with tighter integration of monitoring. We elaborate on these recommendations in chapter 4.

Current approaches to risk assessment are inadequate, cumbersome and slow. Insufficient use is made of environmental monitoring. A new paradigm is needed.

Chapter 3

NATIONAL AND INTERNATIONAL APPROACHES TO CHEMICALS REGULATION AND RISK MANAGEMENT

The European Commission's proposal for a new approach to chemicals regulation is prompted by dissatisfaction with the existing system. But will it suffice? What can be learned from approaches elsewhere, for example in the US, Japan and Canada? How far is regulatory practice and the response of the industry influenced by civil liability and international trade agreements?

THE REGULATORY FRAMEWORK

3.1   This chapter describes national and EU legislation, international agreements, and the associated administrative arrangements for regulating the assessment and management of the environmental risks posed by chemicals. It discusses the shortcomings of the legislation and the steps being taken to address those deficiencies. Several non-regulatory initiatives also bear on the issue and are described here.

3.2   UK legislation on chemicals risk management, as in all EU Member States, derives almost entirely from EU instruments. Because most of these are based, at least partly, on the single-market provisions of the Treaty of Rome, there is little scope for Member States to vary from their requirements. Several international bodies have also developed agreements or conventions on aspects of chemicals risk management, and EU legislation endeavours to implement them where the European Community is a signatory.[1] These include the harmonisation of information requirements and test methods by the Organisation for Economic Co-operation and Development (OECD), and United Nations Environment Programme (UNEP) instruments for addressing global problems caused by the production and use of chemicals.

3.3   For the most part, this chapter deals with the legislation relating to the risks arising from the production and use of industrial chemicals. This legislation, in the main, conflates both occupational and environmental safety. Consumer safety, food safety and the control of emissions fall mainly under separate legislation, which will be discussed here, but which is not the main focus of the report. Chapter 4 considers whether closer links could be made between the administrative arrangements related to these issues.

EUROPEAN UNION

3.4   Three instruments, which are discussed in more detail below, address the assessment and management of risks from general industrial chemicals.[2] The Directive on the Classification, Packaging and Labelling of Dangerous Substances,[3] in addition to classifying chemicals according to their hazards and prescribing packaging and labelling regimes, requires all 'new' chemicals to be notified and assessed. The Existing Substances Regulation[4] sets out provisions for gathering and assessing information about 'existing' chemicals. The

Marketing and Use Directive[5] provides for bans on certain uses of several chemicals and groups of chemicals, and in particular places blanket bans on chemicals with certain hazardous properties, particularly carcinogens, mutagens and reprotoxic chemicals (CMR chemicals). A number of other directives deal with special purpose chemicals such as pesticides, or activities such as sale to consumers. The principal concern of early chemicals policy was to avoid fragmentation of the internal market within Europe.

CLASSIFICATION, PACKAGING AND LABELLING OF DANGEROUS SUBSTANCES AND PREPARATIONS

3.5   This Directive was adopted in 1967 to harmonise the classification, packaging and labelling rules operating in the (then) six Member States. The combined standardised provisions ensured the establishment of a common market in the field of dangerous chemical substances and a harmonised level of protection of human health.

3.6   Some categories of substance are excluded from the provisions of the Directive, including those for which assessment or approvals procedures are provided in other legislation. Exempt categories include medicines, plant protection products (such as pesticides), cosmetics, and chemicals used in food, including additives and flavourings, or in animal feed.

3.7   For the purposes of the Directive, *substances* are defined as chemical elements and their compounds as they occur in the natural state or as produced by industry. *Preparations* are defined as mixtures or solutions composed of two or more substances. The Dangerous Preparations Directive[6] essentially replicates the classification, packaging and labelling requirements of the Dangerous Substances Directive for those chemicals that appear on the market as preparations. Roughly 90-95% of all chemicals on the European market appear as preparations. The Dangerous Preparations Directive is to be consolidated with the Directives on the classification and labelling of plant protection products and biocides in 2004. This will extend the scope of the Directive to include pesticides and biocides for the first time and will add a requirement to classify and label preparations for environmental hazards.

3.8   The classification element of the Directive categorises substances on the basis of degree of hazard and the specific nature of the risks they pose. The packaging requirements seek to ensure that packaging is suitably strong, that it will not react with the contents, that the chances of content loss are minimised, and that appropriate fastenings are used. The labelling of a substance must indicate the name of the substance, details of the manufacturer, the danger symbol for the substance (table 3.1), and refer to any special risks arising from these dangers. This information is presented in a standardised manner using standard phrases on the nature of special risks from substances and standard safety precaution phrases.

NEW SUBSTANCES DIRECTIVE

3.9   The Classification, Packaging and Labelling Directive is regularly updated (through daughter directives) to take account of scientific and technical progress. These amending directives mainly add to the list of dangerous substances and specify the control measures to be applied. The two amendments of most significance for this study are those that introduced, and then extended, provisions relating to new substances: the 6th Amendment[7] (the New Substances Directive) and the 7th Amendment.[8]

Table 3.1

Indications of danger and symbols for dangerous substances and dangerous preparations[9]

Explosive	E	
Oxidising	O	
Extremely flammable	F+	
Highly flammable	F	
Very toxic	T+	
Toxic	T	
Harmful	Xn	
Corrosive	C	
Irritant	Xi	
Dangerous for the environment	N	

3.10　In 1979 the 6th Amendment introduced two new components to the Directive. First, it brought in a new European scheme (incorporating developments suggested by France, Germany and the UK) requiring pre-market notification of certain basic safety data for new chemicals. Second, it extended the scope of the Directive, particularly in respect of the new substances notification scheme, to include consideration of the environmental fate and effects of chemicals. Until this amendment the Directive had been entirely concerned with ensuring occupational safety.

3.11　The EU system operates on the basis of pre-market notification. This means that notification of the manufacture or import of the substance must take place before it is placed on the market (defined by the amended Directive as 'making available to third parties (including importation)'). This is in contrast to the US regime (3.115-3.122) that operates on the basis of pre-manufacture notification. The differences between these two approaches are explored further in 3.138-3.152.

3.12 The new substances notification scheme effectively implements the recommendation in the Royal Commission's Second Report[10] for 'some "early warning system" for the impact on the environment of new substances intended for commercial production'. It requires the manufacturer of a new chemical to submit a notification dossier to a competent authority in one of the Member States before the substance can be placed on the market. The dossier of information about the substance is made up of a number of parts, including:

- a technical dossier of information about the hazardous properties of the substance. Testing requirements (appendix D) are prescribed according to the quantity of the substance to be placed on the market (which, we have argued, is not a good criterion – 2.31). A minimum 'base set' of data are specified;

- a proposal for the classification and labelling of the substance;

- a proposal for a safety data sheet if the substance is classified as dangerous (covering both human health and the environment); and

- a declaration concerning the unfavourable effects of the substance in terms of the various uses envisaged.

3.13 The competent authority[11] is responsible for assessing the dossier's completeness and conformity with the requirements of the Directive. The dossier is then passed to the European Commission's European Chemicals Bureau in a standardised format. Copies are forwarded to all Member States. If no objections are raised within a fixed period (60 days for substances to be marketed in quantities greater than one tonne per year and 30 days for quantities less than one tonne per year), the notifier may then market the chemical throughout the EU. Subsequent notifiers (of the same substance) are required to inform the competent authority when the quantity of the substance placed on the market reaches 10, 100 and 1,000 tonnes per year per manufacturer or when the total quantity placed on the market reaches 50, 500 and 5,000 tonnes. The attainment of these thresholds results in additional testing requirements.

3.14 The 7th Amendment in 1992 introduced the requirement for risk assessments to be carried out on notified substances. The procedure for the risk assessment was published in 1993.[12] Detailed guidance, in relation to assessments for both human health and the environment, has been published by the European Commission.[13]

3.15 For every end-point investigated, the risk assessment for new substances assigns one of four available conclusions:

i. The substance is of no immediate concern.

ii. The substance is of concern ... further information for revision of the assessment is required, but deferred until next tonnage threshold attainment.

iii. The substance is of concern ... further information is required immediately.

iv. The substance is of concern ... recommendations for risk reduction to be instigated immediately.

3.16 The European Chemicals Bureau[14] reports that 'Since adoption of the 7th Amendment of the Directive, more than 800 notifications were submitted with a risk assessment report completed by the Competent Authority. Most substances, about 56%, were of no immediate concern (conclusion (i)). In 34% of the notifications, the need for further information was identified, either when the next tonnage trigger was reached (about 20%, conclusion (ii)) or immediately (about 14%, conclusion (iii)). In about 10% of the cases, the Competent Authorities considered the substance of concern and risk reduction measures were required (conclusion (iv)).'

3.17 In some cases the risk reduction measures were minor, such as an alteration to the classification and labelling of the substance. Other substances have been withdrawn from the market by voluntary agreement of the notifier, and for a number of substances restrictions on marketing and use are under discussion.

3.18 Several special cases are identified under the Directive. One concerns polymers, which were not subject to substances regulations at the time. Polymers are treated separately because those polymers with a high molecular weight, low content of low molecular weight species, as well as low solubility or extractivity in water are regarded as essentially not bioavailable.[15] Following the 7th Amendment, a requirement to notify certain polymers was introduced (polymers containing in combined form 2% or more of any substance which is not on the existing substances list). This change means that some substances that were exempt from notification are now no longer exempt. A European Commission document[16] lists so-called 'no longer polymers' exempt from retrospective notification. A more recent adaptation to the Directive[17] introduced a reduced testing package for strictly controlled intermediates (substances supplied and then consumed in a chemical reaction).

3.19 A register of 'new' chemicals, the European List of New Chemical Substances (ELINCS), is held by the European Chemicals Bureau.[18] The operation of the Directive also required the establishment of a list that defines 'existing' substances. The European Inventory of Existing Commercial Chemical Substances (EINECS) lists all substances that were reported to be on the market on or before 18 September 1981. More than 3,200 new substances have been notified since 1981. However, EINECS contains 100,116 substances, a number likely to have been inflated due to the desire of chemicals manufacturers in Europe to have as many compounds as possible classified as 'on the market before 1981', to avoid the notification requirements of the Directive.

EXISTING SUBSTANCES REGULATION

3.20 Work on assessing the chemicals on the EINECS list, and therefore not subject to the new chemicals legislation, commenced in 1993 with the publication of the Existing Substances Regulation.[19] The procedure for the risk assessment of existing substances was published in 1994.[20] This Regulation aimed to ensure the collection of available data, filling of data gaps, and assessment of those substances on EINECS marketed in quantities in excess of 10 tonnes per annum (approximately 10,000 substances).

3.21 The data collection step was split into three phases. Initially, the 1,884 substances expected to be produced in or imported to the EU in quantities exceeding 1,000 tonnes per year per producer or importer were extracted from EINECS. Producers and importers were obliged to submit a data set for each of these substances to the European Chemicals Bureau by 1994. During the second phase of data collection, industry had to report any other substances with a production volume of more than 1,000 tonnes per year by 1995. The total list of substances reported under phases 1 and 2 of the Regulation is now referred to as the EU–HPVC (European Union – High Production Volume Chemicals) list. The third phase required the submission of data for substances produced in the range of 10 to 1,000 tonnes per year by 1998.

3.22 The data sets varied according to production volume, but included as a minimum requirement: the name and EINECS number of the substance; the quantity being produced or imported; the classification from the Classification, Packaging and Labelling Directive; and a listing of reasonably foreseeable uses of the substance.

3.23 In the case of substances manufactured or imported in quantities in excess of 1,000 tonnes per year, additional data also had to be provided on the physico-chemical properties, ecotoxicity and carcinogenicity of the substance. The European Commission reserved the right to request this information for substances produced in lower quantities.

3.24 Following submission of the data, priority lists of substances for data filling and risk assessment were drawn up on the basis of the following factors:

- the effects of the substance on humans or the environment;

- the exposure of humans or the environment to the substance;

- the lack of data on the effects of the substance on humans and the environment;

- work already carried out in other fora; and

- other Community legislation and/or programmes relating to dangerous substances.

3.25 So far four lists have been agreed, comprising a total of 131 substances. The completion of a risk assessment follows the same rules as those established for new substances in the 7th Amendment to the Classification, Packaging and Labelling Directive. The first drafts of the risk assessment reports are written by competent authorities acting as 'rapporteurs'. The European Commission mediates the meetings that attempt to reach consensus on the conclusions of these risk assessments. After adoption of the risk assessment, the comprehensive reports are published, as is a summary. So far 26 completed risk assessments have been published, leading to 16 risk management proposals of which 2 have resulted in regulatory decisions. We regard the continuation of such slow progress in the assessment of existing chemicals as completely unacceptable.

Marketing and Use of Dangerous Substances and Preparations

3.26 There are two primary routes for introducing measures to restrict or ban dangerous substances: the European Commission has the right of initiative to make proposals for restrictions; and individual Member States are able to develop proposals for national measures, which must be notified to the European Commission under a procedure set out in the Technical Standards Directive.[21] Proposals for restrictions may be made on the basis of both physico-chemical and toxicological risks.

3.27 The Marketing and Use Directive provides the framework for such proposals.[22] The Directive includes a list of substances, which is subject to amendments by daughter directives. Currently there are some 22 amendments, each of which places specific restrictions on particular substances or products. Examples of substances controlled in this way include PCBs, polychlorinated terphenyls, asbestos, creosote and cadmium. There are also blanket restrictions on substances classed as carcinogens, mutagens or substances toxic to reproduction. Only 2 of the amendments (covering short chain chlorinated paraffins and pentabromodiphenyl ether) have been adopted as a consequence of formal risk assessment under the new or existing chemicals programmes. Other amendments have come about as a result of the identification of individual substances meeting criteria of concern established in earlier directives (individual CMR substances) and from recommendations arising from concerns in individual Member States (through the technical adaptation process).

3.28 Restrictions under the Marketing and Use Directive may also be applied to products containing substances of concern, as well as to the substances themselves. This was the case with batteries and accumulators containing mercury, cadmium and lead.[23] Products containing chemical substances dangerous to the consumer may also be controlled or banned under the provisions of the Product Safety Directives (3.64). This was the case for European Commission Decision 1999/815/EC[24] prohibiting the placing on the market of toys and childcare articles intended to be placed in the mouth by children under three years of age and made of soft PVC containing certain phthalates, which fell under General Product Safety Implementing Measures alongside a Marketing and Use Directive amendment (the 22nd Amendment[25]).

3.29 It is worth noting that it is unusual to prohibit the manufacture of the substance of concern, but it is not unknown. One example of such action was the ban on the manufacture of ozone-depleting substances,[26] which implemented the Montreal Protocol in the EU.

STRATEGY FOR A FUTURE CHEMICALS POLICY

3.30 Since the mid-1990s several Member States have expressed dissatisfaction with the rate at which chemicals are being assessed and managed under these instruments. The Swedish Chemicals Policy Committee published its document *Towards a Sustainable Chemicals Policy* in 1997, which proposed that products on the market should be free from certain hazardous substances by 2007. The UK government, during its Presidency of the Council of the EU in 1998, initiated a Ministerial debate about EU chemicals policy, as a consequence of which the European Commission undertook to prepare proposals for improved legislation. These were published as a White Paper, *A Strategy for A Future Chemicals Policy,*[27] in 2001. The passage of the White Paper through Council was a priority for the Swedish Presidency of the Council of the EU, which ended in June 2002. The European Commission is currently elaborating legislative proposals to implement the Strategy.

3.31 This White Paper cited a number of examples, some well known (such as asbestos and the use of DDT) and some more recent (such as the release of phthalates from toys and the presence of brominated flame retardants in human breast milk) as reasons for public concern about chemicals and evidence of the current weaknesses in EU chemicals policy. It noted that no one country has yet been successful in overcoming the huge gap in knowledge about chemical substances, and it highlighted several contributory factors including: the general lack of information about both properties and uses of existing substances; the slow and resource-intensive nature of the existing risk assessment process; the burden of responsibility for assessment of chemicals falling on regulatory authorities rather than on manufacturers and importers; and information about the substances being required from manufacturers and importers only, and not from downstream users.

3.32   The White Paper proposed a new approach to chemicals assessment and management to address these difficulties and to deal with the chemical 'burden of the past'. The objectives of the proposed strategy were:

- protection of human health and the environment;

- maintenance and enhancement of the competitiveness of the EU chemical industry;

- preventing fragmentation of the internal market;

- increased transparency. Consumers need access to information on chemicals to enable them to make informed decisions about the substances they use, and enterprises need to understand the regulatory process;

- integration with international efforts. The global nature of the chemicals industry and the trans-boundary impact of certain chemical substances have made chemical safety an international issue;

- promotion of non-animal testing. Protection of human health and the environment, including wildlife, should be balanced against protection of the welfare of laboratory animals. The European Commission will therefore promote further development and validation of non-animal test methods; and

- conformity with EU international obligations under the World Trade Organization (WTO). No unnecessary barriers to trade should be created and there must not be discrimination against imported substances and products.

The White Paper only addressed chemicals subject to the new and existing substances regimes, so pesticides, biocides, medicines, cosmetics and food additives were excluded from its scope.

3.33   The European Commission's review of legislation 'Simpler Legislation for the Internal Market' (SLIM) included the Dangerous Substances Directive in its fourth round.[28] The review took place alongside developments leading to the publication of the White Paper described above. SLIM sought to rationalise the Directive, separating policy from science, examine the possibilities for making greater use of existing data on substances, speed up the classification process, introduce simpler notification procedures for intermediates, and modify the notification scheme for low volume substances. In all, some 48 recommendations were made. Because of the review of chemicals policy leading to the development of the White Paper it was proposed that only those recommendations from SLIM likely to have short-term impact were implemented, with the remainder being subsumed into the development of the White Paper.

REACH

3.34   The White Paper proposed a new EU system for the assessment and management of the risks from chemicals. It was given the acronym 'REACH', to reflect its key components: registration, evaluation and authorisation of chemicals.

Registration

3.35   Companies must submit basic information for around 30,000 substances (all existing and new substances exceeding a production volume of 1 tonne per annum per manufacturer/importer) for inclusion in a central database. The White Paper suggested deadlines for submission of registration dossiers ranging from 2005 to 2012, depending on production volume. Given subsequent progress, even this leisurely pace is likely to be unrealistic. In chapter 4 we make recommendations regarding the listing of chemicals, and in particular that the government moves swiftly to achieving such a database for all chemicals on the UK market without waiting for the arrival of REACH.

Evaluation

3.36   The registered information for all substances exceeding a production volume of 100 tonnes per annum (around 5,000 substances) will be evaluated by competent authorities, including the development of substance-tailored testing programmes focusing on the effects of long-term exposure; in case of concern, this requirement extends to substances at lower tonnages. For the reasons set out in chapter 2, we believe that current evaluation systems are not adequate for this task and that their use will lead to continued paralysis of the existing chemicals programme. In chapter 4 we describe an approach to evaluation that we believe will lead to faster management, scientifically more supportable results, and better incorporation of public values.

Authorisation

3.37   Substances with certain hazardous properties that gave rise to very high concern would require permission before they could be marketed in the EU, and this permission would be limited to specific purposes demonstrated to be safe. The number of substances likely to be subject to authorisation is estimated at 1,400, comprising carcinogens, mutagens, reprotoxic compounds and persistent organic pollutants. We agree with the proposal to authorise hazardous chemicals for specific uses. However, we believe that more sophisticated approaches to risk management should also be adopted, including economic measures to encourage substitution. We explain this in chapters 4 and 5.

3.38   The authorisation procedure envisaged under the White Paper proposals will cover certain functions of the existing marketing and use restrictions. The White Paper also refers to decisions restricting or banning the use of substances subject to an accelerated risk management procedure being taken within the framework of a modernised Marketing and Use Directive.

3.39 The White Paper claimed that the extra regulatory effort required by REACH could be made available without a net increase in public resources. This has since been questioned by a number of commentators, including the House of Lords Select Committee on the European Union (3.49-3.50).

Central entity

3.40 In order to ensure the smooth running of the new system, the White Paper proposed the establishment of a 'central entity' that would provide services to the REACH system. This entity would act as a receiving body for the registration dossiers and be responsible for establishing and maintaining a comprehensive central database on all registered chemicals. It would also be responsible for providing the operational framework for the authorisation and accelerated risk management procedures. During 2002, consultants were appointed by the European Commission to produce a report detailing the possible options for the structure and operation of the central entity.[29] The main options considered were the enlargement of the European Chemicals Bureau (currently part of the Joint Research Centre at Ispra) to cover all of these functions, or the creation of an independent agency.

3.41 The report favoured the creation of an independent agency, for reasons of impartiality and financial autonomy. Difficulties in recruiting staff with suitable expertise were identified, with the report concluding that the operation of an independent agency would allow more flexible recruiting and charging policies and that staff for the new agency would need to come from the various competent authorities. We believe that it is critically important that the principle of subsidiarity underpins the allocation of functions to the central entity. Failure to allocate adequate responsibility (and commensurate resources) to national competent authorities will result in an operation that is bureaucratic and slow – no improvement, in fact, over the existing system. We return to this in chapter 4.

Cost of REACH

3.42 A business impact assessment of the White Paper was carried out for the European Commission by independent consultants.[30] Different scenarios were developed for the number of chemicals subject to registration and testing, with estimates of costs ranging from €1.4 to €7 billion. With mid-range testing and registration requirements this sum was estimated at €3.6 billion.

Animal testing under REACH

3.43 In a paper presented at the Chemicals Stakeholder Forum in 2002,[31] the UK's Institute for Environment and Health updated their earlier estimates of the number of animals likely to be required as a result of the REACH process. A series of scenarios were presented, with the most realistic prediction being that:

> 'From our calculations, the lowest likely estimate for animal usage for completing testing for the approximately 30,000 chemicals produced at up to 100 tpa [tonnes per annum] falls within the range 2.467 to 2.547 (*sic*) million animals, assuming that 66% of chemicals lack adequate data. Inclusion of the testing to be undertaken at Level 1 and 2 (approximately 4.27 million animals), brings the overall total to at least 6.7

million vertebrate animals (excluding offspring from reproductive studies and any additional studies that may be warranted, e.g. toxicokinetics, mechanistic investigations, endocrine disruption, avian toxicity studies).'

3.44 The Institute for Environment and Health recognised the high degree of uncertainty surrounding their estimates of the numbers of chemicals that may be produced or marketed in the 1 to 100 tonne per annum category. It also noted that acceptable toxicity data might already be available for these chemicals and that substances may be voluntarily removed from the market as a result of increased testing requirements.

New chemicals under REACH

3.45 The White Paper states that the new substances notification scheme is 'generally considered to have been successful in testing and assessing chemicals'. In general we agree, but we are concerned by many of the limitations in the testing methods that we discussed in chapter 2. These limitations apply equally to the new and existing chemicals schemes, and consequently we are of the opinion that much could be done to improve the assessment methods for new substances. The scheme we propose in chapter 4 introduces a new approach to assessing chemicals, whether new or existing, which, if adopted, would address these limitations.

3.46 The White Paper also proposes increasing the weight limit for notification from 100 kg under the current New Substances Directive to 1 tonne in order to provide for enhanced product innovation. The need to reduce animal testing was also a factor in this decision. We disagree with this proposal. We do not consider that raising the weight limit for notification of new substances from 100 kg to 1 tonne is appropriate. In chapter 2 we explained why the wide range of chemical toxicities and the inherent uncertainties in testing for toxicity render tonnage thresholds inappropriate, and though we recognise that for pragmatic purposes some sort of level is needed, we see no justification for increasing the limit. We also explain, in chapter 5, why we do not think it possible to be confident that raising the limit will have any positive effect on innovation. We discuss better ways of minimising animal testing in chapter 4.

3.47 REACH would merge the operation of the new and existing substances schemes. We are of the opinion that the two schemes, for new and existing chemicals, should be kept separate. There is an important difference between them. While systematic information may too often not be available, considerable experience with existing chemicals has been acquired over their long period of use. Assessing existing substances in the same way as new substances are assessed currently would not address the backlog ('the burden of the past') within a sufficiently short time-scale. Enhanced use of monitoring, as described in chapter 4, would yield important information about existing chemicals. This is not the case for chemicals that have not yet been marketed in significant quantities. These should, therefore, be assessed in a different way under a different system.

Responses to the White Paper

3.48 Following the publication of the White Paper, a number of governments and organisations have produced responses and position papers on the legislative proposals needed to implement the White Paper.

3.49 The House of Lords Select Committee on the European Union published its review of the White Paper in March 2002.[32] The Royal Commission provided evidence to this enquiry, noting in particular its doubts about the public acceptability of the increased level of animal testing required under the proposals.

3.50 The report of the Select Committee commented that the proposals contained in the White Paper were over-ambitious and the timetable unachievable, and doubted the wisdom of joining together the schemes for new and existing substances. It also called for a 'no data, no market' clause (see also 4.21) in the proposals to provide an incentive for industry to produce data. The report noted the clear role for the proposed central entity in maintaining the database on substances and requesting further information from manufacturers and importers, but suggested that its involvement in the evaluation and authorisation process might be more limited. The Select Committee noted that the establishment of product registers at national and EU level could assist in the identification and involvement of downstream users in the REACH process. They also noted a clear role for an improved post-market surveillance scheme, possibly overseen by the European Environment Agency. The report recommended that persistent, bioaccumulative and toxic substances and 'very persistent, very bioaccumulative' substances should be subject to authorisation. On animal testing, the Select Committee called for the UK government to take the lead in developing proposals to promote non-animal testing and to identify a programme of funding in the UK to develop alternatives.

3.51 In December 2002, the UK government published its position paper based around three main aims for the new chemicals policy:[33] creating a fast and workable system to control substances of concern; minimising animal testing; and maintaining or improving the competitiveness of the chemical industry.

3.52 The government paper expressed concern that resources should not be wasted on re-testing existing substances about which a great deal was already known (such as lead) but that the focus should be on relatively new substances for which there was little or no data. It called for piloting of the new system prior to full introduction, identified the need for further development of alternatives to animal tests alongside greater international recognition of the results of tests carried out using alternative methods, and improved data sharing to avoid the need for repeat testing. The paper emphasised the special needs of the chemical industry in the UK, given the importance of small and medium-sized enterprises (SMEs) in the specialty chemicals sector that would be particularly vulnerable to the introduction of the REACH system. The paper proposed a self declaration system to deal with chemicals in imported articles and noted that such a system would need to be carefully designed to avoid challenge under WTO rules (3.153). The government documents set out their vision of a workable version of the REACH system. The government's proposals are data intensive at the registration stage and do not allow for as rapid risk management decisions on substances of extreme concern. We elaborate on the comparison of the government's scheme and the European Commission's REACH proposals with our own proposals for a new system in appendix I.

3.53 The USA government response[34] to the proposals took the form of a 'non-paper' on EU chemicals policy. The non-paper expressed concerns that the EU was moving away from the efforts at global harmonisation on chemicals policy being orchestrated by OECD. The paper also contained sections expressing concern about WTO neutrality and the use of the precautionary principle as a means to provide cover for politically motivated trade restrictions. In November 2002, a number of US non-governmental organisations (NGOs) and community groups prepared a response to the non-paper, which called for its retraction and a more positive approach from the US administration towards the REACH proposals.

3.54   The Swedish government issued a series of three papers in response to the White Paper. These covered transparency, industry accountability, and authorisation.[35] The Swedish government recommended increased transparency to allow more informed consumer choice about the use of chemicals and to benefit industry through enhanced data sharing, a view that we very much share. It also called for authorisations issued under REACH to be time-limited, and for the inclusion of a review clause in the implementing legislation to permit extension of the authorisation system to include some specific categories of concern (such as endocrine disruption) once these have been defined at EC level. They also called for persistent, bioaccumulative and toxic, and 'very persistent, very bioaccumulative' substances to be included within criteria for authorisation. The Swedish government considered that a general clause on chemical safety should be included within the White Paper, to oblige industry to provide basic information about all chemicals, irrespective of production volume. This proposal is also in line with the recommendations we make in chapter 4, and would be made more feasible even at very low production methods by the use of the mass screening methods that we recommend.

ENFORCEMENT OF CHEMICALS LEGISLATION

3.55   We have heard from regulators that the effort put into enforcing the new and existing substances legislation is not high. European studies have found low levels of compliance. In one study instigated by the European Commission, nearly 4,000 substances were checked at 96 companies. Of these, 305 could either not be identified (163 substances) or were found to be new (142 substances). The inspections revealed that 37% of these new substances were not notified and thus illegally marketed.[36] In another study, about 15-20% of controlled synthetic products contained more cadmium than permitted, and in a third, covering 178 companies and 1,400 substances, companies could not identify 30% as new or existing substances. Concern about enforcement effectiveness has led to the establishment of a new network, CLEEN (Chemicals Legislation European Enforcement Network),[37] as a forum for information exchange that sets priorities for enforcement projects within the EC.

3.56   The White Paper on chemicals noted that:

> 'Recent studies in the Netherlands and the United Kingdom found high levels of non-compliance with the Safety Data Sheets legislation. Flaws in compliance and enforcement activities related to current legislation for new and existing substances were also noted by recent Community-wide enforcement projects.'

3.57   The White Paper also noted that individual Member States would be responsible for enforcement of the new legislation in their own territories and that current levels of fines awarded by the courts for breaches of substance legislation did not provide a sufficient deterrent. It is envisaged in the document that, following the enacting of new legislation, a network of authorities within Member States would be set up to develop minimum enforcement criteria.

3.58   We are concerned by this failure in enforcement. If legislation is to be effective it must be enforced, proportionately but transparently. There is more that could be done to improve this situation, particularly by making it more feasible for users of chemicals to ensure that the chemicals have been properly registered and assessed, and making them more aware of their responsibilities and potential liabilities should they purchase chemicals which are on the market illegally. In chapters 4 and 5 we make recommendations that will facilitate enforcement in this way.

OTHER EU LEGISLATION ON CHEMICALS

3.59   Several other directives govern the use of chemicals in products. These different regimes have arisen for a number of specific reasons. Some of the products come into direct contact with sensitive parts of the human body or are directly ingested (cosmetics and food additives), others are deliberately designed to be toxic and are released widely in the environment (plant protection products and biocides), while others are designed to be biologically active in small doses (pharmaceuticals and veterinary medicines).

3.60   Table 3.2 lists schemes that operate on a positive approval system, under which a chemical substance may not be used unless specifically approved for a particular use. This is the function of the authorisation step for hazardous chemicals under the REACH proposals, but is in contrast to the current industrial chemical control system that operates on a negative list principle – substances may be used unless specifically restricted.

3.61   The EU's 6th Environment Action Programme has proposed the development of a Thematic Strategy on the Sustainable Use of Pesticides, with a communication from the European Commission on the subject.[38] This noted one important shortcoming of the current Plant Protection Products Directive, in that it is primarily based on assessment of the effects of individual compounds, whereas potential additive or synergistic effects of mixtures containing several active substances are only evaluated to a very limited extent (2.46).

3.62   The regimes for pesticides, biocides, veterinary medicines and animal feed additives all contain provisions to assess harm to the environment. A proposal for the assessment of pharmaceuticals for environmental risk is also in development. The environmental effects of pharmaceuticals were discussed previously (2.119-2.123). The regimes for food additives and cosmetics are concerned exclusively with human health and do not contain provisions for ecotoxicological testing.

3.63   The assessment, authorisation and monitoring requirements vary between each of these categories of substance. The assessment scheme that we propose in chapter 4 is equally applicable to each of these types of substance. There is also greater scope for sharing of assessment tools and we elaborate on the use of techniques from the pharmaceutical industry in the assessment of industrial chemicals in chapter 4.

Table 3.2

Regulations governing products other than industrial chemicals

Chemicals group	Directive	Features of interest
Plant protection products	91/414/EEC	• Two-tier registration system with active ingredients being assessed at Community level for inclusion on a 'positive list' and products subsequently being registered by Member States • All approved pesticide products are subject to routine review, but may be reviewed at any time if any evidence emerges concerning their safety. If appropriate an approval can be restricted or revoked entirely
Biocidal products	98/8/EC	• Substances that will be supported under the Biocides Directive must be notified • Substances which will not be supported will be identified and phased out from the market over a few years • Introduced the concept of comparative risk assessment, whereby substances can be prevented from being marketed if there is an alternative substance that presents a lower risk to human health or the environment
Veterinary medicines	81/852/EEC (A further EU regulation sets maximum residue limits for approved medicines in food)	• All veterinary medicines have to be approved either nationally, in the UK by the Veterinary Medicines Directorate, or centrally by the European Medicines Evaluation Agency • Assessment includes effects on the animal, people handling the medicine, the consumer and the natural environment; the latter involving a risk assessment procedure similar to that for pesticides
Cosmetics	76/768	• Directive includes a series of annexes listing banned cosmetic substances and those cosmetic ingredients permitted for specific uses (such as colouring agents) and does not permit products to be marketed where they are composed of other substances • There are no pre-market controls for cosmetic products, the system relies on testing by producers and importers and a market surveillance and liability scheme • 27th Amendment to the Directive introduced a ban on the carrying out of animal experiments for cosmetic product testing and to prohibit testing of cosmetic product ingredients on animals once validated *in vitro* methods had been put forward

(continued overleaf)

(table 3.2 continued)

Chemicals group	Directive	Features of interest
Pharmaceuticals	65/65/EC	• Harmonised process since 1993, with central registration (under the European Medicines Evaluation Agency) for new products and a Member State mutual recognition procedure for existing products • No formal environmental risk assessment process (although one is currently in development) • The European Medicines Evaluation Agency oversee good manufacturing, laboratory and clinical testing practices as well as carrying out after-market surveillance and advising on actions to be taken
Food additives	Framework Directive (94/34/EC) Daughter Directives covering sweeteners (94/35/EC), colours (94/36/EC) and other food additives (95/2/EC)	• The Directives all operate on the principle that only those additives that are specifically authorised can be used • Prior to authorisation, the EC's Scientific Committee on Food evaluates additives • Purity criteria set out in a further series of directives • Directives also require monitoring of consumption. Preliminary findings from the last review noted that intake of the majority of food additives authorised in the EU was below the acceptable daily intake (ADI) set by the Scientific Committee on Food
Presence of undesirable substances in animal feedingstuffs	1999/29/EC	• Maximum limits were set for the presence of heavy metals, dioxin, aflatoxin, certain pesticides and botanical impurities in animal feed and feedingstuffs • A proposal has been put forward to replace this Directive as a result of the Belgian scare over dioxin contamination of animal feed additives
Authorisation, marketing and labelling of animal feed additives	70/524/EEC	• Authorisation procedure driven by a scientific evaluation demonstrating that the additive has no harmful effects, on human and animal health or on the environment • Before authorisation, a dossier of information on the substance is required, which is then evaluated by Member States and the Standing Committee for Feedingstuffs • Time-limited authorisation procedure for coccidiostats (used to treat infections caused by a micro-organism in poultry) and other medicinal substances, antibiotics and growth promoters • European Commission White Paper on Food Safety[39] led to proposals to ban the use of antibiotics as growth promoters from 2006. Antibiotics used in human medicine are already prohibited from being added to animal feed

PRODUCT SAFETY DIRECTIVES

3.64 In addition to controls on substances (covered under the Marketing and Use Directive), there are also directives relating to the safety of products. Where substance controls can be shown to be ineffective at controlling the risks to consumers, these Product Safety Directives can be used. In the case of the presence of phthalates in children's toys, general product safety measures were implemented alongside marketing and use restrictions.

3.65 The EC General Product Safety Directive[40] regulates the safety of consumer products and aims at ensuring that products placed on the market are safe for the consumer. The products covered are those intended for consumers, or which are likely to be used by consumers when supplied in the course of a commercial activity. The Directive places obligations on producers to place only safe products on the market and to provide consumers with the relevant information to assess the risks associated with a product. It defines criteria for assessing product safety and deciding under which conditions a product should be deemed to be safe, and sets out Member States' obligations to secure compliance.

INTERNATIONAL ARRANGEMENTS

THE ORGANISATION FOR ECONOMIC CO-OPERATION AND DEVELOPMENT

3.66 OECD Member Countries established a programme in 1971 to undertake work at the international level on the safety of chemicals such as the organochlorine pesticides, PCBs, lead, mercury and cadmium. This followed the recognition in these countries of the widespread contamination and accompanying adverse effects caused by such chemicals. In the mid-1970s, the programme received a major boost and underwent a change in emphasis as a result of the development of the Toxic Substances Control Act (3.116) in the US and of the New Substances Directive (3.9) in the EU. OECD Members recognised that if barriers to trade and multiple testing of chemicals were to be avoided, then there was a need to develop common approaches to safety testing and risk assessment. The size and expertise of the OECD Secretariat was increased and the programme extended, funded by a levy on the participating countries.

3.67 The OECD Secretariat and the 29 Member Countries work together, often on a 'lead country' basis, to develop and co-ordinate environmental health and safety activities on an international basis. Such activities include: harmonising chemical testing and hazard assessment procedures; harmonisation of classification and labelling; developing principles for good laboratory practice; co-operating on the investigation of existing high production volume chemicals; work on pollutant release and transfer registers; and sharing and exploring possible co-operative activities on risk management from chemicals. While this work is focused primarily on the production, processing and use of industrial chemicals, it is also closely co-ordinated with other work in OECD, particularly with work on pesticides, chemical accidents and biotechnology.

3.68 The principal objectives of the OECD Chemicals Programme are to:

- assist OECD Member Countries' efforts to protect human health and the environment through improving chemical safety;

- make chemical control policies more transparent and efficient; and

• prevent unnecessary distortions in the trade of chemicals and chemical products.

3.69 OECD is not a supranational organisation, but rather a forum for discussion where governments from the developed world and the European Commission express their points of view, share their experiences and search for common ground. If Member Countries consider it appropriate, an accord can be embodied in a formal OECD Council Act, which is agreed at the highest level of OECD, the Council. OECD decisions on chemicals policy require EU action before they can be implemented into UK law.

3.70 An OECD hazard assessment programme investigates the hazards of chemicals produced in quantities of at least 1,000 tonnes per year in at least one OECD country. The chemicals programme has also co-ordinated the development of a set of test guidelines, which are widely used across the world to measure and evaluate the toxicity and other properties of chemicals (transposed in the 6th Amendment Directive, see 3.10).

3.71 OECD has also stipulated a minimum data package required to determine whether or not a chemical requires further investigation. Member Countries work together to provide this minimum data set for a particular chemical. Information is collected from government, public and industry sources and, where necessary, by additional testing. Once all the necessary information has been collected on a chemical, a lead country makes an evaluation that includes conclusions on potential risks and, if appropriate, recommendations for further action. The information collected and the sponsor country's report are subjected to peer review. The results are co-ordinated by the international organisations and made widely available to all countries through the United Nations International Programme on Chemical Safety (as Concise International Chemical Assessment Documents or CICADs). The mutual acceptance of data generated to internationally accepted standards prevents unnecessary duplication of testing. The test data are used within a number of national and international risk assessment programmes, including that under the Existing Substances Regulation (3.20).

3.72 The International Council of Chemical Associations has announced a voluntary programme of accelerated testing and hazard assessments of about 1,000 of the 4,100 high production volume chemicals currently identified by OECD by 2004. There will be some overlap with OECD's programme, and the industry organisations are co-ordinating testing efforts to avoid duplication. The High Production Volume Chemicals programme has led to the formation of consortia of companies, which will enhance data sharing. The initiative will be open to include chemicals nominated by OECD Member Countries, developing countries, countries in economic transition, other Intergovernmental Forum on Chemical Safety participants, and other interested parties.

THE UNITED NATIONS ENVIRONMENT PROGRAMME (UNEP) CHEMICALS PROGRAMME

3.73 The UNEP Programme on Chemicals covers a number of activities. It has developed the International Register of Potentially Toxic Chemicals, which contains a wealth of information although the format is not particularly user-friendly. UNEP also initiates and co-ordinates many capacity-building initiatives in the developing world, and as part of this the Programme on Chemicals aims to ensure that expertise on chemicals safety, and resources to manage risks from chemicals, are enhanced in recipient countries.

3.74 Primarily, UNEP is the forum for the negotiation of multilateral environmental agreements – conventions that, once in force, are legally binding on ratifying parties. Two conventions that directly relate to chemicals risk management are the Rotterdam Convention on the Prior Informed Consent Procedure for Certain Hazardous Chemicals and Pesticides in International Trade (the PIC Convention)[41] and the Stockholm Convention on Persistent Organic Pollutants (the POPs Convention).[42]

Prior Informed Consent (PIC) Convention

3.75 The Rotterdam Convention establishes a procedure for obtaining and disseminating the decisions of importing countries as to whether they wish to import specified chemicals, and for ensuring compliance with these decisions by exporting countries. The aim is to promote a shared responsibility between exporting and importing countries in protecting human health and the environment from the harmful effects of such chemicals. Decisions taken by the importing party must be trade neutral; that is, if the party decides it does not consent to accepting imports of a specific chemical, it must also stop domestic production of the chemical for domestic use or imports from any non-party.

Persistent Organic Pollutants (POPs) Convention

3.76 The Stockholm Convention is an agreement to phase out the production, use and emissions of chemicals that are capable of moving long distances through the environment from their point of release, and causing environmental effects in countries other than those where they are used. Twelve substances were initially included in the Convention, though limited derogations were provided for DDT when used as a malaria vector control, and for PCBs because of their widespread use in electrical equipment. The Convention is broadly based on the United Nations Economic Commission for Europe (UNECE) Convention on Long-Range Transboundary Air Pollution Protocol on Persistent Organic Pollutants, agreed in 1998,[43] though its scope extends beyond atmospheric dispersion to include other global transport modes.

Other UNEP instruments

3.77 Other measures that establish global risk management regimes for chemicals include:

- the Montreal Protocol on Substances that Deplete the Ozone Layer[44] (a protocol to the Vienna Convention for the Protection of the Ozone Layer), which introduces measures to restrict the production and use of chemicals that damage the ozone layer; and

- the Basel Convention on the Control of Transboundary Movements of Hazardous Wastes and their Disposal, which, *inter alia,* defines which wastes are to be considered hazardous and the criteria to be taken into account in so defining them.

OTHER INTERNATIONAL BODIES

3.78 Global programmes generally operate under the auspices of several bodies. National and European activities on chemicals are part of a wider international structure, co-ordinated by the Intergovernmental Forum on Chemical Safety and the Inter-Organization Programme for the Sound Management of Chemicals. These bring together a range of chemical programmes under UNEP, the International Labour Organization, the UN Food and Agriculture Organization, the World Health Organization, the UN Industrial Development Organization, the UN Institute for Training and Research, and OECD. Further details of some of these programmes are given in appendix F.

3.79 The Intergovernmental Forum on Chemical Safety adopted the Bahia Declaration on Chemical Safety in 2000, in which the participating partners undertook to achieve a set of key goals. These goals included targets for better provision of data about chemicals, the management of stocks of pesticides and other chemicals that are no longer in use, action against illegal traffic with chemicals, and assisting countries with work on chemicals safety issues.

CONVENTION FOR THE PROTECTION OF THE MARINE ENVIRONMENT OF THE NORTH EAST ATLANTIC

3.80 Of particular significance in the context of this study is the OSPAR Convention (the Convention for the Protection of the Marine Environment of the North East Atlantic). The OSPAR Convention introduces controls on the use of certain hazardous chemicals and, in particular, a system for identifying chemicals that meet certain hazard criteria. In 1992, OSPAR replaced two previous Conventions – the Oslo Convention for the Prevention of Marine Pollution by Dumping from Ships and Aircraft, and the Paris Convention for the Protection of the Marine Environment of the North-East Atlantic.

3.81 The new Convention, drafted to merge and modernise the Oslo and Paris Conventions, requires, *inter alia* the application of the precautionary and polluter pays principles, and the concepts of best available technology and best environmental practice, and establishes rights of access to information about the maritime area of the Convention.

3.82 The aim of the OSPAR hazardous substances strategy is to:

'prevent pollution of the maritime area by continuously reducing discharges, emissions and losses of hazardous substances (that is, substances which are toxic, persistent and liable to bioaccumulate or which give rise to an equivalent level of concern) with the ultimate aim of achieving concentrations in the marine environment near background values for naturally occurring substances and close to zero for man-made synthetic substances'.

3.83 The Convention will implement the strategy progressively:

'by making every endeavour to move towards the target of the cessation of discharges, emissions and losses of hazardous substances by the year 2020'.

3.84 Measures to achieve these aims will take into account the sustainability of the marine ecosystem, guiding principles such as any need for precautionary action and the use of risk assessment to set priorities, with the most cost-effective measures given the highest priority.

3.85 After the OSPAR Ministerial Meeting in 1998, the OSPAR Ad-hoc Working Group on the Development of a Dynamic Selection and Prioritisation Mechanism for Hazardous Substances was tasked to develop the DYNAMEC mechanism, apply this mechanism for the first time and prepare proposals regarding which substances could be prioritised by the OSPAR Commission (the administering body for the Convention).

3.86 During its first application, an initial selection procedure and a ranking procedure were developed and applied to identify priority substances that should be added to the OSPAR List of Chemicals Identified for Priority Action, which was first established in 1998. Currently some 40 substances have been identified for priority action. Work in 2000-2002 on the further development of DYNAMEC[45] has led to the establishment of the OSPAR List of Substances of Possible Concern. This list of around 400 substances that meet particular thresholds for persistence, toxicity and bioaccumulation was agreed at OSPAR 2002. The list is a result of the initial selection procedure and is published on the OSPAR website,[46] with an invitation to those who have an interest in these substances to submit any new relevant information to OSPAR. Data sheets for all substances of possible concern are also accessible on the OSPAR website. The list is updated from time to time, and substances can be added or deleted as further information becomes available.

3.87 The cut-off values for persistence, bioaccumulation and toxicity agreed by the OSPAR Commission in 2001 are used as criteria to select substances for inclusion in the List of Substances of Possible Concern. Substances that do not meet the criteria but for which there are other reasons for concern may also be listed via the 'Safety Net Procedure', provided that suitable monitoring data and associated information are presented which demonstrate the presence of the substances in the marine environment. The DYNAMEC procedure does not yet contain criteria for endocrine disrupters, but recognises that this is an area for development.

3.88 OSPAR develops comprehensive background documents on the substances for priority action which cover the main sources and pathways to the marine environment, provide monitoring information, examine the existing national and international controls, and make recommendations on the actions needed to achieve the OSPAR objectives on hazardous substances.

NATIONAL ARRANGEMENTS

UNITED KINGDOM

UK National Strategy

3.89 Chemicals regulation in the UK is derived largely from action at the EU level. However, because of its growing disenchantment with the way the EU regulatory instruments were being implemented (3.30), the government commissioned a strategy document in 1997, which was published as *Sustainable Production and Use of Chemicals* in December 1999.[47] This recognised that any regulatory measures that were secure against legal challenge under European legislation or international agreements would have to flow from the EU, and that this would take time. Because of this, the UK raised the issue at a meeting of EU Environment Ministers during the UK Presidency in 1998, and this led to the European Commission proposals discussed previously (3.30-3.54).

3.90 The UK Strategy focused on the marketing and use of chemicals where such activity may be harming human health or the environment. Groups of chemicals subject to a 'positive approval procedure' (for example, pesticides, biocides, veterinary medicines and human pharmaceuticals) were not covered. The Strategy expressed concern at the slow pace at which chemical risk assessments were being carried out, and it sought ways to speed up the process. The Strategy also sought to encourage industry's duty of care on chemicals, by developing a package of information that could be passed down the supply chain in a suitable format for all users to evaluate risks to human health and the environment. In addition, it sought a reduction in exposure to hazardous chemicals and advocated substitution wherever possible. The Strategy also gave guidance on the use of the precautionary principle.

3.91 The Strategy set out a series of challenges to industry, backed by the creation of an open forum (the Chemicals Stakeholder Forum) to oversee and report on their implementation, and the clear intention to seek regulatory underpinning through Europe when possible. The challenges included:

- testing and assessment of the priority high production volume (HPV) substances (through the International Council of Chemical Associations' programme (3.72)) by 2004;

- all HPV chemicals to be assessed by 2015;

- hazard assessment data for all chemicals by 2020;

- priority chemicals (persistent, bioaccumulative and toxic (PBT), carcinogenic, mutagenic or reprotoxic (CMR) and other chemicals identified by the Chemicals Stakeholder Forum) to be fast-tracked and publicly assessed by the Forum, and risk management measures to be put in place by industry by 2010, to implement the precautionary principle;

- a continuing programme of substitution of hazardous chemicals with less hazardous ones (to implement the substitution principle); and

- information to be publicly available and passed down the supply chain.

Chemicals Stakeholder Forum

3.92 The Strategy led to the establishment of the Chemicals Stakeholder Forum. Its role was to set criteria for the identification of priority chemicals and to seek voluntary commitments from industry to introduce appropriate risk management measures for chemicals which met these criteria (which were based largely on the OSPAR criteria, see 3.86).

3.93 The Forum also aims to promote a better understanding between stakeholders of the concerns that people have about chemicals in the environment. Its scope covers the impact that the production and use of industrial chemicals has on the environment, and on human health through environmental exposure. The Forum has a wide range of organisations as members. These include industry associations, environmental NGOs, trades unions, non-departmental public bodies, the Royal Society of Chemistry, and the National Association of Women.

Implementation and enforcement in the UK

3.94 The administrative arrangements for the assessment and management of chemicals in the UK are complex, involving a number of government departments, advisory bodies and enforcement authorities. Responsibilities have been allocated to organisations in response to European legislation as it has evolved. The role of the devolved administrations is complex, as while environment and public health matters are generally devolved, health and safety at work and product safety are generally reserved matters. This complexity has often meant that control of chemicals has been dealt with on a GB or UK basis[48].

3.95 The key departmental, advisory and enforcement bodies are shown in figure 3-I. The Health and Safety Executive is responsible for chemicals safety in the workplace and as a consequence of occupational activities, and the Environment Agencies and the Environment and Heritage Service in Northern Ireland are responsible for ensuring the environmental safety of chemicals. The competent authority for work on new and existing substances and marketing and use restrictions is jointly the Health and Safety Executive and the Environment Agency on behalf of the Department for Environment, Food and Rural Affairs (3.13). Consumer protection is the responsibility of the Department of Trade and Industry, which has an enforcement role through the work of local authority trading standards officers, as well as sponsoring the chemicals industry. The Food Standards Agency monitors and regulates the presence of chemicals in food (both as contaminants and as food additives). The efficacy and safety (to patients, but not environmental safety) of pharmaceuticals are regulated by the Medicines Control Agency, which reports to the Department of Health, and the efficacy and safety (including environmental safety) of veterinary medicines and pesticides are regulated by directorates that report to the Department for Environment, Food and Rural Affairs. The departments and agencies are supported by several expert advisory committees.

Figure 3-I

Main sources of scientific advice to the government on hazardous chemicals[49]

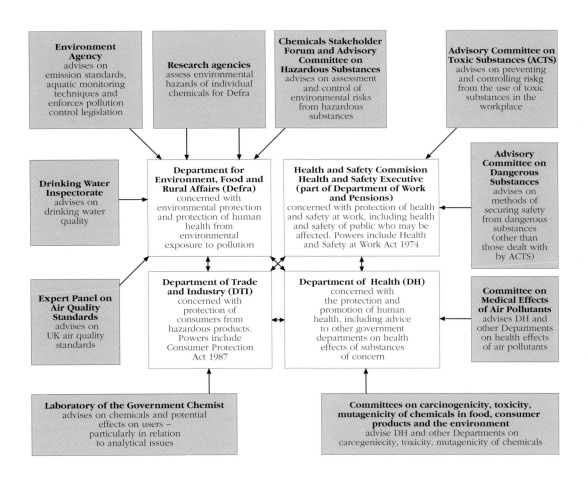

3.96 While it is useful to develop government policy on chemicals alongside other related policies, such as environmental, occupational or food safety, and important to have some chemicals expertise to inform the policy-makers, we believe that this fragmentation of responsibility and expertise has been allowed to continue for too long. A single body of experts in chemicals legislation would more efficiently and effectively address many of the issues raised in this report. It would be responsible for implementing and enforcing all aspects of chemicals legislation, advising policy-makers in departments, taking advice from experts in other bodies, for example the environmental monitoring experts in the Environment Agency and British Geological Survey, and acting as a single competent authority for EU legislation relating to chemicals. We return to this in more detail in chapter 4.

3.97 In addition to these assessment and management roles, a large number of bodies are involved in the collection of monitoring data relevant to chemicals. Data collection systems range from highly systematic monitoring regimes, such as the health data monitored by the National Health Service, to more *ad hoc* arrangements, such as wildlife monitoring by volunteers. All are important, and their role in monitoring for chemicals is discussed in chapters 2 and 4.

3.98 During 2002, the Environment Agency published a consultation draft of its strategy *Managing Chemicals for a Better Environment*, setting out proposals for work on chemicals to 2007.[50] The Strategy states that the Environment Agency's future management of chemicals will be underpinned by an increased understanding of the environment and how chemicals affect it, and will promote research and improved monitoring approaches, set environmental targets and develop new approaches to support chemicals management. We strongly agree with this approach. The key to managing the environmental risks from chemicals is a better understanding of their fate and effects, including an enhanced role for monitoring. We elaborate further on this in chapter 4.

OTHER NATIONAL APPROACHES WITHIN THE EU

3.99 Other EU Member States have also expressed dissatisfaction with progress under the Existing Substances Regulation, and have developed their own chemicals management procedures. Of particular interest are the approaches taken in Sweden and the Netherlands.

Sweden

3.100 Swedish government policy has been associated with a radical approach to chemicals control for many years. In the 1980s Sweden introduced a Chemicals Products Act[51] and created a National Chemicals Inspectorate (KemI). The operation of this national inspectorate and its work on establishing a Swedish chemical products register are particularly worthy of note (box 3A). The Swedish 'sunset chemicals' initiative to phase out the use of certain chemicals and heavy metals was highly influential in fostering international programmes in OECD and UNECE.

3.101 However, with their accession to the EU in the mid-1990s, the Swedish government realised that its room for manoeuvre for introducing unilateral controls had been severely curtailed. On the other hand, its ability to influence a major trading bloc had grown. This was one of the reasons for the 1997 Swedish report of the Chemicals Policy Committee.[52]

BOX 3A   **SWEDISH CHEMICAL PRODUCTS REGISTER**

One of the tools used by KemI is a chemical products register. The register contains information on approximately 65,000 chemical products from 2,000 companies. Also, 130,000 substances with synonyms are contained in a special file in the database. Cosmetics and pharmaceuticals are not included on the register (although constituent chemical products may be). Data are required on all substances manufactured or imported in quantities greater than 100 kg. The register stores details of function, industrial category, classification, composition, and quantity of chemical products imported to or manufactured in Sweden and is updated annually. Manufacturers/importers pay an annual fee to cover the costs of maintaining the register, which varies according to the tonnage of the product on the market.

The information collected is used to support work on risk assessments, statistical calculations, substance flow analyses and supervision. Although the database information is used mainly to support the activities conducted by the National Chemicals Inspectorate itself, other authorities, researchers, organisations and the public may use the information. Each application for data is treated on a case-by-case basis and there are controls in place to protect commercially sensitive information.

3.102 This Swedish report, along with the UK Chemicals Strategy, was influential in the review of EU chemicals policy that resulted in the European Commission's White Paper. Unlike the UK Strategy, the Swedish report is not a statement of Swedish government policy on chemicals – the Chemicals Policy Committee is an advisory body, not a government department. The report has nevertheless strongly influenced the line taken by Sweden in EU negotiations on chemicals policy.

3.103 Chapter 4 of the Chemicals Policy Committee report proposed several 'cornerstones' of chemicals policy. These were the precautionary principle, substitution, grouping of substances, publicly-funded technical support for industry, more green chemistry and green procurement, and economic instruments:

> 'to facilitate the marketing of environmentally adapted products when they compete with substantially cheaper poorly adapted products; the income from a financial instrument should be used for specific purposes; manufacturers and importers of poorly adapted products containing dangerous chemicals should be subject to the economic measures in relation to the marketed amount of those substances.'

3.104 The National Chemicals Inspectorate (KemI) is a supervisory authority under the Ministry of the Environment. Each year it receives instructions from the Ministry on areas of priority. The Ministry itself only employs a small number of staff on chemicals policy. KemI is the competent authority for a large part of the EU work on chemicals (chemicals policy, classification and labelling, notification of new substances, existing chemicals, pesticides and biocides). KemI has responsibilities both for health and environmental effects of chemicals. The National Board on Occupational Health has responsibility for supervising the regulations on chemical hazards in the workplace. The Environment Protection Agency is responsible for supervising the risks related to emissions of chemicals (for example from production sites), for hazardous waste, and for monitoring chemicals in the environment.

The Environment Protection Agency also has a supervisory role related to the Swedish Environmental Quality Objectives. KemI has a supervisory role for one of these objectives, for 'a non-toxic environment'.

3.105 KemI co-operates with other stakeholders such as research and development bodies, educational institutions, trade and industry, the trade unions, environmental organisations and central, regional and local authorities.

The Netherlands Strategy on the Management of Substances (SOMS)

3.106 The Dutch government adopted a new chemicals policy in April 2001.[53] The Strategy on Management of Substances, or SOMS, is rather more ambitious than the European Commission's White Paper on chemicals, setting extremely challenging targets for Dutch industry and business to produce data, propose 'levels of concern' for the chemicals they produce and use, and take appropriate measures to reduce hazard and risk.

3.107 SOMS aims to be a comprehensive system for the management of chemicals. It seeks to ensure 'that the potential risks and health hazards associated with the use of substances in each stage of their life cycle … are sufficiently controlled so as to remove, or reduce to negligible levels, any harmful effects caused by substances on man or the environment. In addition, safety and health hazards in the working environment due to the use of substances must be minimised'. Unlike the White Paper, it is intended eventually to cover medicines, veterinary medicines and agricultural and non-agricultural pesticides, as well as new and existing industrial chemicals.

3.108 In this and other areas the Dutch Strategy has much in common with the Swedish Chemicals Policy Committee recommendations – greater use of the precautionary principle, public access to information, improved information flow through the product chain, control of chemicals that are either persistent, bioaccumulative and toxic or carcinogenic, mutagenic or reprotoxic, and a greater onus on business to assume full life cycle responsibility for its products all feature in both documents.

3.109 The SOMS memorandum sets out the responsibilities of the business community. As well as expectations for responsible use of chemicals, risk management throughout the life cycle, and free access to information, the Strategy outlines more specific duties. Suitably trained staff and expertise are expected to be available, working under management systems that 'guarantee objective assessment and decision-making'. Public registers of chemical products and risk inventories must be maintained.

3.110 Through SOMS, the government promises:

> 'to create a clear and concrete framework within which the business community can take its responsibility, and, on the other hand, to ensure that there is an adequate system of monitoring and enforcement. Further, the government, where possible, will stimulate the industry in adopting the required quality improvements, and anchoring the product chain responsibility.'

As in Sweden, the Dutch government envisages providing considerable practical help to small and medium-sized enterprises (SMEs) throughout the product chain to meet these requirements.

3.111 The most radical aspect of the Dutch Strategy is the planned 'three-tier approach' to identify and control chemicals of concern. The timetable for implementing these proposals is very ambitious. The essence of the three steps is as follows:

    i. All substances sold or used to have 'substance profiles' prepared of available data and 'quick scans' by the (box 3B) in order to allocate the chemical to one of five 'levels of concern' (to be verified by the end of 2004). Any substances not meeting the deadline are to be banned or severely restricted, as will any causing serious concern.

    ii. Chemicals of concern produced in quantities over a certain threshold will have data gaps filled and risk assessments completed by 2010. This process is not to cause postponement of controls under step 1.

    iii. By 2015 all substances will have completed base data sets and risk assessments where necessary, and all necessary measures will have been implemented by 2020.

3.112 In a similar way to the UK Strategy, SOMS is seeking to assign a greater share of chemical assessment and management to industry. The Dutch approach to substance prioritisation is also similar to that taken in the UK Strategy. However, we were particularly impressed by the clear, systematic approach to prioritising and classifying chemicals through SOMS, linked directly to risk management options. In chapter 4 (4.8-4.39) we make recommendations for screening and categorising chemicals in a way rather similar to that in the SOMS quick scan.

3.113 In July 2002, the draft Netherlands Ministerial order to implement the quick scan approach in national legislation was notified to the European Commission. The Commission objected on the procedural grounds that it was already preparing a proposal for new chemicals legislation.[54]

3.114 As part of SOMS, legislation is being prepared on information transfer through the supply chain. This is discussed further in chapter 5.

OTHER NATIONAL REGIMES

The United States

3.115 The Royal Commission has heard opinions in evidence[55] that while the US approach to chemicals management offers advantages to industry, it is less precautionary, giving rise to doubts as to whether it offers the same degree of protection to human health and the environment as the current and proposed EC schemes. The situation in the US also needs to be seen in the context of its more litigious society and the possibility of greater damage awards than in the UK (3.146 and 3.178-3.198).

3.116 In the United States, the Toxic Substances Control Act (TSCA) regulates industrial chemicals. TSCA was enacted in 1976[56] to identify and control industrial chemical hazards that are toxic to human health and the environment. The Act is administered by the US Environmental Protection Agency (EPA) through its Office of Prevention, Pesticides and Toxic Substances. The EPA has broad authority under TSCA to regulate new and existing chemicals. The Act also included a provision requiring the EPA to take specific measures to control the risks from PCBs. Subsequently, additions have been made to address concerns about other specific toxic substances: asbestos in 1986; radon in 1988; and lead in 1992.

BOX 3B   **SOMS QUICK SCAN**

As a result of the delays in the EU chemicals policy revision process and partly as a result of the Dutch view on the feasibility of the proposed REACH process, the Dutch Ministry of Housing, Spatial Planning and the Environment (VROM) has developed an alternative 'quick scan' approach. This quick scan is the first stage of the chemicals management process of SOMS.

The quick scan seeks to use all available pre-existing hazard information about a chemical in order to prioritise those substances where risk management may be necessary. The full SOMS approach uses full risk assessments where these are available, but in the absence of such information, uses hazard-based criteria for chemicals management. A minimum information requirement is specified, but more data are welcomed. A 'no data, no market' clause is included to introduce sanctions against those not providing this basic data. The use of this hazard-based system also reduces considerably the number of animals used in testing. The quick scan does include a very simple estimation of exposure, by partitioning use into one of four categories (see figure below). In addition to these use categories, hazard-based criteria (persistence, bioaccumulation and toxicity (PBT), carcinogenicity, mutagenicity and reprotoxicity (CMR), endocrine-disrupting properties and health damage in humans) are also used.

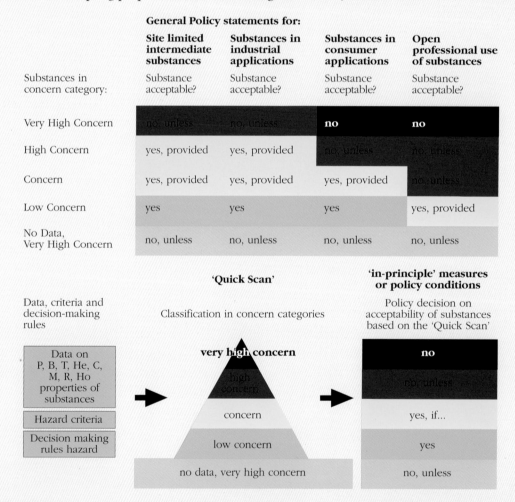

The hazard information and the use category information are taken together to allocate each substance to one of five categories of concern. Each of these categories is then linked to a policy statement on the acceptability of use of the substance.

Following the completion of quick scans for all substances currently available on the Dutch market, VROM will verify that these are complete at the end of 2004. There is a voluntary agreement with industry to prepare an inventory of all substances on the market and to indicate the availability of information on quick scans by October 2003.

3.117 The Act directs the EPA to use the least burdensome option that can reduce the risk to a level that is reasonable given the benefits provided by the chemical product or process. While the EPA implements most of the Act's provisions, individual states have some responsibilities, particularly where knowledge of local conditions is important.

3.118 An inventory is kept of all substances regulated under the Act, which also serves to distinguish existing from new substances. The EPA has identified a priority-testing programme to gather information about existing substances, which is currently focusing on high production volume chemicals.

3.119 For new substances, a process of Pre-Manufacture Notification (PMN) has been adopted, analogous to the EU's pre-market approach (3.11). This requires manufacturers, importers, and processors to notify the EPA at least 90 days prior to producing or otherwise introducing a new chemical product into the US. In addition to the notification, any pre-existing information about the chemical should also be submitted at the same time. The EPA then has 45 days after notification (or up to 90 days if it extends the period for good cause) to evaluate the potential risk posed by the chemical. The assessment process is described further in box 3C.

3.120 There is no defined base set of data required as part of notification, and the EPA reports that less than half of the notifications submitted include toxicological data.[57] An assessment of the substance is also required within the 45-day time-scale. This therefore means that the US EPA assessment of new substances is heavily reliant on quantitative structure activity relationships (QSARs). (These techniques are described in further detail in chapter 4 (4.51-4.59)). In cases where insufficient data are available and these QSAR tests are inconclusive, the EPA can request additional information from suppliers as part of the PMN process. If it is determined that the substance will pose an unacceptable risk, requirements must be proposed to protect against this risk. The EPA estimates that action to control potential risks to health or the environment is taken on approximately 10% of the notifications submitted.[58]

3.121 The US General Audit Office carried out a review of the Toxic Substances Control Act in 1994[59] that found it to be lacking in effectiveness regarding the attainment of its protective aims, and recommended the US Congress to introduce changes more akin to the European system. The review noted that the Act's requirements reflected an underlying philosophy that manufacturers and processors had the right to produce and market chemicals, and that before the EPA could take any legal action to restrict this right, it had to demonstrate that the risks outweighed both the costs to industry and the lost benefits of the unrestricted use of the chemical. The burden of proof was therefore on the EPA to demonstrate that a chemical may pose an 'unreasonable risk'. The Act does not define 'unreasonable risk' and provides little guidance on what level of risk should be considered unreasonable under the Act. It also requires producers of substances or products to report test results suggesting hazardous risks to the EPA immediately. There is, therefore, a disincentive to carry out non-regulatory testing.

BOX 3C	US EPA PRE-MANUFACTURING SCREENING[60]

The US EPA Pre-Manufacture Notification (PMN) review for new substances consists of four distinct and successive technical phases:

The chemistry review phase This establishes a chemical profile for each new substance and provides chemical information for use in further review phases. The EPA notes that 'Most PMNs contain few physicochemical data. Consequently, the majority of physicochemical properties used for risk assessment of PMN substances are obtained by EPA scientists, usually by estimation'. The EPA aims to estimate physico-chemical properties to provide over-estimates of exposure and risk, so that it is in the notifier's interest to submit data.

The hazard (toxicity) evaluation phase This phase includes a review of available literature on the substance, likely to be minimal in the case of new substances. This phase is therefore heavily reliant on the use of structure-activity relationships, which are used to estimate qualitatively human acute and chronic toxicity of PMN substances (including carcinogenicity; mutagenicity; developmental toxicity; neurotoxicity; reproductive toxicity; and systemic toxicity, irritability, and sensitisation). Estimates of the probable human pharmacokinetics of the PMN substance are made (evaluating absorption, distribution and redistribution, metabolism (biotransformation), and excretion of the substance). QSARs are used to estimate chronic and acute toxicity values for fish (vertebrates), *Daphnia magna* (invertebrates), and algae (plants). An environmental fate assessment is made (including consideration of: relative rates of environmental biodegradation, hydrolysis, and photolysis; adsorption to soils and sediments; treatability (generally in publicly-owned treatment works); and half-lives in the atmosphere, surface waters, soils, and sediments). This assessment is carried out on the basis of the physico-chemical properties of the substance.

The exposure evaluation phase This phase evaluates the potential for occupational exposure and for releases to the environment expected from the manufacturing, processing, and commercial or industrial use of the substance. This evaluation is again reliant on physico-chemical data.

The risk assessment/risk management phase Following an assessment of the risk posed by the substance, it is assigned one of 11 possible outcomes, which can be summarised into three groups:
- the substance will not present an unreasonable risk and is dropped from further review,
- the substance may present an unreasonable risk but risk management decisions can be made without additional review, and
- the substance may present an unreasonable risk but requires additional review for risk characterisation.

Approximately 80% of PMNs are dropped between the end of the chemistry review phase and the outcome of the risk assessment phase. Some of the remaining 20% may also be subject to control on the basis of the EPA's categorisation approach under the new chemicals programme, which groups together chemicals with similar hazard concerns and testing requirements. These controls may include restrictions on production pending the outcomes of further testing.

In order to conserve resource, these phases are structured to remove substances of low risk from the review process and focus on those substances of greater risk as the review progresses.

3.122 The US also operates separate regimes for pesticides and other groups of chemicals. The Federal Insecticide, Fungicide and Rodenticide Act requires EPA registration for all pesticides sold in the US. The Federal Food, Drug and Cosmetic Act regulates the establishment of pesticide tolerances (maximum residue levels). The Emergency Planning and Community Right-to-Know Act requires industry to notify their communities and states about releases to the environment. It is under this Act that the US national inventory of toxic chemical releases (the Toxics Release Inventory[61]) was established.

Canada

3.123 The Canadian Environmental Protection Act 1999 requires the Minister of the Environment and the Minister of Health to categorise and, if necessary, conduct screening assessments of substances listed on the Canadian Domestic Substances List to determine whether they are toxic or capable of becoming toxic.[62] This categorisation must be carried out within seven years of the passage of the Act, which occurred on September 14, 1999.

3.124 Under the Act, a substance is defined as 'toxic' if it is entering or may enter the environment in a quantity or concentration or under conditions that:

- have or may have an immediate or long-term harmful effect on the environment or its biological diversity;

- constitute or may constitute a danger to the environment on which life depends; or

- constitute or may constitute a danger in Canada to human life or health.

3.125 The Domestic Substances List includes substances that were used in Canadian commerce for manufacturing purposes, or manufactured in or imported into Canada, in a quantity of 100 kg or more in any calendar year between 1984 and 1986. The purpose of the Domestic Substances List was to define what was 'new to Canada'; it has been amended from time to time following assessment under the New Substances Notification Regulations and currently contains approximately 23,000 substances. The Domestic Substances List is, therefore, roughly equivalent in purpose to EINECS (3.19) but contains only those chemicals that have actually been marketed.

3.126 The categorisation criteria under the Environmental Protection Act identify those substances that:

i.   may present, to individuals in Canada, the greatest potential for exposure; or

ii. are persistent (P) or bioaccumulative (B), in accordance with the Persistence and Bioaccumulation Regulations, and inherently toxic (iT) to human beings or to non-human organisms, as determined by laboratory or other studies.

Substances that are identified as P *or* B *and* iT will proceed to the second phase, a screening assessment.

3.127 Data are likely to be lacking for many of the substances contained on the Domestic Substances List and heavy reliance is therefore placed on the use of QSARs for this initial categorisation of substances, including the assessment of inherent toxicity. Environment Canada has produced detailed guidance[63] on how and when expert judgement and issues of practicality are to be considered to categorise substances on the list. In particular, guidance is given, based on rules of thumb, on using expert judgement to categorise substances when no experimental data (or acceptable closest analogues) are available or QSAR predictions are unreliable, and for determining the P, B and iT properties of 'model-difficult' substances.

3.128 Substances meeting the categorisation criteria proceed to a second phase, a screening assessment. This involves a more detailed assessment of toxicity (integrating effects and exposure).

3.129 The screening assessment results in one of the following outcomes:

i.   no further action is taken at this time in respect of the substance, if the assessment indicates that the substance does not pose a risk to the environment or human health;

ii. the substance is added to the Canadian Environmental Protection Act Priority Substances List in order to assess more comprehensively the risks associated with the release of the substance, if the substance is not already on the List; or

iii. it is recommended that the substance be added to the List of Toxic Substances in Schedule 1 of the Canadian Environmental Protection Act; substances on Schedule 1 can be considered for regulatory or other controls.

3.130 The initiative is currently at the information gathering stage.

Japan

3.131 Japan is the second largest producer of chemicals worldwide, its production being approximately half that of the USA and four times that of the UK. Over the last two decades there has been a progressive reduction in the export of organic chemicals from Japan, which has been almost replaced by the export of end-products of which half constitute pharmaceuticals.

3.132 In 2001 there were major reforms in the Japanese government administration to strengthen policy co-ordination. As part of this a new Ministry of Economy, Trade and Industry has been created to replace the Ministry of International Trade and Industry (MITI), and the Japanese Environment Agency has been upgraded into a full Ministry. The National Council for Science and Technology Policy was created within the Cabinet Office.

3.133 Responsibility for chemical substance management falls under the remit of the Ministry of Economy, Trade and Industry; the Ministry of the Environment is responsible for monitoring. The basic concept of the Japanese Chemical Substance Management Policy is to 'identify the characteristics of harmful effects of chemical substances, assess the risks of these through their life cycle and implement appropriate management activities through science-based risk assessment'. This 'science-based' approach operates through voluntary regulation by agreements between government and industry.

3.134 In 1973 the Chemical Substances Control Law was introduced to evaluate the toxicity of chemicals and regulate their manufacture. All chemical substances, either manufactured in Japan or imported, are subject to pre-market toxicity evaluation. This is designed to deal with approximately 300 chemicals per year. Chemicals are divided into two classes:

- *class 1* – chemicals that exhibit persistence, high bioaccumulation and long-term toxicity (11 chemicals identified since 1973); and

- *class 2* – chemicals that exhibit persistence, low bioaccumulation and long-term toxicity (23 chemicals since 1973). This class also includes designated chemicals that are suspected of being persistent, having low bioaccumulation and long-term toxicity (616 chemicals since 1973).

A total of 1,280 chemicals manufactured or imported up to March 2002 have been evaluated. Two government-funded programmes have been launched to monitor systematically the environmental fate of existing substances, one for class 1 and one for class 2 substances.

3.135 The Law for Pollutant Release and Transfer Register and Promotion of Chemical Management directs manufacturers of chemicals and end-products to ascertain and notify the release of designated chemical substances. This has so far embraced 354 chemicals and a further 435 for which a material safety data sheet has been required. The register covers chemicals manufactured or handled in amounts greater than 5 tons per annum, and this will fall to 1 ton per annum in 2004.

3.136 The Ministry of Economy, Trade and Industry guides its requirement for toxicology studies through contracts with the associated Chemical Evaluation Research Institute, which has five laboratories across Japan that carry out toxicity and ecotoxicity testing. Of the 616 chemicals that have been assessed only 11 have been withdrawn (including DDT) and 13 are being tightly regulated on the basis of persistence and bioaccumulation.

3.137 Recent publicity about endocrine disruption and changes to the physical environment has raised awareness among those producing chemicals and products containing chemicals that genuine public concern exists. Thus, the Japanese Chemical Industry Association (JCIA) takes very seriously its role to undertake research on chemical production, distribution and use, to engage in educational activities with the public, and to enable easy access to information on chemicals. The JCIA is an active participant in Responsible Care (3.199) and has established a Chemical Product Liability Consultant Centre, which provides information in an easily accessible form on chemicals and their impact on the environment and health. One output is the 'JCIA EHS Net', which provides an e-mail news network on chemicals.

COMPARISON OF REGULATORY REGIMES

3.138 It is instructive to compare the chemicals notification schemes of the EU, the US and Japan in terms of their main features, their effectiveness and their possible impact on business. A summary comparison between the regimes is given in table 3.3.

Data requirements

3.139 The main differences in data requirements are that mandatory base sets are required under EU and Japanese law, both of which lead to an element of classification or categorisation. The US Toxic Substances Control Act does not specify a base data set, and does not lead to classification. This reflects the criticism of the General Audit Office, that the Act leaves a severe burden of proof on the EPA. It may also explain an element of the US's disquiet over the EU REACH proposals, which move even further towards requiring data from industry.

3.140 The most significant difference, though, is in US industry's right to confidentiality. While, under the EU notification of new substances scheme, manufacturers are able to request a one-year exemption from the data disclosure requirements of the scheme, disclosure of information is taken to be the norm. This contrasts with the situation in the US, where confidentiality (for example on the intended uses of a substance) is ensured under legislation. The American Chamber of Commerce[64] has expressed concern about proposals on data sharing within the European Commission's White Paper. It has called for the protection of confidential business information, which in the US can even include the specific chemical identity of a hazardous substance (except in health-related emergency situations).

Table 3.3

Comparison of the notification procedures for chemical substances[65]

	EU	Japan	US
Name of procedure	Notification, (Dangerous Substances Directive)	Notification Chemical Substances Control Law	Pre-Manufacture Notification Toxic Substances Control Act
Corresponding legislation and year of first publication	European Council Directive 67/548/EEC (1967) and 7th Amendment 92/32/EEC (1992)	Chemical Substances Control Law No. 117 (1983) and amended in 1986	Toxic Substances Control Act (1976)
Purpose of legislation	Protect humans and environment	Protect humans from contamination through environment	Protect humans and environment
Inventory type	EINECS (static, old) ELINCS (dynamic, new)	ENCS (dynamic)	TSCA inventory (dynamic)
Polymer listed	No	Yes	Yes
Approach for new substances	Pre-market	Pre-manufacture	Pre-manufacture
Good Laboratory Practice requirement	Yes	Yes	No
Classifications of substances	On the basis of intrinsic property	Designated Specified class 1 Specified class 2	None
Legal delay before manufacture	60 days (before marketing)	Japan: 90 days Import: 120 days	PMN: 90 days NCMI: 30 days
Responsible body	National competent authorities and European Commission DG XI	MITI MHW	US EPA
	EU	Japan	US

(continued overleaf)

(table 3.3 continued)

	EU	Japan	US
PROCEDURE FOR NEW SUBSTANCES			
Approach and obligation to notify	Pre-market based on volume trigger	Pre-manufacturing beginning with 1 tonne per year	Pre-manufacturing (first time)
Information requirements	Physico-chemical properties	Physico-chemical properties	Physico-chemical properties
	Use and production volume data	Use and production volume data	Use and production volume data
	No obligation to declare new use of chemical	–	Obligation to declare new use of the chemical
	–	–	Expected exposure for humans and the environment
	Automatic requirement for ecotoxicological data	Simple ecological data; then more detailed data are required in case chemicals are non-biodegradable and/or bioaccumulative	Obligation to submit only available data on toxicology
Structure of testing requirement	Fixed testing requirements	Flexible risk contingent testing	Flexible risk contingent testing
Estimated cost for a notification	$117,000	$80,000	$40,000
Exemption	Marketed product less than 100 kg per year per manufacture	Produced less than 1 tonne per year	Less than 10 tonnes per year
	Polymers (but see 3.18)	High molecular weight polymer	Polymers
	Substance for scientific R&D	Substances manufactured or imported for testing and research	R&D chemicals
	Substances for process-oriented R&D		Record-keeping requirement for process-oriented R&D
	Manufacture for export use only	–	Manufacture for export use only
	Intermediate manufactured and consumed in the same site	Substances manufactured in the same site	–
	–	Some specific substance such as paints and films	–
	–	Reagents for detection	–
	–	–	Low release and exposure substance
PROCEDURE FOR EXISTING SUBSTANCES			
Scope	Extensive notification requirement	–	Testing of priority substance
High volume chemicals	Additional data need to be submitted	–	US program on high volume chemical
State-aided (co-) financing	No state-funded program	Existing substance are tested by the state	US National Toxicological Program

3.141 We have already referred to the need for transparency in the management of chemical risks and in chapter 4 we will discuss ways of securing as open a mechanism as possible. Whereas the American Chamber of Commerce regards the confidentiality of business information as an absolute value of right, we see it in instrumental terms. In particular we would be concerned if our recommendations in this, or other, respects, could be shown to be likely to restrict innovative activity – a matter taken up in chapter 5. **We recommend that the UK government argues strongly for adherence to the EU model despite pressure to the contrary from the US.**

Notification

3.142 Following receipt of a notification from a manufacturer/importer, regulatory agencies are expected to respond as to (a) the adequacy of the tests reported, and (b) the (likely) ruling as to whether the benefits of the prospective uses warrant incurring the risks and environmental externalities.

3.143 Three questions arise in relation to this procedure:

i.   At what point is the notification to be made in the process of developing, manufacturing and marketing a new product?

ii. How definitive is the agency's ruling? Or might a product cleared before manufacture still be banned after marketing? and

iii. How much protection does clearance by the agency offer the producer against being sued in courts by users, consumers or NGOs (on behalf of the environment)?

3.144 If the regulator is to have only one opportunity for intervention, there is a potential conflict between the requirements of potential producers and consumers. The producer wants a relatively early decision so as to know that the product will be marketable before committing themselves, and investors' resources, to pilot, or particularly, full-scale production. Thus the producer wants pre-manufacturing notification – and clearance – as in the US. The consumer on the other hand wants notification (and clearance) as late as possible so that as much data and experience as possible have been accumulated – as in the European pre-marketing notification regime. In practice the choice is not quite so clear. One reason is that in most regulatory regimes there is opportunity for dialogue between industry and regulator in a way that blunts the sharpness of the distinction between the two models. Also, in the US the threat of litigation is an incentive for producers to be more cautious than might be the case in the EU.

3.145 A further, related, distinction is that under the US system the notified chemical is most often submitted as a 'pure' compound (of 95% or greater purity), while under the EU notification of new substances regime, the notice pertains to the substance 'as marketed', which is often a mixture. This distinction has important implications for the predictability of physical and chemical properties, biodegradation, and potential hazard concerns.[66] In the US, the new chemical and any impurities reported by the submitter or identified as being likely contaminants by the EPA are considered when assessments are performed. In the EU, the submitter is required to provide purity information for the product as marketed and any test data pertaining to this product.

3.146 The answer to question iii (in 3.143) is not merely a question of formal law but also of legal culture. In the more litigious US society a manufacturer might (in the absence of any formal regulations) be more cautious about launching a new product than in less-litigious Europe. It may be that this explains the relative 'light-handedness' of formal US regulatory regimes. It is worth noting that liability costs in the US following marketing are much higher than those in Europe (3.178). Dow Chemicals reports figures from 1996[67] showing that in the US one dollar was spent on litigation for every 160 dollars of US sales, whereas in Europe, one dollar was spent on litigation for every 40,000 dollars in sales, for similar products.

Testing methodologies

3.147 The European and Japanese systems require specific tests to be carried out in line with Good Laboratory Practice. This is not the case in the US, where 'all available data' must be submitted and there are no mandatory testing requirements. Following the submission of this basic set of data, the EU system prescribes further tests to be carried out on the basis of tonnage thresholds, whereas the US and Japanese systems operate on a risk-contingent basis, tailoring the testing package to the nature of the substance. The US approach is heavily dependent on QSAR and other computational techniques, while the testing scheme in the EU requires more animal testing.

3.148 In chapter 4 we set out why we believe that the UK approach to screening chemicals should move much more in the direction of using computational techniques such as those used in the US and elsewhere, instead of relying on the extensive testing procedures stipulated in EU legislation.

Costs (and who pays)

3.149 A study by the Institute for Prospective Technological Studies[68] compared the regulatory regimes in the EU, US and Japan. They noted that the costs of notification were generally highest in the EU due to the list of tests to be performed. The precise costs of testing in the EU vary according to the tonnage of product to be placed on the EU market (see details in table 3.4). Details of costs for testing under the Japanese system are given in table 3.5.

Table 3.4

Testing costs for notification in the EU[69]

Test requirements under Directive 92/32/EEC	Laboratory costs (Euros)
Annex VII C (< 100 kg)	15,000-20,000
Annex VII B (< 1,000 kg)	25,000-30,000
Annex VII A (< 10 tonnes)	75,000-85,000
Annex VIII Level 1 (< 100 tonnes)	175,000-250,000
Annex VIII Level 2 (< 1,000 tonnes)	275,000-325,000

Table 3.5

Testing costs for notification in Japan[70]

Level	Laboratory costs (Euros)
Advanced report	10,000-12,500
Specified class 1	–
Designated	20,000-25,000
Specified class 2	50,000-60,000

3.150 The US system has no fixed testing requirements, although laboratory tests may be requested as a result of Pre Manufacture Notification screening. It is therefore difficult to estimate costs. We have heard evidence from the Chemicals Industry Association[71] that chemical firms are moving their R&D facilities from Europe to, *inter alia,* the US, to enable candidate chemicals to be trialled without the need for providing extensive test data on each one before deciding which to place on the market.

3.151 In addition to these testing costs, further costs are associated with the compilation of the dossiers of results and fees for filing the dossier with the relevant authority. A recent German study[72] noted that when comparing the regulatory systems, it should be borne in mind that Toxic Substances Control Act places practically the entire burden of work and proof of risk assessment on the EPA. By contrast, the European White Paper on chemicals pursues exactly the opposite aim, placing more of the burden of initial assessment on industry, which, under the polluter pays principle, is exactly where the costs should lie. In effect, the US government is subsidising the US chemicals industry, firstly by not requiring tests to evaluate the environmental and health effects of the chemicals they produce, and secondly, by using public funds to pay for the tests which are required. On the other hand it is possible to envisage a much lower cost testing regime than Europe's, while providing equivalent security, and we return to this in chapter 4.

Effects on innovation

3.152 We have considered the influence of regulation on innovation in some detail and the results of a consultant's study on this topic are described in further detail in chapter 5 (5.117-5.127). The overall conclusions of the work were that there is no consensus about whether regulation inhibits or stimulates innovation in industry, but that the introduction of new regulation causes a temporary shock to innovative activity in firms that has a negative effect on the overall rate of innovation. Each of the elements of the notification schemes described above could potentially act on companies' thinking in terms of the registration process and thus influence the overall number of notifications.

OTHER RELEVANT LEGISLATION

INTERNATIONAL TRADE

3.153 The General Agreement on Tariffs and Trade (GATT), and subsequent related trade agreements, now in the remit of the WTO, requires non-discrimination in trade matters between countries, and particularly, under Article III, between 'like products', whether imported or domestically produced. However, GATT's Article XX permits exemptions for national measures that are necessary to protect human health, animals or plants, or relate to the conservation of exhaustible natural resources, provided that they do not entail 'arbitrary and unjustifiable discrimination' between countries, or constitute 'a disguised restriction on international trade'. The burden is on the country imposing such measures to justify the exemptions.

3.154 The quoted text has been variously interpreted in subsequent trade agreements to mean that in order to be consistent with Article XX, measures should be based on scientific evidence and should be the least trade-restrictive measures available to achieve the desired outcome. There is obviously scope for considerable difference of opinion as to precisely what measures would satisfy these criteria.

3.155 Trade disputes are adjudicated by a Disputes Panel, an independent panel of experts in WTO jurisprudence set up by the WTO itself. A separate Appellate Body adjudicates appeals against the judgements of the Disputes Panel.

3.156 The France-Canada dispute over France's 'effective' ban on asbestos imports from Canada was, in 2001,[73] the first application of a trade-restrictive measure to protect human health to be ruled justified under GATT Article XX. Canada had argued that the measure discriminated in favour of other non-asbestos substances and products with similar functions. The Dispute Panel ruled that there was indeed discrimination between like products, but that the measure was justified under Article XX. On appeal the Appellate Body considered for the first time the meaning of 'like products' in Article III, and held that a difference in toxicity may be sufficient to differentiate for trade purposes between otherwise 'like products'. Hence the ban did not infringe the basic prohibition in Article III. It remains to be seen to what extent the concept of likeness and non-likeness will extend to products with less obvious toxic properties than asbestos, but the decision is an important extension of thinking in this area.

3.157 Given its decision on Article III, it was not strictly necessary for the Appellate Body to consider whether the measure could be justified under Article XX. Nevertheless the decision contains important rulings on Article XX, which suggest that a less rigid approach will be applied in future. The Apellate Body confirmed that WTO Members had the right to determine the level of protection of health they considered appropriate, and that when it came to considering whether measures were 'necessary' it was not necessarily correct to judge by majority scientific opinion: 'a Member may also rely in good faith on scientific sources which at that time may represent a divergent but qualified and respected opinion'.

3.158 Trade measures for the conservation of natural resources have not, so far, stood up to challenge. In celebrated cases such as the Mexico-US tuna-dolphin dispute,[74] it has been found that countries have no right to impose discriminatory trade measures on the basis of process and production methods in other countries, or to protect natural resources outside their own jurisdiction.

3.159 However, the Appellate Body's 1998 ruling in the shrimp-turtle dispute between the US and a number of developing countries[75] seemed to signal a change in interpretation of Article XX in both these respects. The restrictions on shrimp imports imposed by the US were ruled as legitimate in principle under Article XX, despite the fact that the turtles which the measures sought to protect were outside the US's territorial jurisdiction, and that the measures were triggered by other countries' process and production methods. However, the Appellate Body also found that the way in which the measures had been applied by the US (including failing to consult adequately and applying US standards blindly without taking sufficient account of different conditions in other countries) constituted 'unjustifiable and arbitrary discrimination', and therefore were not consistent with Article XX on those grounds. Further judgements are probably necessary to give definitive clarification of these issues.

3.160 The European Commission's White Paper on chemicals did not deal with the issue of chemical substances present in imported products in any detail. The section of the White Paper on trade barriers noted that:

> 'The new policy shall not discriminate against imported products. In that respect, the EU should conform with Article 2.1 of the WTO's Technical Barriers to Trade, which sets out that imported products shall be accorded treatment no less favourable than that accorded to like products of national origin. Without a sound scientific evaluation of the potential threats to human health and the environment, the EU will not be able to defend a measure being challenged by third countries. In accordance with Article 2.2 of the Technical Barriers to Trade, the EU shall ensure that "technical regulations will not create unnecessary obstacles to international trade".'

3.161 For European chemicals regulation to both protect human health and the environment in Europe, and not have adverse impacts on the European chemicals industry, more consideration will need to be given in the REACH system to the regulatory treatment of chemicals in imported products. Some suggestions in this regard are presented in chapter 5.

OTHER EU ENVIRONMENTAL LEGISLATION RELEVANT TO CHEMICALS

3.162 The legislation described so far in this chapter has been specifically directed towards securing the environmental safety of chemicals and products containing those chemicals. There is, however, a much larger block of legislation related to the control of emissions, the management of waste, and securing the quality or safety of various environmental media, which has a bearing on chemicals in products, and therefore on the subject of this report. This section briefly describes the more relevant of these European instruments.

WATER FRAMEWORK DIRECTIVE

3.163 The Water Framework Directive was adopted by the European Parliament and the Council in September 2000.[76] The Directive contains a legal framework and methodological basis for the prioritisation of substances of concern in water. The European Commission has proposed a list of 32 substances[77] based on a 'combined monitoring-based and modelling-based priority setting' (COMMPS) procedure. Data were reviewed on 658 substances to identify the list of 32 priority substances. The priority substances include pesticides, biocides, industrial chemicals (including metals) and others.

3.164 Under the scheme, it is suggested that the proposed substances should be subject to emission controls and quality standards at European Community level in order to achieve a 'progressive reduction of discharges, emissions and losses'. Within the list of priority substances, a proposed list of priority hazardous substances (PHS) that are of particular concern for the freshwater, coastal and marine environment has been identified. These substances will be subject to 'the cessation or phasing out of discharges, emissions and losses … including any appropriate timetable for doing so … [which] … shall not exceed 20 years'.

3.165 The Directive also contains requirements to monitor water quality, including detection of the presence and levels of these priority substances.

WASTE

3.166 EU waste policy contains a specific Directive dealing with the management of hazardous waste.[78] The hazardous waste stream will include by-products of chemical production, chemical substances, and products incorporating such substances.

3.167 Annex III of the Waste Directive lists the properties of wastes that render them hazardous, derived from the definitions in the Basel Convention (3.77). These are listed in appendix G.

3.168 The need for accurate classification and labelling information to enable recovery of material (such as waste electrical equipment) from the waste stream is discussed further in chapter 5.

PRODUCER RESPONSIBILITY

Integrated Product Policy

3.169 In 2001, the European Commission published a Green Paper on Integrated Product Policy[79] that proposed a strategy to strengthen and refocus product-related environmental policies, and to promote the development of a market for greener products. Part of the purpose of the Green Paper was to improve environmental performance of a range of products and services throughout their life cycles. It was noted that as a result of this life cycle approach, there could be no single instrument to deliver Integrated Product Policy. The success of the approach depended upon successful design and consumer uptake of greener products.

3.170 The European Commission noted that pricing mechanisms would be important in the adoption of Integrated Product Policy, including fuller reflection of life cycle external costs in the price of goods and services. They also proposed that Community level measures, such as reductions in VAT for eco-labelled goods should be explored.

3.171 Part of Integrated Product Policy also relates to Producer Responsibility (Extended Producer Responsibility or EPR). This means that producers take responsibility for recovery of goods once they have reached the end of their service life. Such schemes have been introduced in the Directive on End of Life Vehicles and the Directive on Waste Electrical and Electronic Equipment (see below). The Green Paper also suggested that such approaches could be usefully extended to other areas, such as deposit-refund systems.

End of Life Vehicles

3.172 The intention of the Directive on End of Life Vehicles[80] was to reduce the amount of waste from vehicles at the end of their lives, and to increase opportunities to re-use and recycle components from vehicles.

3.173 Under the provisions of the Directive, Member States must set up collection systems for end of life vehicles and for waste used parts. The Directive stipulates that vehicle manufacturers and material and equipment manufacturers must:

- endeavour to reduce the use of hazardous substances when designing vehicles;

- design and produce vehicles which facilitate the dismantling, re-use, recovery and recycling of end-of-life vehicles;

- increase the use of recycled materials in vehicle manufacture; and

- ensure that components of vehicles placed on the market after 1 July 2003 do not contain mercury, hexavalent chromium, cadmium or lead (with some exceptions).

3.174 Provisions were also introduced to facilitate the labelling of different types of materials in use to facilitate separated dismantling and component re-use.

Waste Electrical and Electronic Equipment

3.175 The Directive on Waste Electrical and Electronic Equipment[81] resulted from concerns about growth in the amount of electronic equipment waste and its increasing importance in the municipal waste stream. The Directive applies to a wide range of electrical and electronic consumer goods, and business and medical equipment.

3.176 Under the Directive, Member States must set up free collection systems and distributors are obliged to take back the materials after use. Producers must provide information for users to enable them to identify the various components and substances used in the product as well as any hazardous substances contained in the equipment.

Restriction on the Use of Certain Hazardous Substances in Electrical and Electronic Equipment (ROHS)

3.177 A Directive covering the use of hazardous substances in electrical equipment[82] is linked to the Waste Electrical and Electronic Equipment Directive. This requires that from 1 January 2008, lead, mercury, cadmium, hexavalent chromium, polybrominated biphenyls and polybrominated diphenyl ethers should no longer be used in the production of electrical equipment and these substances should be substituted.

NON-REGULATORY REGIMES AND INITIATIVES

CIVIL LIABILITY

3.178 As the previous sections have indicated, the legal framework concerning the manufacture and distribution of chemicals is now dominated by a complex regulatory system. But it is important not to ignore the principles of law governing the civil liability of manufacturers and others involved in the system, where chemical products cause damage to people, property, or the environment. They may well influence both the production of chemicals, the design and composition of products, and the nature of the regulatory system itself. A vigorous civil liability system is sometimes described as a shadow regulator, and has on occasion been advocated as a more efficient, market-based solution than more traditional public regulatory techniques. We were informed[83], for example, that the lighter regulatory system governing chemicals in the US as compared to Europe had to be viewed against the much tougher system of civil liability that exists in the US (3.146). This section, therefore, considers some of the key existing principles in the UK, but highlights significant differences to the US system. There has been some important recent case law that is likely to influence the future development of the law in this area. Chapter 5 makes a number of recommendations.

Product liability – from fault to defect

3.179 Until 1987, the law in England and Wales was that a manufacturer was liable in civil law to someone who suffered damage from a chemical product only if the manufacturer could be proved to have been negligent, in the sense of falling below the standards that might reasonably be expected of that type of manufacturer. Scottish law, based on delict, also contained a similar requirement of fault on the part of the manufacturer. An alternative form of remedy was for the consumer who had actually bought the product to sue the retailer for breach of contract, in which case the principles are dependent not on fault but essentially on whether the product worked as it should have done. The retailer could sue the wholesaler and so on up the line. Contractual remedies, though powerful, may be of limited value since only the person who had made the contract could sue, and in any event the immediate supplier might have limited resources.

3.180 Basic principles of fault-based and contractual liability are still important, and counterparts are found in many continental jurisdictions and in the US. But the thalidomide tragedy brought a general recognition in Europe that a purely fault-based system provided unacceptable hurdles for consumers who had suffered as a result of defective products. As a result the European Commission agreed a new Product Liability Directive in 1985,[84] transposed into UK law under Part I of the Consumer Protection Act 1987.[85] Where the Directive applies, negligence is no longer an essential ingredient to liability, though a number of specific defences are available to manufacturers and producers. Any UK claim involving health or property damage from a product is now likely to be based on the Consumer Protection Act rather than negligence or delict.

3.181 The Japanese Product Liability Law[86] is similar in content to the EC Directive. In the US, in contrast, since the early 1960s, it was the courts rather than the legislature that developed a much stricter liability approach for manufacturers and sellers of products, starting with a number of key decisions in the 1960s. There is no Federal legislation providing a consistent set of principles (despite a number of legislative attempts) and principles differ somewhat from state to state. In addition, many individual states permit the award of punitive damages in addition to compensation, where the defendant is shown to have acted recklessly or with utter disregard for safety – hence some of the enormous awards sometimes reported. It should also be noted that in the US, it is usual for juries to determine the amount of damages, which also accounts for some of the very high awards (though these are often cut down on appeal). In the UK, civil liability claims are determined by judges alone, and damages are based strictly on compensation needs. Punitive damages are unheard of in the UK in this type of claim. Without taking account of such fundamental differences, one has to be very cautious in comparing US and European systems.

3.182 The basic provision of the EC Directive is that a producer is 'liable for damage caused by a defect in his product', with liability resting on (a) the manufacturer of the product, (b) a company that puts its name on the product holding itself out as the producer, or (c) an importer of the product into the European Community. Unlike in the US, wholesalers or retailers are not liable under the Directive unless, in relation to a potential claim, they fail to identify the name of the producer as defined in (a)-(c).

3.183 The claimant has to prove the damage and the fact that the defect caused it. What, then, is a defect? A product is defined in the Directive as defective 'when it does not provide the safety which a person is entitled to expect, taking all the circumstances into account'. 'The safety' is not what a reasonable manufacturer would expect to provide, nor what the public might actually expect, but what the court determines the consumer is 'entitled to expect'. This means that there may be no entitlement to expect that an inherently and known risky product (such as a knife, alcohol, or tobacco) could be 'defective'; this is similarly the case for drugs with advertised side-effects. For similar reasons, the New York Court of Appeals has recently rejected negligence claims by victims of gun wounds against gun manufacturers.[87] It is equally clear that it is not an absolute level of safety.

3.184 There have been few reported cases on the Directive or the transposing provisions of the Consumer Protection Act – only five reported cases in the UK and a similar small number in other European countries. This may disguise numerous settled cases, or could indicate that the legislation has proved successful in improving manufacturing safety. The European Commission has adopted two application reports on the Directive, one in December 1995[88] and one in January 2001.[89] The first essentially launched a consultation exercise on whether the objectives pursued by the Directive were being achieved within Member States. The second concludes that there are still major information gaps, and problems of late implementation and little case law, but that there was no case as yet for major change. However, it proposed to launch two studies; one concerned with the economic impact of the Directive on industry insurance companies and consumers, and the second to be concerned more with the impacts of the different systems within Member States and whether there was a case for a uniform product liability system within the Community.

3.185 The most recent and extensive UK case on product liability is the 170 page judgement of Mr Justice Burton in the HIV-infected blood case.[90] Before this case, a number of UK commentators had argued that the effect of the EC Directive, taking into account all the defences, was not significantly different from pre-existing fault-based liability. But it is clear from this decision that there is now a clear break between product liability and previous common law concepts, and that we have moved from fault-based to defect-based liability. The judge (rather than, say, standard industry practice) plays a much stronger role in determining what are socially acceptable risks, and issues concerning the amount of information provided to the consumer become more important. It is clear that the definition of defectiveness requires the court to determine what is a socially acceptable risk in this context.

3.186 In the US, judges sometimes engage in what has been described as the 'risk/utility' test – the more difficult it is to make the product safe and the more socially beneficial the product, the less is expected and *vice versa* – but this approach was rejected by Mr Justice Burton. On analysis of the Directive and its purpose, he concluded that the concern of the court was whether the product was safe according to legitimate expectations. Alternative production and design methods might be relevant to a defence but not to the initial issue as to whether the product was 'defective'.

State of the art defence

3.187 The EC Directive includes a defence if the defendant could prove 'that the state of scientific and technical knowledge at the time when he put the product into circulation was not such as to enable the existence of the defect to be discovered'. Member States had the option to exclude this defence if they wished in their national transposing legislation; Germany, for example, did not transpose the defence, but the UK did under section 4(e) of the Consumer Protection Act 1987.

3.188 In any event, subsequent legal interpretation of the defence indicates that the state of knowledge refers to the most advanced available and not simply what was available to the producer, and is a tough test. In a key decision of the European Court of Justice for example,[91] the Advocate General stated that 'where in the whole gamut of scientific opinion at a particular time there is also one isolated opinion (which as the history of science shows might become, with the passage of time, *opinio communis*) as to the potentially defective and/or hazardous nature of the product, the manufacturer is no longer faced with a unforeseeable risk since, as such, it is outside the scope of the rules imposed by the Directive.' However, it has been accepted that the information must be 'accessible' in the sense of published research. The European Court also made it clear that it was not relevant for this defence that no one in the particular class of manufacturers in question took avoidance measures.

Compliance with regulatory requirements

3.189 Compliance with regulatory requirements does not generally provide a defence to a civil liability claim, though where a claim (such as one of negligence) requires fault to be proved, it may provide useful evidence. The Product Liability Directive does, however, contain an express defence where the defect can be proved to be in compliance with a mandatory requirement of a public authority.

Causation and risk exposure

3.190 Even strict liability regimes such as the Product Liability Directive still depend on the claimant proving a causal connection between the damage suffered and defendant's actions or product, albeit in civil cases on the balance of probabilities. In cases involving human or environmental exposure to chemicals where the limit of scientific understanding and detection is being reached, this may often prove fatal to a successful action. The recent House of Lords decision, however, in the mesothelioma litigation indicates that the courts are prepared to adopt new approaches to causation tests in complex areas.

3.191 Fairchild v. Glenhaven Funeral Services Ltd.[92] concerned a number of claimants who had contracted mesothelioma through being exposed to asbestos during their working life, involving a number of different employers. Asbestosis is familiar in litigation, and is described as a cumulative disease in the sense that the more an individual is exposed the greater the severity of the disease. Where more than one employer is involved, and has failed to provide adequate safety measures, the courts have readily imposed joint and several liability, that is, each employer can be liable for all the damages, and it is up to them to sort out their individual responsibilities (in practice, insurers tend to split responsibility on a time/exposure basis). The problem for the courts with mesothelioma was that medical evidence suggested that it was caused by exposure to a single fibre, but it was impossible to prove which was the 'fatal fibre'. The Court of Appeal felt that in such circumstances causation could not be proved. The Court recognised the decision was unjust but felt that the government should produce a statutory scheme.

3.192 The House of Lords overturned the Court of Appeal, and felt less inhibited in developing notions of causation. Lord Hoffman noted that judges often describe causation as a question of common sense and fact, but he felt there was sometimes an appeal to common sense to avoid explaining one's reasons. In his view, causal requirements were just as much a part of the legal conditions for liability as the rules that prescribe the type of conduct which gives rise to liability:

> 'Once it is appreciated that the rules laying down causal requirements are not autonomous expressions of some form of logic or judicial instinct but creatures of law, part of the conditions of liability, it is possible to explain their content on the grounds of fairness and justice in exactly the same way as the other conditions of liability.'

3.193 He considered that for the Court of Appeal to say there was no causative relationship between the defendants' conduct and the disease was wrong:

> 'It depends entirely upon the level at which the causal relationship is described. To say, for example, that the cause of Mr Matthews' cancer was his significant exposure to asbestos during two employments over a period of eight years without being able to identify the day on which he inhaled the fatal fibre is a meaningful causal statement.'

Essentially, the basis of the decision of the House of Lords was that in this type of situation an employer who gave rise to a substantial risk of contracting the disease should be considered to have caused it for purposes of liability. It is clearly a significant decision, though the Law Lords were keen to emphasise the particular facts of the case. At present the ruling is confined to situations where two or more defendants were negligent in exposing employees to exposure, and the damage is initiated by a 'single' exposure but it is impossible to prove the time of inception. Should scientific evidence be able eventually to pin-point the time of inception, liability would clearly rest with that employer.

Multiple defendants and market share liability apportionment

3.194 Problems of causation and exposure to multiple sources have been handled by courts in some states of the US in a rather different way. Sindall v. Abbott Laboratories[93] involved a generic drug, diethylstilbestrol (DES), produced by many manufacturers and later found to cause cancer in children of mothers who had taken it during pregnancy. Given the time lapses involved, it was impossible to identify the specific manufacturers of the drugs taken by the claimants, and the California Supreme Court imposed liability on all the manufacturers before the court apportioned on the basis of their market share. Joint and several liability was considered unfair because of the total number of manufacturers involved (several hundred) and the fact that only a small proportion were named as defendants. The decision has been confined to cases where the product concerned is described as 'fungible', that is, produced and manufactured in a similar way and with similar marketing approaches. For those reasons, the New York court in the case referred to above (3.183) held that the principle could not apply to gun manufacturers. Nevertheless, in the Fairchild decision, Lord Hoffman referred to the Sindall principle as an imaginative approach, and it is one that might eventually be developed in this country.

Genetic susceptibility

3.195 In the longer term, the developing science of genetic susceptibility to exposure from chemicals could have significant implications for civil liability concepts. Traditional civil liability rules already include concepts such as '*volenti not fit injuria*' (no liability where someone voluntarily accepts a risk), the 'over-sensitive' claimant (who should not impose liabilities in nuisance law over and above what a 'reasonable' person might expect), and the 'egg-shell skull' claimant (provided the type of damage was foreseeable, a defendant has to take his victim as he finds him even if he is unusually vulnerable to the particular damage). These principles are not always reconcilable with each other, but could come into play where, say, an individual was advised of genetic susceptibility to a particular chemical, but nevertheless decides to live near exposure sources. We suspect that initially the issue may arise in relation to emissions from particular manufacturing processes rather than product exposure as such, but it is a subject where joint scientific and legal research would be valuable. A familiar response of government is to wait for litigation to raise these issues, but **we recommend that government should fund a joint scientific/legal study in order to anticipate the moral, legal and practical challenges to traditional civil liability concepts posed by increasing knowledge of genetic susceptibilities to specific chemicals.**

Liability for environmental damage

3.196 Civil liability claims under the EC Product Liability Directive are confined to damage to humans (death or personal injury) or private property. Many examples of environmental damage may in law involve damage to private interests (such as damage to crops growing on land, or fishing rights). But equally there are aspects of the environment not subject to private ownership and, therefore, not encompassed by current private civil liability concepts, examples include the upper atmosphere, the high seas, and wild animals and flora. Rather than extend concepts of private rights, the legal response has generally been to develop the powers of public bodies, or introduce special compensation schemes such as that concerning oil pollution at sea.

3.197 In 1993 the European Commission began discussions[94] on possible civil liability regimes for environmental damage, leading to the publication of a proposed Directive in 2002,[95] which is now before Member States and the European Parliament. Although some of the original discussions concerned the expansion of private civil rights of compensation to cover environmental damage, the final proposals are much more focused on providing powers to public authorities to require operators of specified processes to remedy environmental damage they have caused, or to prevent imminent environmental damage. Public authorities will have the power to recover costs where they have carried out clean-ups. Essentially, no fault is required for liability, but there are proposed defences, including compliance with a permit, and where emissions or activities were not considered harmful according to scientific and technical knowledge at the time; these last two defences would not apply if the company was negligent. The proposed Directive does not, however, contain any special provisions concerning concepts of causation.

3.198 Private parties and NGOs would not have the right to take a company directly to court, but could seek judicial review against the competent authority that has failed to act. The proposed Directive will take several years to negotiate. As proposed by the European Commission it does not represent a radical shift in the sorts of powers already available to bodies such as the Environment Agency concerning clean up and recovery of costs, though it will increase their responsibilities and exposure to legal review of the decisions they take.

INDUSTRY INITIATIVES

Responsible Care

3.199 The chemical industry's Responsible Care programme is a voluntary programme of action by member companies, and seeks to deliver continual improvement in health, safety and environmental performance and increased openness in communication. The Chemical Industries Association has led Responsible Care in the UK since it was adopted in 1989. The programme seeks to earn public confidence and trust through a number of guiding principles, including stakeholder engagement and product stewardship. The International Council of Chemical Associations reported in 1998 that companies in 46 countries representing 87% of global chemicals production by volume have committed themselves to Responsible Care.

Confidence in Chemicals

3.200 Confidence in Chemicals[96] is the chemical industry's programme of risk assessment, product stewardship, and long-range research into the effects of chemicals on health and the environment, which includes incorporation of stakeholder dialogue at each stage. It has four main elements:

i.   **Chemicals assessment and management – the HPV programme**   One thousand high production volume (HPV) chemicals have been selected for priority assessment by industry, from a total of 4,000 (3.72).

ii. **Enhanced product stewardship** This builds on existing product stewardship commitments and is seeking the implementation of product stewardship management systems, measurement of performance through approved indicators, and the introduction of improved customer support.

iii. **Long-range Research Initiative** Under the Long-range Research Initiative the chemical industry globally has pledged the equivalent of £85 million over five years to support independent research evaluating the interaction between chemicals, human health and the environment. The industry has pledged to take action on the basis of the outcomes of risk assessments being carried out under the Initiative.

iv. **Stakeholder engagement and communication** This element aims to involve stakeholders in designing and implementing Confidence in Chemicals.

NGO CAMPAIGNS

The Copenhagen Chemicals Charter

3.201 This Charter arose out of the 'Chemicals in the Spotlight' conference held in Copenhagen in October 2000. It was published jointly by the European Environmental Bureau, the European Consumers' Organisation, the Danish Consumer Council, the Danish Society for the Conservation of Nature, and the Danish Ecological Council, and to date has been signed by over 60 European environmental and consumer groups.

3.202 The Charter makes five key demands for future EU chemicals policy:

1. *A full right to know – including what chemicals are present in products.* This seeks to redress the lack of information about chemicals and their effects and calls for improved labelling of consumer products and publicly accessible information about sources of chemicals. The Charter also calls for greater openness, with increased availability of chemical testing information for consumers, regulatory authorities and downstream users.

2. *A deadline by which all chemicals on the market must have had their safety independently assessed. All uses of a chemical should be approved and should be demonstrated to be safe beyond reasonable doubt.* The authors suggest a deadline of 2005 for high production volume chemicals and 2010 for those produced in lower volumes. The eventual establishment of an EU-wide approval scheme based on the precautionary and substitution principles is also advocated.

3. *A phase-out of persistent and bioaccumulative chemicals.* This, is in addition to the removal of skin sensitisers, carcinogenic, mutagenic and reprotoxic and other substances hazardous to human health from consumer products.

4. *A requirement to substitute less safe chemicals with safer alternatives.* The Charter seeks a legislative adoption of the substitution principle. It is suggested that this can be done practically by providing information to the public and introducing approval schemes for product groups through an Integrated Product Policy.

5. *A commitment to stop all releases to the environment of hazardous substances by 2020.* The Charter calls for the adoption by the EU of the 'Generation' target agreed at a conference in Esbjerg in 1995. This target is the cessation of discharge of hazardous substances to the sea by 2020. It is suggested in the Charter that the list of hazardous substances could be determined using selection processes similar to the DYNAMEC (OSPAR persistence, bioaccumulation and toxicity criteria) and Swedish chemicals policy procedures (3.85-3.87 and 3.100-3.105).

FAILURE TO DELIVER DECISIONS

3.203 In this chapter and in chapter 2 we have set out the present system of chemical risk assessment at a technical and institutional, and national and international level. We have highlighted many problems and concerns about the present system. We now bring together the main conclusions of these two chapters.

3.204 Several submissions of evidence to the Royal Commission have commented on the length of time taken to deliver decisions using the current risk assessment system.[97] It is clear that a huge amount of effort has been expended over many years to develop the chemicals assessment procedures described in chapter 2. But despite a considerable amount of resources and time spent on testing and assessing chemicals there are still many unknowns about the possible impacts of chemicals on the environment. More than 20 years after the introduction of the new chemicals scheme and almost 10 years since that of the Existing Substances Regulation, the proportion of chemicals on the market that have been properly tested and assessed remains small. The House of Lords report on the EU Chemicals White Paper highlighted the lack of progress under the Existing Substances Regulation, with only a handful of substances having been regulated in the past eight years. The European Commission's Joint Research Centre has also reported on data available to the public on high production volume substances covered by the Existing Substances Regulation.[98] The report stated that (in 1999) only 14% of EU high production volume substances had data at base data set level, 65% had less than base set data, and 21% had no data.

3.205 Chemical risk assessment is a very expensive process. But even given access to unlimited funds we could not hope to perfect it. Current risk assessment procedures follow a rule of diminishing returns, in that additional effort will not increase our ability to protect the health of the environment by a proportionate amount. Chemical risk assessments, due to the uncertainties and information gaps in available ecotoxicological knowledge, often involve over-reliance on simple models embodying a number of flaws and assumptions that limit their efficiency. As with human toxicity testing, to counter this problem the risk assessment process usually incorporates a number of safety factors, acute to chronic ratios, and a precautionary approach. But the basis for using these factors is often a political or regulatory decision, and subjective interpretation can dominate the risk assessment.

3.206 Despite this lack of progress, many regulators and industry bodies continue to argue strongly that control must be on the basis of known risk, regardless of other indications of concern.[99] This is in spite of the fact that problems continue to occur due to unforeseen risks and that the system is unable to react quickly to emerging concerns. However, while doubts about the scientific basis of risk assessments applied in the context of chemical control are valid, the current approach is at least evidence-based, and can be transparent. But given the inherent problems with the current risk assessment system identified in chapter 2 and the delays and procrastination reported in this chapter, both of which seem to be a feature of approaches based on rigorous risk assessments, a fundamental re-think of the processes for managing risks from chemicals is overdue.

3.207 The challenge posed by evaluation of existing chemicals in the coming decades and rapid changes in technology associated with this area indicate that a more robust approach will be required in the future. This approach will need to balance precaution with an evidence-based approach, and provide decision-makers with timely advice. To speed up the assessment of environmental risk of all industrial chemicals to a time-scale far shorter than either that of the current regime, or of that which might flow from the forthcoming EU REACH legislation, we propose a faster and more transparent screening process, moving towards a better understanding of environmental processes, and with tighter integration of monitoring into regulatory decision-making. We elaborate on these recommendations in chapter 4.

3.208 But this in itself will not be enough. Some of the uncertainty in our understanding of the environmental fate and effects of chemicals will not be resolved for many years, and an intrinsically precautionary approach must, therefore, be adopted. In this context, precaution is best implemented through a systematic process of substitution, the replacement of hazardous substances by less hazardous substances or processes. Chapter 5 explores the importance of substitution and recommends a package of measures that, together with the chemicals assessment and monitoring programme we propose in chapter 4, will stimulate it.

Current proposals for improving the regulation of chemical products will not do enough to address the deficiencies in the present system, and a more concerted effort is needed to correct both the scientific approach and the societal framework within which it operates.

Chapter 4

INFORMING DECISIONS: A BETTER APPROACH TO CHEMICALS MANAGEMENT

The large number of chemicals on the market cannot be assessed within a reasonable timescale with conventional methods. What alternatives exist? Would better use of environmental monitoring help? Who should be responsible for this new approach?

A STEP CHANGE

4.1   In the preceding chapters we described the ways in which chemicals are assessed for their potential to harm the environment and human health, and how the risks of harm are managed. We discussed the shortcomings of these methods and evaluated current proposals for change, particularly the European Commission's REACH proposals (3.34-3.47), and suggested why they were unlikely to be satisfactory.

4.2   This chapter explores other options for improvement, and makes recommendations for alternative approaches to the assessment and management of chemicals. The challenge facing regulatory authorities is to satisfy themselves and the public, over a reasonable time-scale and without undue reliance on scarce resources, that the great number of chemicals on the market will not damage the physical or biological environment or harm human health. We pointed out in our Second Report, *Three Issues in Industrial Pollution*, that absolute proof that a chemical will not cause harm will always be beyond reach. But there are better ways of reducing the overall risk of harm than are employed at present.

4.3   The goals of our chemicals assessment and management programme include the rapid examination of all chemicals on the market, the selection of some for further, more detailed investigation leading to risk management measures, and arranging to keep the remainder under review. In line with the recommendations in our Twenty-first Report, *Setting Environmental Standards*, the programme should be fully transparent, and informed and steered by public values. Where there is evidence of concern about a chemical, decisions about risk management measures must be taken and acted upon promptly, even when the evidence is not conclusive. We also consider that the requirements to provide information about chemicals and to implement the risk management measures that arise should be backed by law. In chapter 5 we recommend some non-statutory measures that would complement this statutory approach.

4.4   The current system for assessing and managing existing chemicals is paralysed by the task of evaluating even the small number of chemicals presently selected as priorities. This is largely due to the antiquated, cumbersome and expensive procedures used for hazard characterisation, which were in place 30 years ago and are still in used today. Had the recommendation that the Royal Commission made in its Second Report in 1972 been acted upon then (1.28), regulators would now have a basis for using advanced computational screening methods. The US and Canada already apply such techniques to the assessment

and management of chemical risks. Similar techniques are routinely used in the pharmaceutical industry to screen huge numbers of chemicals rapidly for evidence of a range of physiological activities.

4.5 We believe that the time is long overdue for a complete change to the chemicals risk assessment paradigm in the UK and in Europe. In this chapter we recommend a new approach to chemicals assessment and management and discuss the alternative approaches to hazard characterisation that would be needed. The greatest changes to the present approach are required for existing chemicals, many of which have found their way into the environment already and where an urgent assessment for all is required. In this report we define existing chemicals as those on the European Inventory of Existing Commercial Chemical Substances, EINECS, that is, the 100,116 substances that were reported to be on the market on or before 18 September 1981 (3.20). Marketed chemicals will be much fewer in number. New chemicals which have not yet been released into the environment, are already subject to a more cautious approach, recognising that we knew little of their effects on ecosystem or human health.

4.6 We noted in chapter 2 the relative lack of interaction between chemicals risk management and environmental monitoring activities (2.108-2.116). Integrating the results of certain types of environmental monitoring into the chemicals assessment and management programme would result in a much more effective system without a major increase in costs. We discuss ways of doing this and make recommendations in this chapter.

4.7 In chapter 3 we pointed to the existing fragmentation of responsibility for chemicals policy and regulation between many government departments and agencies. To improve chemicals assessment and management in the way we recommend, there will need to be a central co-ordinating body to drive forward changes and implement the new approach. The final section of this chapter makes proposals for such a body (the 'chemicals safety co-ordination unit'), and describes its composition and function.

A NEW APPROACH

4.8 Figure 4-I outlines our proposal for a chemicals assessment and management programme that will deliver the goals set out above (4.3). It requires 4 steps: **listing** – compilation of a list of all chemicals on the UK market; **sorting** – using modern techniques to determine key properties of the listed chemicals, for comparison with publicly accepted criteria; **evaluation** – further investigation of chemicals selected by the sorting process; and **action** – risk management based on use, including regulatory measures to restrict use and non-regulatory drivers of substitution (which we will discuss in more detail in chapter 5). Environmental monitoring is more tightly integrated into this system.

4.9 We have discussed in chapters 1 and 2 the low public confidence in the chemicals industry, and in the risk assessment process. The process of design and implementation of the chemicals assessment and monitoring programme should be informed by public values. The public should be involved in defining problems, framing questions and clarifying policy aims. This is not just to restore reputations but more importantly to ensure that the process is influenced by the widest possible range of opinions, to reduce the chances that some factor in this complex area might be overlooked. Setting the level of the standards to be adopted at each stage, and determining the level of risk management for chemicals of concern, should be overseen and influenced by stakeholders and a wider deliberative process, as described in our Twenty-first Report.[1]

Figure 4-I

RCEP proposals for managing the risks from existing chemicals in products

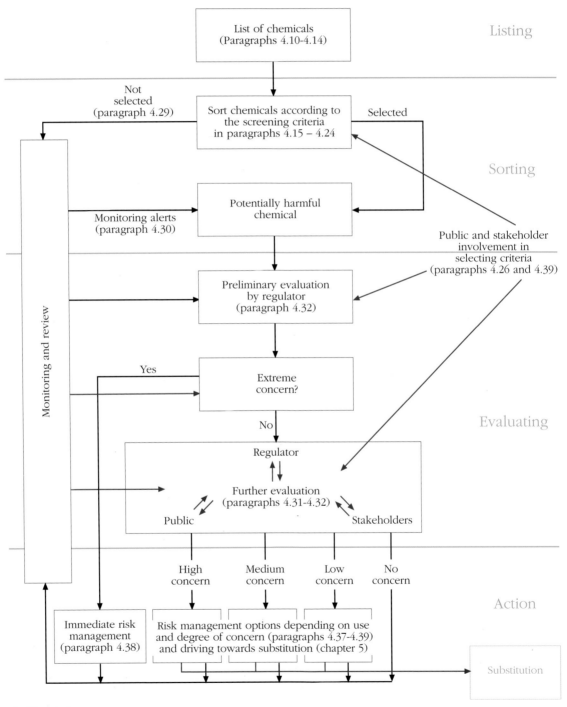

➤ Chemicals
➤ Influence

STEP 1: A LIST OF MARKETED CHEMICALS

4.10   After several decades of chemicals safety legislation, regulatory authorities in the UK still do not maintain a simple published list of the chemicals manufactured in or imported into the country. Without this basic management tool, it is difficult to imagine how any enforcement of chemicals legislation is feasible. Without such a list, the improvements necessary to secure better chemical control regimes would be difficult to achieve.

4.11   Many chemicals already appear on lists for one reason or another, for example under the Notification of New Substances scheme (3.9), the Environment Agency's Pollution Inventory (5.8b), the OSPAR Convention (3.80) and occupational safety legislation. A number of countries, such as Canada (3.123), the US (3.115) and Sweden (box 3A) already have such lists, and others, such as the Netherlands, are in the process of drawing one up (3.106). Inventories of chemicals on the market in these countries would not be too different from that for the UK, but these existing inventories could form a starting-point for a UK register of marketed chemicals. Government alone could not draw up a complete list and industry would need to be encouraged, or required, to submit chemicals for inclusion on the list – concern over liability would be one non-regulatory incentive for industry to do this (5.71-5.79).

4.12   Maintaining this list of marketed chemicals would require the addition of new chemicals and the removal of chemicals when it is clear that they would no longer be manufactured. The use of modern information technology will allow links to further information about each chemical on the list: estimated tonnage, safety analyses, primary uses and, for example, relevant entries in the Environment Agency's Pollution Inventory.

4.13   To be effective the list should be owned by the chemicals safety co-ordination unit (which we propose later in this chapter (4.107-4.111)), include details of the manufacturer or importer of the chemical, and be publicly available on the Internet. A mandatory list would be more effective than a voluntary scheme, but in anticipation of legislation we encourage the chemicals industry to participate in the development of a list on a voluntary basis. Such a list would be an essential prerequisite for the operation of REACH, and work started now would not be wasted should REACH come into effect. We discuss which agency should manage the list later in this chapter and suggest ways of securing statutory backing (4.40-4.45). Probably some tonnage limit would be necessary to limit the size of the list and the 100 kg currently used in the New Substances Directive is appropriate for this purpose (3.46). But we have pointed out (2.31) that the widely divergent behaviour of chemicals in the environment and the very wide range of concentrations over which effects might be seen make tonnage a very poor substitute for a proper exposure analysis.

4.14   **We recommend that the government compile and publish a list of all chemicals currently marketed in the UK.** Later, we will be recommending additional information to be included in the list – it should, therefore, take the form of a database.

STEP 2: SORTING, TO SELECT CHEMICALS OF CONCERN

4.15   The first stage in dealing with the backlog of untested chemicals is sorting – that is, the application of simple, transparent criteria to the large number of potential candidates for investigation, to select a more manageable number that can be studied in greater detail. The

Dutch Strategy on the Management of Substances (SOMS) scheme (box 3B), the current UK National Strategy (3.89), the OSPAR DYNAMEC process (3.85), and the Canadian scheme (3.125) each rely on a few key properties to select chemicals for further investigation, using available data, computational methods or laboratory testing. We propose that, where data are not already available, the main approach to sorting should be through techniques that are already well established in the pharmaceutical industry, where they are used to screen chemicals for likely physico-chemical properties and physiological effects (appendix J and 4.53). We discuss approaches to data collection and testing in the next section (4.50 onwards). But it is also important to ensure that the properties assessed, and the criteria against which they are assessed, are themselves tested against public concerns as well as expert judgement.

4.16   The Chemicals Stakeholder Forum has identified persistence and bioaccumulation as two properties of particular value in screening. These properties also form the basis for screening in SOMS, OSPAR DYNAMEC and other national and international schemes and they will play a key role in REACH. Persistence and bioaccumulation indicate the potential for long-term damage. Information about these properties already exists for almost all the chemicals likely to be on the market. In the main this information has been derived from computational processes. Doubts have been raised about the validity of such methods (4.55), but in addition to the scientific rationale for using persistence and bioaccumulation, these properties also have pragmatic advantages: where information is not already available, or its validity is doubted, certain basic tests for persistence and bioaccumulation are rapid, easy to perform, cheap to carry out, and use no animals.

4.17   Toxicity information from animal tests and other sources will already be available for some of the chemicals currently on the market, particularly those for which there are occupational safety concerns, and should be investigated using modern informatics techniques for literature searching. To avoid undue delay and unnecessary use of animal tests, the sorting process should not be delayed while experimental toxicity information is generated *de novo*. Indicators toxicity and ecotoxicity can be derived from knowledge of chemical structure using various computational approaches. The US EPA's procedure for assessing pre-market notifications (chapter 3) is heavily reliant on the use of structure activity relationships, which are used qualitatively to estimate human acute and chronic toxicity, including: oncogenicity; mutagenicity; developmental toxicity; neurotoxicity; reproductive toxicity; and systemic toxicity irritability and sensitisation. Estimates of the probable human pharmacokinetics of the chemical are made, evaluating absorption, distribution and redistribution, metabolism and excretion of the substance. QSARs are used to estimate chronic and acute toxicity values for fish, daphnids, and algae. **We recommend that the government put in place now sorting procedures based extensively on computational approaches to hazard assessments, using the US EPA and Environment Canada procedures as models where applicable.**

4.18   A sorting process of this type would be fast, and applicable to all chemicals on the market. Under this scheme there would be no need to rely on tiered tonnage thresholds, with the disadvantages that we described in chapter 2 (2.31), as under the current scheme or proposed under REACH.

4.19   This screening information ought already to have been appearing in a systematic way for all existing and new chemicals on the UK market. The UK National Strategy[2] (adopted in 1999) invited the chemicals industry and its customers to accept a duty of care under which a basic package of environmental and human health safety information should be passed along the supply chain. The Strategy also committed the Chemicals Stakeholder Forum to identify chemicals of concern by 2005, which would not be feasible without these basic data. We should, therefore, expect the imminent arrival of these data for all chemicals on the market. We have not, however, been able to find a systematic account of the persistence, bioaccumulation or toxicity of chemicals on the UK market, other than the very broad listing prepared for OSPAR purposes.

4.20   The list of chemicals on the UK market (4.14), published on the Internet, should be enhanced by the addition of these data, so that they were also publicly available. This would not be a large or expensive undertaking. It would facilitate the degree of self-regulation foreseen in the UK National Strategy. Companies making or importing chemicals would need to register their data with the agency owning the list, and the agency would make it available on an Internet site. Companies using chemicals would then be able to assure themselves, quickly and easily, that the chemicals they were buying had been registered and tested for persistence, bioaccumulation and toxicity. Failure to carry out this simple investigation, and thus purchasing non-registered chemicals, could raise questions about liability should harm subsequently be caused. We explore the question of liability in more detail in chapter 5.

4.21   Self-regulation is unlikely to be enough. If it were, it is likely that more chemical companies would have followed the example of those who already test their products and publish the data. Greenpeace, in its evidence to this study, used the expression 'no data, no market'.[3] We endorse this concept in connection with the information on toxicity, persistence and bioaccumulation necessary to select chemicals for further evaluation, and **recommend that new legislation should prohibit the marketing of any chemical for which these basic environmental safety data have not been registered on the list.** The legislation should also provide for information to be passed with the chemical from supplier to user to allow rapid identification of the chemical's entry on the list.

4.22   **We recommend that the government publish all necessary toxicity, persistence and bioaccumulation data on the Internet for all chemicals on the UK market, using the list we recommend above (4.14).**

4.23   For most chemicals, other information will be available relevant to their fate and behaviour in the environment. Preliminary sorting should not be delayed because of the absence of any of this information, and any available information should be taken into account. Additionally, provision should be made in any sorting programme for available information to be used as evidence (for example, by the manufacturer of the chemical, or an environmental or consumer group) that a sorted chemical has been inappropriately classified.

4.24   Using available data and advanced computational techniques the sorting process itself will be fast. We recognise, however, that some lead time will be necessary to provide the necessary infrastructure, obtain the technology and train personnel, and that some dialogue about the results might subsequently be necessary (though any extensive debate about particular chemicals would be part of the further investigation described below). We believe that installing the sorting process and carrying it out on all chemicals on the list should take no more than 3 years.

CHOOSING THE CRITERIA

4.25 A key prerequisite in the sorting procedure is to set the criteria standards on the basis of which a conclusion can be drawn that a chemical is 'of concern'. A number of organisations have already carried out this exercise, notably the Chemicals Stakeholder Forum which consulted widely and on that basis adopted the standards on persistence, bioaccumulation and toxicity reproduced in summary here in table 4.1.[4]

Table 4.1

Chemicals Stakeholder Forum's first tier criteria for persistence, bioaccumulation potential and toxicity

Property	Substances of greatest concern	Substances of high concern
Persistence	$t_{1/2}$ water > 2 months or $t_{1/2}$ soil/sediment > 6 months	$t_{1/2}$ water > 2 months or $t_{1/2}$ soil/sediment > 6 months
Bioaccumulation potential	log $K_{o/w}$ > 5 unless Bioconcentration Factor < 5,000	log $K_{o/w}$ > 4 unless Bioconcentration Factor < 500
Toxicity	Acute $L(E)C_{50}$ < 1 mg/l or long-term NOEC < 0.1 mg/l Category 1 or 2 carcinogens, mutagens or reprotoxins Category 3 mutagens	Acute $L(E)C_{50}$ < 1 mg/l or long-term NOEC < 0.1 mg/l Category 1 or 2 carcinogens, mutagens or reprotoxins Category 3 mutagens

4.26 The criteria standards adopted by the Chemicals Stakeholder Forum are useful but are predicated on test procedures that are of limited value, as we discussed in chapter 2. We have recommended a better approach to identifying toxic and ecotoxic chemicals (4.17). Criteria will need to be selected accordingly, but in any case **we recommend that the standards be reviewed regularly, through an inclusive process taking into account public views, and adjusted accordingly.**

4.27 Once this information is available and included on the list that we have proposed, sorting of chemicals to identify those of concern becomes an automatic process. A scan of the data on the register will screen out chemicals that meet the criteria. This process will identify chemicals as either meeting the hazard criteria or not. A check against lists of chemicals of concern produced against similar criteria for other purposes, particularly the 400 or so chemicals identified in the OSPAR process, will lend authority to the list. **We recommend that the putative list of selected chemicals is shared with other countries and their observations used to inform the process.**

4.28 This process is similar to that proposed in the UK National Strategy and under REACH. By basing this selection on a list of chemicals on the UK market and by using readily available information it can be carried out quickly and cheaply. **We recommend that the government carry out this sorting process on the listed chemicals within three years, and annotate the list to show those exceeding the sorting criteria.**

NON-SELECTED CHEMICALS

4.29 Chemicals that are not selected by the sorting process and that have not been identified for further investigation through environmental monitoring would not be required to undergo full testing but would be kept under review. Reappraisal might be triggered by the results of environmental monitoring, changes in use (and in particular the inclusion of chemicals into new or changed products), or improved understanding of the fate and effects of the chemicals in the environment (or developments in methodologies). We discuss some ways in which methods for understanding the fate and effect of chemicals might develop (4.118-4.121), and the role that environmental monitoring might play (4.96-4.101).

4.30 Many of the problems that have arisen with chemicals in the environment have come to light through monitoring. We listed examples in chapter 1 (box 1A). This suggests that in selecting chemicals for further study, the results of environmental monitoring need to be taken into account, in addition to the outcome of the sorting process. To some extent this already happens. For example, the risk reduction strategy for the flame-retardant brominated diphenyl ethers was brought forward on the discovery that certain of the chemicals were accumulating in human breast milk. We have concluded that a more systematic integration of monitoring into the chemicals assessment and management programme is necessary. Reflecting this, figure 4-I shows a link from the list to the selection of chemicals via a monitoring alert. **Chemicals found in unexpected environmental compartments or at unexpected concentrations, or associated with unusual biological phenomena, should be selected for further investigation.** We discuss the new approach to monitoring necessary to achieve this later in this chapter (4.72-4.101).

STEP 3: EVALUATION OF SELECTED CHEMICALS

4.31 Chemicals of concern selected through sorting or monitoring should be subject to investigation. **We recommend that all new chemicals should be considered as potentially harmful and evaluated with chemicals of concern**. This would reflect the fact that they have not yet been released into the environment and we know little about them. The investigation would be overseen by the agency hosting the proposed chemicals safety co-ordination unit (4.107), but must be a fully transparent and accessible process. This will require a statutory advisory body constituted in a way similar to the current Chemicals Stakeholder Forum (though see 4.45), and with a similar but not identical remit. But the Forum will also need access to a much broader range of opinion, so that both its decision-making procedures and the decisions themselves may be informed by public values. We reviewed methods suitable for articulating public values in our Twenty-first Report.[5] To secure a proper relationship between the regulator (the unit) and its advisory body (the Forum), a clear separation of roles would be needed. In paragraph 4.45 we recommend that the Forum be reconstituted as a statutory advisor to the unit and we return to the respective roles of the unit and the Forum in paragraphs 4.107 onwards.

4.32 The process of further investigation must permit fast recourse to regulatory action against the chemical in urgent cases (4.38) or where environmental monitoring identifies particularly severe problems. In other cases there should be an opportunity for companies producing or using selected chemicals to provide evidence that they should not be so selected, and for groups or individuals concerned about the chemical to challenge such evidence. Strict time limits must be applied to this process to avoid deliberate procrastination. Throughout the process, the chemical's entry on the list will retain the 'of concern' annotation, and purchasers and users of that chemical will need to be alert to potential liabilities should harm result.

4.33 The further investigation is aimed at categorising the degree of hazard offered by the chemical into three categories, of high, medium and low concern. This categorisation will have two functions – to inform decisions about the level of risk management action required (4.37) and to drive the process of substitution (chapter 5). The category to which a chemical of concern has been assigned, and the risk management response, should be indicated on the published list of marketed chemicals. If the sorting criteria are suitably precautionary some chemicals should be found by further investigation to be of less concern than the sorting process had indicated, and should be no longer considered to be selected. They would, though, still be subject to monitoring and review, as indicated in figure 4-I (4.29).

4.34 **We recommend that chemicals selected by the sorting process or identified through environmental monitoring as 'of concern' be categorised according to their degree of potential risk on the basis of agreed criteria, to determine the level of risk management and charge to which they should be subject.**

4.35 **We recommend that the government should ensure that 90% of the chemicals selected by sorting have been evaluated and categorised within three years of selection (4.24).**

4.36 For the reasons that we give above (2.31, 4.13) we do not recommend that the extent of evaluation be determined by tonnage, as is the practice under current legislation and proposed for REACH. A chemical that has been selected by the sorting process should be subject to further investigation regardless of the volume of the market. But the uses to which the chemical is put, and therefore its sources and pathways into the environment, must be integral to the investigation.

STEP 4: RISK MANAGEMENT ACTION

4.37 The category to which a chemical is assigned will determine the necessary level of risk management action. The detailed measures necessary for each chemical would have to be determined on a case-by-case basis but would generally be:

high concern – risk management is likely to include severe restrictions on the use of the chemical, or a total prohibition on marketing and use;

medium concern – certain uses would be restricted; and

low concern – there might not need to be restrictions on the use of all the chemicals in this category, but they would continue to be regarded (and indicated on the list) as being of concern.

4.38 There will be some chemicals for which risk management action should be taken as a matter of urgency. These might include, for example, chemicals identified as very persistent and very bioaccumulative, or chemicals shown to have particularly unacceptable effects on the environment or in humans. The results of environmental monitoring will also play an important role in identifying such chemicals, particularly where elevated concentrations are found in the upper trophic levels of the food web. At the very least, **we recommend that where synthetic chemicals are found in elevated concentrations in biological fluids such as breast milk and tissues of humans, marine mammals or top predators, regulatory steps be taken to remove them from the market immediately.**

4.39 **We recommend that the chemicals safety co-ordination unit (4.107-4.111), guided by a statutory advisory committee (4.45) and within a wider deliberative process (4.26), should indicate at an early stage the criteria that will trigger this higher level of concern**.

STATUTORY UNDERPINNING

4.40 The approach described above could be made to operate through non-statutory means by renewed emphasis on the duty of care recommended in the UK National Strategy, a recommendation that has not so far been pursued by government or regulatory agencies. However, non-statutory schemes have not yet delivered satisfactory control of chemicals safety, either in the UK or elsewhere. It is important, therefore, to seek statutory underpinning of key components of the scheme.

4.41 There are no regulatory provisions for the risk management elements of the programme described in this section under current EU (and therefore UK) law. A recent attempt by the Dutch government to secure European acceptance of the SOMS system was successfully opposed by the European Commission on the grounds that it anticipated REACH (3.112). We wonder how successful or determined the European Commission's objection might have been if the Dutch application had, instead, been a joint approach by several Member States.

4.42 It is possible that there is also no regulatory backing for the provision of data to form the list of marketed chemicals, or for the provision of information about basic environmental properties that could assist with the sorting process. However, the Chemicals (Hazard Information and Packaging for Supply) Regulations[6] call for information about the environmental hazards of chemicals. The current interpretation of the Regulations appears to be that this applies to information that is already available, and that it does not represent a call for further assessment. We are of the opinion that the Regulations should be re-examined with a view to their use to help draw up the list of marketed chemicals.

4.43 If REACH comes into force it will not do so for several years from now. An early concerted approach by several Member States to introduce mandatory listing and reporting of persistence and bioaccumulation for all marketed chemicals might be sufficiently robust to resist challenge by the European Commission. Indeed, the European Commission might well share some of the concerns about REACH set out in this report and might welcome a joint approach by several Member States, so long as the approach could either demonstrate clear advantages over the REACH proposals or be represented as an interim measure pending REACH. Risk management measures on individual chemicals (or groups of chemicals) could be introduced through national measures under the Directive on adaptation to technical progress,[7] but we are aware of the considerable resource burdens this would place on relevant government departments. Joint action by several Member States might ease this burden but inclusion of blanket provisions in this pre-REACH measure would be an even more satisfactory approach.

4.44 **We recommend that the government open discussions with other Member States with similar national approaches to chemicals management, and seek EU legislation to underpin a satisfactory listing, sorting and management scheme for chemicals.**

4.45 **We further recommend that, as part of the UK implementation of this statutory development, the Chemicals Stakeholder Forum be reconstituted as a statutory advisory body to the chemicals safety co-ordination unit to enable it better to carry out the role proposed in this chapter, and that this is reflected in a change of name to the 'Chemicals Standards Forum'.**

4.46 Appendix I compares the scheme we describe here with the current UK system and with the European Commission's REACH proposals (3.34-3.47). The main advantages of our proposal are that it will be feasible to examine all chemicals on the market within 3 years, that categorisation of chemicals of concern will be rapid and inexpensive, and that the burden of proof for chemicals of concern will be transferred to industry. We foresee reluctance on the part of some authorities to move from the traditional and slow testing protocols described in chapter 2 to the much more rapid, and in many ways simpler, computer-based systems we propose here. Therefore, **we recommend that the UK government, jointly with like-minded Member States, press for an EU-wide initiative to demonstrate and promulgate the effectiveness of these techniques, and to secure their international acceptance through OECD.** This should build on the work of ECVAM.[8]

4.47 This raises three questions: how should the selected chemicals be evaluated? how might environmental monitoring be integrated into the process? and, who will organise the work? The remainder of this chapter addresses these questions.

ALTERNATIVE TESTING TECHNIQUES

4.48 Tests required under new and existing substances legislation are cumbersome to undertake, expensive, and often have considerable intrinsic uncertainties, requiring heroic assumptions to convert the results into decisions about risk and hazard (chapter 2). They also rely heavily on the use of animals, against which there are pragmatic and ethical objections. The approach we recommended in the previous section offers scope for a new paradigm, which emphasises the sorting of very large numbers of chemicals rapidly and with minimal effort, followed by selecting a relatively small number for detailed further attention. Such arrangements could greatly speed up society's ability to judge a chemical, would release resources to allow better use of environmental monitoring (4.72-4.101) and would confine animal testing to the minimum consistent with society's essential needs for safety. It would require, however, a substantial rebalancing of the current priorities of testing regimes and an international effort to apply the high throughput testing arrangements widely used in the pharmaceutical industry.

4.49   We described in chapter 2 how concern about commercial confidentiality and about protecting the investment made in developing information about the hazard and other properties of chemicals has hindered the free exchange of such information between companies. We also described the steps currently underway partially to resolve this problem through consortia of companies involved in the International Council of Chemical Associations' high production volume chemical programme (3.72). Similar arrangements seem to be envisaged for REACH, if a pre-registration stage is introduced (appendix I, I.4). The sharing of data and testing resources in this way is clearly in the interests of industry, and will become more so as pressures increase to deliver comprehensive evaluations of marketed chemicals. We encourage industry to continue to find ways of overcoming difficulties with commercial confidentiality and intellectual property rights in order to reduce unnecessary duplication of testing.

4.50   We examine next the scope for a more productive approach to acquiring data about the fate and effects of chemicals in the environment. It would include:

computational techniques – techniques already widely used for screening pharmaceuticals are increasingly being adapted for environmental safety assessment of chemicals;

***in vitro* testing** – again the pharmaceutical industry has been the pioneer in adopting the widespread use of *in vitro* tests to screen out any compounds which show seriously adverse biological actions; and

animal testing – where the approaches above have left unresolved doubts about the safety of a chemical, a decision will be needed as to whether to test it on animals.

COMPUTATIONAL TECHNIQUES

4.51   The chemical and physical properties of a chemical depend on its molecular structure and the ambient environment in a complex but predictable way. Techniques for predicting the behaviour of chemicals in particular environments – for example in ocean sediments, in organisms, or in the upper atmosphere – have been evolving for some years. They have already been used in screening exercises to predict certain properties that influence behaviour, such as a chemical's solubility in lipids (bioaccumulation), or its tendency to be destroyed by biological or physico-chemical action (degradation).[9]

4.52   The acceptance of computational techniques into regulatory processes for assessing chemicals safety is still limited. This is not necessarily because the science is too difficult. As computing capacity is now freely accessible these techniques are becoming more available. We have heard that the main obstacle is the acceptability to regulators of safety data derived from these techniques. There are probably several reasons for this: regulators are used to interpreting information from animal tests; such tests are the subject of international agreements on the mutual acceptability of data; some international agreements, for example on the transport of dangerous goods require data from tests in animals; and there may be concerns that information generated by new tests will not be completely comparable with existing data banks and a lack of confidence that the results are reliable, leading to demands for the re-testing of chemicals.

4.53 One expert witness stated that in the pharmaceutical industry a library of 100,000 chemicals potentially active against a given disease could be reduced by more than 99% following a computational analysis seeking out physiologically-active chemical structures within a molecule.[10] These methods of computational analysis include expert systems, extensive databases of chemical properties, and QSARs. The objective of high-throughput screening is to identify compounds with potential pharmacological properties but to eliminate all those with strong counter-indications. As computational techniques for properties relevant to a chemical's fate and effects are already available, it should be possible to develop analogous high-throughput systems to augment and eventually replace current screening methods for environmental safety.

4.54 The reliability and performance of structure-activity relationships is likely to increase with enhancements in technology. Also there are now software-based systems that compute and automatically validate assessments of the toxic and environmental effects of chemicals, using information-rich descriptors of molecular structure based on graph and information theory, and on rigorous diagnostic procedures (appendix H).[11] The Danish Environmental Protection Agency has carried out research to show that QSARs may play a role in allowing initial screening of substances with little or no available experimental data.[12] US and Canadian authorities already use the QSAR approach as the basis for screening chemical substances (3.120 and 3.127).

4.55 Structure activity relationships are, however, not yet fully acceptable for regulatory purposes, at least in the EU. Concerns that have been raised include that:[13]

- the validity of data used to establish the correlations between structure and activity is critical to the performance of the method but cannot be guaranteed (though this objection could be raised against any assessment procedure);

- QSARs can predict potency with respect to the mechanism of action of a group of compounds but cannot predict an unanticipated type of activity;

- toxicity is influenced by factors other than the physico-chemical properties of chemicals used to derive the models;

- models derived from large databases of heterogeneous chemicals do not normally model a single mechanism; and

- if too many independent variables are used with small sets of substances, there is a high probability of adventitious correlations occurring.

We do not believe these concerns are sufficient to outweigh the advantages, and a more concerted attempt to introduce a clear role for structure activity relationships into EU chemicals legislation would be worthwhile.

4.56 OECD is currently undertaking an assessment of computer-based modelling techniques with a diagnostic system, to determine whether the structure activity relationships are producing the correct output. OECD is developing an accredited database of chemical information to underpin the structure activity relationships. Structure activity relationships will also need to be evaluated against well-tested chemicals as part of the validation process.

4.57 The predictive value of structure activity relationships can be greatly enhanced when toxicokinetic data on the absorption, distribution, metabolism and excretion of the substance under study is available, as certain substances are biotransformed to active metabolites that are responsible for toxicity. Toxicokinetic modelling (box 4A) can be used to describe the absorption, distribution, metabolism and elimination of xenobiotics as a function of dose and time within an organism.

BOX 4A   **TOXICOKINETIC MODELLING**

Toxicokinetic models can be divided into two main classes: data-based and physiologically-based models. In both, the models simulate the biological complexity of the body by the use of two or more tissue compartments.[14]

In data-based compartmental models the human body is usually represented by a system that describes uptake, distribution and metabolism. The simplicity of data-based models, and the limited number of parameters, means that a model structure can be rapidly established and parameterised on the basis of the results of *in vivo* studies. However, these models are merely descriptive of the data; they do not describe the mechanisms governing the processes that they model, and in particular they cannot estimate the concentration of a substance at the affected site.

Physiologically-based toxicokinetic (PB-TK) models describe the body in terms of a series of compartments based on the known anatomy and physiology of the organism. Much of the chemical-specific information necessary for PB-TK modelling can be obtained from *in vitro* studies including tissue-blood partition coefficients, the kinetics of any active transport processes, and the kinetics of metabolism by the liver and any other organ capable of biotransforming the compound. The blood-air partition coefficient, important in the uptake and exhalation of volatile compounds, can also be determined *in vitro*. PB-TK models can predict the kinetic behaviour of the compound on the basis of a mechanistically-based model structure, produced using independently-derived parameters. This facilitates route-to-route, dose-to-dose, and inter-species extrapolation.

Models of this sort have already been use to evaluate a range of chemicals of particular regulatory concern, such as chloroform, formaldehyde and trichlorethylene.[15]

4.58 While, therefore, we cannot conclude that the use of these techniques would offer significantly more certainty in describing the effects of chemicals than conventional testing methods, it is clear that they would provide useful information very much more quickly – allowing progress to be made in clearing the backlog of chemicals. And future development is likely to result in considerable enhancement of their power to predict effects. We return to the need for research to this end in paragraph 4.114.

4.59 As we have recommended (4.17), there needs to be a substantial shift to the use of computational methods, including QSARs and expert systems, already used in the pharmaceutical industry for assessing the safety of chemicals. QSARs have been developed for pharmaceuticals to meet a market need, and requiring tests on these lines for chemicals will also elicit a market response. Future risk assessments should all contain information derived from these techniques, strongly coupled with monitoring, as we describe in 4.72 onwards.

'IN VITRO' *TECHNOLOGIES*

4.60   It is axiomatic that the effects of virtually any new chemical upon a biological system can be detected at the cellular level. The 'new biology' (used particularly by biomedical scientists and the pharmaceutical industry) has developed a host of technologies that allow processes to be analysed in tissue culture with the end-points being the key cellular events of gene activation (*genomics*), protein expression and organisation (*proteomics*) and alterations in metabolic pathways (*metabolomics*) (appendix H). This applies as much to toxic chemicals as to other agents.[16] Equally importantly, these technologies are suitable for scaling up so that, for example, the effects of very large numbers of chemicals upon a specific cellular end-point can be measured rapidly. Consequently, measurement of the products of cell metabolism can reveal valuable information about the potential toxicity of chemicals and make possible improved hazard identification and more predictive safety evaluation. The extensive information available from such studies requires access to powerful informatics, bringing together *bio-informatics,* dealing with genes and proteins, their regulation and functions, and *chemi-informatics*, defining molecular structures and properties, binding sites and reactivities.

4.61   It should be noted, however, that these technologies are still in their infancy, especially in their application to the field of toxicology. Any technology that is used for regulatory purposes in relation to risk assessments must be reliable and robust. For example, micro-array technology (appendix H) requires improvements with respect to reproducibility, speed, cost and sensitivity, and a significant number of questions remain regarding both experimental protocol and gene expression data. There are also limitations within proteomics technology and only a limited proportion of proteins can be identified with present techniques. There is a major effort needed both in biotechnology and pharmaceutical companies and in academia to understand the scope and limitations of these techniques. There is a need to identify and research the areas that are specific to chemicals in the environment. There is considerable existing knowledge, some of it in the form of databases but much of it scattered in the literature, of known effects from chemicals with well-characterised toxicities. We need to make sure that agencies assessing the impacts of chemicals have access to the best forms of literature search. There is also a need to correlate gene expression data with traditional toxicological end-points.

4.62   Despite these caveats, rapid progress in genomics and proteomics, in combination with the ever-increasing power of bio-informatics, creates a unique opportunity to improve the predictive power of safety assessments by offering a more effective way to identify toxic hazards. In particular, toxicogenomic research will provide fundamental information on the mechanism of action of chemicals on cell metabolism, and modulation of gene expression is of paramount importance in understanding chemically-induced toxicity. The potential of proteomics and genomics in toxicological risk assessment will require further research and validation (4.114), before these techniques can be considered for routine use in regulatory toxicological risk assessment.

4.63   It does appear, therefore, that the techniques emerging from the 'new biology', in particular those which permit better understanding and measurement of the interaction between synthetic chemicals and the biochemistry of cellular processes, offer the prospect both of a deeper insight into the effects of chemical pollutants and improved assessment methods. Many experts are pessimistic about the prospects for *in vitro* test methods replacing the current suite of *in vivo* tests. This is partly due to the complexity of the task involved and partly because of the time taken to validate the procedures for use at an international level. Despite these misgivings it is apparent that *in vitro* techniques are already useful in particular areas of toxicology, for example, in relation to assessing genotoxicity. They could play an important role in candidate selection during the development of new chemicals, for establishing priorities for regulatory consideration and assisting in the investigation of underlying mechanisms.

4.64 Because of the phase-out of animal tests for risk assessment of substances used in cosmetics, the European Commission will be petitioning the OECD for acceptance of data derived from *in vitro* studies for cosmetic ingredients, using validated alternative methods that have been conducted to fulfil the requirements of Directive 76/768/EEC,[17] in an initiative to gain regulatory acceptance of alternative methods on a global scale. **We recommend that the government press for wider application of this approach, using screening tests, existing data and computational techniques, together with *in vitro* studies, to describe the hazards of chemicals in all but exceptional cases**.

ANIMAL TESTING

4.65 There is much that could and should be done to reduce the need for testing chemicals on higher organisms. Not only are there important questions about the morality of using animals for testing chemicals, but also there are also inherent uncertainties in many of the methods. This is particularly so in ecotoxicology, where a few species are used as surrogates for entire ecosystems, but is also the case in toxicology, where non-human species are used in an attempt to predict the potential effects of chemicals on humans. While the general biological and toxicological relevance of other mammalian species to humans is acknowledged, the selection of species used for hazard identification may be made on the basis of practicality, rather than of knowledge about their relevance to humans with respect to the chemical in question.[18]

4.66 On the other hand, *in vivo* models are particularly useful because they allow the integration of factors such as toxicity and metabolic profiles with absorption and elimination aspects. In particular, *in vivo* studies allow the identification of organ- or system-specific toxicities and of effects that are apparent at only high levels of integration, aspects that have not thus far been addressed by *in vitro* techniques. Whole animal testing is especially important when assessing the effects of chemicals on higher functions (such as the central nervous system), on the integration of immune responses (such as hypersensitivity), and on tissues or functions that vary greatly in their responsiveness to chemicals (for example, endocrine functions). The occurrence of totally unpredictable responses to a chemical, as well as effects only seen with chronic dosing, is also an argument put forward for whole animal testing.

4.67 Whether animal testing can be justified by some increment of safety must be a matter for societal judgement, taking account of the function of the chemical concerned. This would be difficult to prescribe, especially in European legislation, which must be acceptable in countries with widely varying attitudes towards animals. There is, though, a precedent: such a decision has been taken already in connection with chemicals used in cosmetic products, which may not be tested on animals under EU legislation (4.64).[19] There may be scope for taking such decisions in the chemicals assessment and management programme.

4.68 By using, wherever possible, assessment approaches such as those outlined above, the need for testing chemicals on animals should arise in substantially fewer cases, for instance:

- by adopting the computational approach to sorting there should be no need for animal test data to be generated at that stage. However, there might already be information available from animal tests, or animal tests might be needed for some purpose not connected with the chemicals assessment and management programme. Such information might be relevant and useful, and must not be discarded;

- in cases of extreme concern, where risk management action on chemicals needs to be taken without further delay (4.38) and testing procedures using animals would be too protracted; and

- the further investigation of selected chemicals, the process leading to categorisation (4.33), will need to consider both the effects of the chemical and the uses to which a chemical will be put. Estimating environmental concentrations will not require animal testing and, in many cases, is likely to resolve questions about the degree of risk management required.

4.69 Further evaluation of the effects of certain chemicals may, however, need to be informed by tests on higher animals. This will be the case where sorting, evaluation or monitoring have revealed, exceptionally, uncertainties about the effects of the chemical. But, there are several questions to be addressed before this decision is taken, such as:

- have all available data about the chemical been collected and assessed? There should be a presumption for all possible data sharing, through industry consortia where appropriate (3.72), before the need for any new animal tests is accepted.

- have all alternative test regimes, such as advanced computational techniques and in vitro methods, been considered?

- what degree of confidence is there that tests on higher animals will resolve the uncertainties about the chemical to an acceptable level? and

- is there a publicly acceptable case for testing this particular chemical on higher animals?

4.70 **We recommend that in implementing the chemicals assessment and management programme that we have described here, all practicable steps should be taken to avoid the use of higher animals as test organisms, and decisions to move to such tests should be made on a case-by-case basis following transparent discussion.**

4.71 Relevant to this is the 2002 report by the House of Lords Select Committee on Animals in Scientific Procedures,[20] which recommended that:

> 'The Government should be developing a strategy to fund the development and validation of replacements for animal tests (*in vitro* and *in silico*), possibly via a centre for the 3 Rs.'[21]

We endorse this conclusion.

INTEGRATING ENVIRONMENTAL MONITORING

OBJECTIVES OF MONITORING

4.72   We have identified the need for the tighter integration of environmental monitoring into the process for sorting, assessing and managing chemicals. Monitoring data would serve three purposes: to identify chemicals of concern that have escaped the sorting process; to check that risk management measures are working; and to assure the overall success of new approaches to chemicals management:

- The sorting process that we recommend (4.15-4.24), or indeed any rapid sorting process for chemicals, cannot be made failsafe. Sorting focuses regulatory attention on a small proportion of the chemicals on the market on the basis of fairly crude criteria. Some of the chemicals not selected for further investigation might still be hazardous in ways not reflected in the criteria. Under the chemicals assessment and management programme proposed, such chemicals would, however, be subject to review, and this review would include assessment of monitoring information.

- Monitoring is also necessary to ensure that risk management programmes are effective, and to help identify adjustments where necessary. Even chemicals that have been removed from the market might remain in the environment, potentially causing damage, for long periods (chapter 2).

- The regulatory and other measures being introduced throughout Europe are both critical to the protection of the environment (including human health) and expensive to society. It is important to know that they are working, and environmental monitoring, attached to key indicators, will permit measurement of their effectiveness.

4.73   The environmental monitoring currently being carried out by organisations such as the Environment Agency and the British Geological Survey has been designed to meet a variety of objectives. Consequently, the data produced are not always well suited to the objectives discussed here. Possibly as a result of this, little attempt is being made to use existing environmental monitoring data as part of the process of managing chemicals risks. To correct this, mechanisms are needed to facilitate a flow of information between the monitoring programmes and the chemicals management process, allowing the design of monitoring programmes to be influenced, and the results used, by those managing chemicals risks. One of the opportunities presented by this tighter integration would be that less emphasis would be needed on risk assessment and the associated laboratory testing requirements, releasing resources for enhanced monitoring programmes. We discuss possible mechanisms for this later in the chapter (4.96-4.101).

TYPES OF MONITORING

4.74   We have discussed existing environmental monitoring programmes in chapter 2. We now discuss some of the developments in monitoring techniques most likely to complement the approach to chemicals management we have proposed.

Analytical techniques

4.75   New computational techniques mean that chemical analysis is now generally much more accurate, sensitive and sophisticated than in the past. Sample preparation and separation techniques are also more sophisticated and can be operated in a semi-automated way. Knowledge of the properties of chemicals that determine both their environmental behaviour and toxicity are better understood. New biological techniques are available, and others are foreseen, that will establish cause and effect more powerfully.[22] New ecological knowledge can be used to supplement chemical and toxicological information.

4.76   Distinguishing between possible origins of the observed chemical is also important where the objective is to assess the operation of risk management measures. One important tool that has emerged in recent years is isotopic analysis. This utilises the fact that chemicals from different sources differ in their content of particular elemental isotopes (isotope signatures), which can be detected by mass spectrometry.[23]

Monitoring the effects of chemicals on non-human biota

4.77   Environmental epidemiology (the study of non-human populations) has provided some powerful input to debates on chemicals in the environment. Monitoring the impact of chemicals on natural populations has two main applications. Firstly, monitoring key species can provide early warning of the impact of chemical contamination on ecosystems. Secondly, higher organisms can act as sentinels to identify chemicals that may affect the health of human populations.[24] However, exposure to chemical contaminants is just one stressor of natural populations among many, and the effects of chemicals on the abundance and types of wildlife species are often difficult to quantify in relation to larger-scale environmental changes. A major challenge in assessing the impact of a chemical pollutant is separating its effect from others such as habitat destruction or alteration and the background effects of natural fluctuations.[25]

4.78   Population monitoring thus picks up evidence of the effects of chemicals, known and unknown. This means that it alone cannot identify the cause of ecosystem change. However, the use of biomarkers has the potential to generate information with which to identify chemical threats based on a weight of evidence argument.[26] Biological changes following exposure to chemicals can occur at different levels of biological organisation, ranging from the cellular to the community and ecosystem level. Following chemical exposure, effects at the organism or population level are preceded by biochemical changes at the cellular level, including the expression of enzymes, proteins and other macromolecules associated with detoxification mechanisms, that can be used as molecular markers (biomarkers; appendix E, box E1). Such biomarkers are frequently detectable prior to the occurrence of any overt effects, such as morphological or behavioural changes, and can provide an earlier or more sensitive warning of impending problems. For example, measurement of the release of lysosomal enzymes in bivalves has been used to detect chronic, sub-lethal exposure to toxicants.[27]

4.79   Mechanisms of uptake of synthetic chemicals are often poorly understood, however, as are the relative contributions of contaminants from different environmental compartments (water, soil, air). Therefore, a quantitative relationship between the concentration of chemicals in the environment and in the tissue being monitored is rarely established. It remains difficult to link or translate biochemical effects caused by chemicals at the cellular level into significant changes at the population level because of the present low level of understanding of the inherent complexity of biological systems.[28]

4.80 A combination of long-term population monitoring and the use of biomarkers has the potential to generate information with which to identify chemical threats based on a weight-of-evidence argument.[29] The archiving of both data and biological samples will permit re-evaluation as understanding develops and techniques become more powerful.

Toxicity Identification Evaluation

4.81 An emerging method of investigating possible causal links is bioassay-directed chemical analysis techniques, or Toxicity Identification Evaluations (TIEs), which allow the identification of a compound or groups of compounds that are exerting a biological effect. TIE bridges the gap between environmental effects and chemical hazard assessment by integrating biological effects and chemical analyses into a single analytical framework. As a tool it is a very powerful technique in identifying unknown causes of biological effects. The Centre for Environment, Fisheries and Aquaculture Science has successfully applied TIEs to characterise unknown chemicals of concern in sediments and water, for example, the identification of oestrogen and androgen steroids in effluents and estuaries, and the presence of mutagenic chemicals in marine sediments.[30]

4.82 The approach is based on the use of fractionation techniques that separate substances with different properties (for example, adsorptive substances from water-soluble ones or volatile from non-volatile ones), through a series of sample manipulations that effectively reduce complex mixtures of chemicals in a sample to simple components for analysis. Following each manipulation the toxicity of the sample is assessed using a bioassay to determine which fraction of the sample is responsible for the overall effect. Where it is possible to extract and recover the toxic agents, chromatographic techniques are used to isolate them. Chemical analysis by gas chromatography and liquid chromatography coupled to mass spectrometry is then used to identify the substances.[31]

4.83 A range of plant-based and animal-based bioassay techniques (for example, on bivalves, *Daphnia magna,* or algae) could be used as part of an integrated approach, but more sensitive bioassays have now been validated, such as *in vivo* tests using genetically-modified bacteria that detect the presence of toxins.[32] Other promising bioassay techniques include *in vitro* reporter gene assays, such as the receptor-mediated chemical-activated luciferase expression (CALUX) assays, which can be employed to determine the toxic equivalency factor of a particular group of compounds. These assays are now as sensitive as traditional chemical analysis techniques and have been successfully used as broad-spectrum assays in several studies.[33]

Utilising ad hoc observations

4.84 Many of the impacts of chemicals on wildlife have been detected as a result of casual observations by members of the public, for example, the detection of the effects of endocrine disrupters on fish from reports made by anglers. It is important that any monitoring network for the effects of chemicals on biota should use this information. At present the Wildlife Incident Investigation Scheme (WIIS), run by the Pesticides Safety Directorate and other responsible departments within the devolved administrations in the UK, is designed to provide early warning of potential pesticide problems. The scheme depends on animal deaths being reported, and investigates cases only where pesticides can be implicated.[34] The system could be expanded to include all cases where a chemical is implicated in observed adverse environmental impacts, and should encompass wider definitions of environmental damage than sick or dead mammals (for example, mass mortality of plant life or invertebrate biota), to avoid the current bias towards easily visible species and those species of particular interest to the public, such as foxes and badgers.

4.85   One model worth considering in this context would be to ask members of the public and special interest groups (angling or birdwatching clubs) to report suspected adverse effects of chemicals in a system similar to the 'yellow card' scheme for therapeutic agents (in which doctors are asked to report any suspected adverse reactions to the Committee on Safety of Medicines), or the Suspected Adverse Reaction Reporting Scheme for veterinary medicines (administered by the Veterinary Medicines Directorate).

4.86   **We recommend that the chemicals safety co-ordination unit (or other relevant agency) assess the feasibility of a 'yellow card' scheme for use by the public to report unusual environmental events that might be related to chemical exposure.**

Exposure data and biomarkers in humans

4.87   The dietary habits, and subsequent disease occurrence, of more than 3 million people are currently under observation on a worldwide basis in cohort studies. Many of these involve the use of a biobank – an archive of biological samples that can be used in designing epidemiological studies. The majority of these studies have been designed to study the effects of diet and other possible risk factors on chronic diseases with relatively long induction times.[35] The reasons for collecting large archives of human, as well as non-human, biological material for prospective epidemiological studies are many. They include the need to understand how metabolic processes relate to exposure to toxic chemicals, and to be able to refer back to samples in the light of improving knowledge about metabolic and cellular processes.

4.88   A recent report by the European Environment Agency and the European Science Foundation[36] recommends the establishment of environmental and human tissue banks to enable an ecosystem-orientated characterisation and evaluation of representative environmental and human samples. This would yield data on the current state of environmental and human contamination, and establish base lines and relevant time trends. Such environmental and human specimen banks have already been established in Germany, Sweden and, more recently, Norway.

4.89   Epidemiological investigations depend on knowledge of the levels of exposure over time and a lack of exposure data may be the major obstacle in establishing a causal relationship between a pollutant and a disease. An increased amount of a pollutant or its breakdown products in the body fluids or tissues of exposed individuals may reflect exposure to a chemical, and measurements of these levels may provide a useful index of an individual's exposure for epidemiological purposes.[37] Pollutants, their metabolites or characteristic biological changes associated with pollutant exposure are usually referred to as biomarkers.

4.90   The number of well-characterised biomarkers, such as the presence of β-microglobulin in urine as an indicator of renal damage by cadmium,[38] is still limited, but the development and validation of biomarkers is vital for epidemiological studies. Biomarkers can potentially offer more detailed information than traditional methods of measuring exposure. Ideally a biomarker should specifically reflect exposure and adverse health outcomes, as it is difficult for epidemiology to detect subtle effects arising from environmental exposure in the absence of unique or easily obtainable biomarkers. Biomarkers also accurately reflect an individual's internal dose,[39] that is they reflect an individual's genetic ability to metabolise foreign substances, as well as their lifestyle, diet, age, and other factors that may affect their overall susceptibility to chemical exposure.

A NEW APPROACH TO MONITORING

4.91 Under the chemicals assessment and management programme we propose, those chemicals that are not selected through the sorting process for further investigation will need to be subject to some degree of monitoring to check that they are behaving as expected. A conventional monitoring scheme to investigate all the tens of thousands of chemicals on the market would be costly and ineffective. However, better use of monitoring data could be made to prioritise chemicals for further consideration and, in certain circumstances, directly provide the data required for risk management decisions.

4.92 We have noted that current environmental monitoring activities in the UK are not well directed towards the systematic assessment of the fate and effects of chemicals in the environment (4.73). Improving this would require, *inter alia*, better co-ordination and integration of chemical and biological monitoring activities. The value of these activities is greatly enhanced if mechanisms are found to integrate them, for example, by helping to establish cause-effect relationships. In addition, existing monitoring schemes need to develop a more flexible approach, conducting periodic observational campaigns on new aspects of environmental chemicals from time to time, as part of a review of chemicals safety in changing circumstances, and incorporating *ad hoc* observations of the sort described above (4.84-4.86). There are risks in this approach, in that false positives may be obtained (due to the uncertainties that will exist in the identification of compounds) but this could be regarded as an important precaution.

4.93 In order to achieve this degree of co-ordination and integration, **we recommend that monitoring activity related to the fate and effects of chemicals in the environment should be co-ordinated by the proposed chemicals safety co-ordination unit (4.107-4.111). However, the monitoring activity itself should continue to be carried out by the relevant expert organisations as at present.**

Reconnaissance monitoring

4.94 In its report to the Royal Commission,[40] the Centre for Environment, Fisheries and Aquaculture Science pointed out that an improved balance between biological and chemical monitoring programmes would permit a change in the emphasis of monitoring to enhance the reconnaissance[41] aspects of existing programmes and detect problems more quickly. A better relationship could be established between assessment and management by implementing such reconnaissance monitoring. This would provide more information about both the chemical and the biological status of the environment, which would be used to determine whether a chemical present in the environment presented a hazard to a biological system, such as ecosystem structure or function, a key food chain element, a top predator or a person. On this basis an informed risk assessment could be made, not on all chemicals but only on those that were actually detectable in the environment or affecting living organisms. Compliance monitoring would follow risk management to ensure that risk management measures were effective. When a chemical is withdrawn from use, the need for monitoring does not disappear entirely, as some chemicals can still appear in the environment due to the effects of trans-boundary processes, trade or waste management.

Environmental epidemiology

4.95 Substantial developments in measuring the health of both human and environmental populations will be needed before epidemiology can become a more generally useful tool in the assessment of chemicals in the environment (4.77). However, the importance of epidemiological data in the process of hazard identification is well recognised. While in the past the sparseness of data was a barrier to their use in risk assessment, environmental epidemiological studies will be essential in the future development of policies for the control of chemicals in the environment. For the vast majority of chemicals that are released into the environment, testing for chronic, low-level effects is not conducted – neither is it practical. **We recommend that environmental epidemiological studies of human and animal populations be used by the chemicals safety co-ordination unit to identify chemicals, and combinations of chemicals, with the potential to damage animal and human health**.

Effective use of monitoring data

4.96 Figure 4-I summarises how monitoring might be used more effectively in a chemicals assessment and management programme. Current systems in place, which we have discussed above, are already able to detect new threats posed by chemicals. Considerable gains can thus be made by integrating the reconnaissance aspects of monitoring explicitly into the sorting and evaluation processes that we propose (4.15-4.36). As well as (or, in due course, perhaps instead of) the physico-chemical and toxicological criteria proposed for this approach, chemicals would also be selected for further investigation if they were found:

- in unexpected environmental compartments;

- in environmental compartments where biological anomalies had been detected;

- at higher concentrations than expected;

- in the tissues of top predators; or

- through reconnaissance monitoring, in some other anomalous situation.

Reconnaissance monitoring would also form the basis of the subsequent follow-up monitoring once risk management action had been taken (or a decision taken that risk management action was unnecessary for that chemical).

4.97 **We recommend that the chemicals safety co-ordination unit, in co-ordinating monitoring as recommended above, direct effort towards reconnaissance monitoring and environmental epidemiology, using an integrated approach to**

detecting the presence or possible effects of chemicals in the environment as part of its risk management programme. Again we stress that responsibility for carrying out publicly-funded monitoring should remain with the expert bodies.

4.98 Monitoring for this purpose needs to recognise fully the value of biological quality status monitoring, the need to gather adequate geochemical data, and the importance of detecting spatial and temporal trends. This means conducting long-term studies in which data management and quality assurance procedures are prominent. Work could start on reconnaissance monitoring immediately, indeed it is already in hand in some UK research centres, although to realise fully the potential of modern techniques, research will be required to develop and validate operational procedures.

4.99 The responsible regulatory body will need to make use of diagnostic techniques that should help determine whether biological change is due to a chemical, or whether a chemical in the environment poses a hazard to biota. Two approaches that could help at this stage are modern approaches to QSARs (4.51-4.59), and the Toxicity Identification Evaluation systems (4.81-4.83). Using these two approaches, and others such as certain types of biosensor should provide the main elements of a screening system to identify chemicals needing further investigation. Research is needed to develop the operational approaches.

4.100 One key element of this system is that risk assessment would become more focused, avoiding the need to generate large quantities of data from tests on higher organisms (4.69). Risk assessment can be expensive, and funding saved by avoiding much of the need for expensive testing and assessment procedures could become available for monitoring. Conventionally, monitoring programmes tend to be publicly funded, so there is a danger that this change of emphasis could result in an extra burden on the public purse, with industry benefiting.

4.101 **We recommend that, following the introduction of reconnaissance monitoring as recommended above, the regulatory approval of chemicals includes requirements for post-approval monitoring by (or at the expense of) the producer or importer.**

ADMINISTRATIVE ARRANGEMENTS

4.102 In this chapter we have recommended a number of changes to the ways in which the environmental fate and effects of chemicals are assessed and managed, and have pointed to the scope for an enhanced role for environmental monitoring in achieving these changes. We have identified a need for scientific research to deliver some of our longer-term recommendations, and for policy initiatives to secure statutory underpinning sooner than the new EU proposals would deliver. We have already referred to the need for an agency to take ownership of the list of marketed chemicals and the research programme, and here we consider options for constituting such an agency.

4.103 Chapter 3 described the bodies responsible for chemical safety in the UK and in other countries. In the UK, many different organisations are involved and their responsibilities are assigned according to exposure routes (such as, environmental, domestic, occupational, consumer use, food) or to the use to which the chemical is put (for instance, pesticides, biocides, veterinary medicines, pharmaceuticals). In Sweden, many of these responsibilities are centred in the National Chemicals Inspectorate (KemI) (3.100). Other countries have arrangements that generally fall between these two positions.

NATIONAL

4.104 We have considered whether the UK arrangements for managing the risks from chemicals are too diffuse. Many of the policy and regulatory issues discussed in this report, and others such as those related to consumer safety and food safety, have common features that would benefit from a common approach and a single, dedicated source of policy on chemicals safety. Without one organisation clearly in the lead, and responsible for ensuring that national objectives are identified and delivered, the separate chemicals programmes in government departments and agencies cannot efficiently be co-ordinated, and resource allocation will be driven by the changing priorities of the various bodies instead of the need to deliver an effective chemicals programme.

4.105 Strategic planning also suffers from scattered responsibilities. The government's National Chemicals Strategy[42] covers only environmental safety, recognising only through reference to the need for 'an holistic approach' the close links between environmental, occupational and consumer safety – even then it excludes 'positive approval schemes' from its scope. Nowhere can we find evidence of this holistic approach in the current national policy on chemicals.

4.106 The Health and Safety Executive has until relatively recently provided a lead on the implementation of some European chemicals legislation, particularly that relating to the marketing and use of dangerous chemicals. We have heard, however, that the Health and Safety Commission has decided that occupational safety priorities lie elsewhere, and that the Executive's current role on chemicals will have to be reduced to some extent.[43] If so, this will exacerbate the absence of co-ordination of the various chemicals policies in government just at a time when chemicals policy in Europe is about to undergo major changes.

4.107 We have considered whether the UK needs a chemicals inspectorate, similar to KemI in Sweden. On balance, the resource implications of establishing such a major body seem substantial, and we have considered lower-cost ways of ensuring the necessary degree of co-ordination and leadership. A 'chemicals safety co-ordination unit', formed from experts in chemicals policy, regulation and science already in government departments, would be adequate. It would be charged with co-ordinating a national chemicals management programme, and would be responsible, *inter alia*, for:

- maintaining the list of all chemicals on the UK market;

- establishing and using the chemicals assessment and management programme (figure 4-I), guided by a statutory advisory body, and securing appropriate risk management;

- keeping under review chemicals not identified by initial sorting as of concern;

- co-ordinating relevant monitoring programmes (including a system for public reporting of chemical related incidents) and assessing the results;

- securing and co-ordinating research by industry and others into the adaptation of high-throughput screening, and the use of emerging science to develop future testing and assessment protocols;

- securing regulatory underpinning for the chemicals management programme as soon as possible;

- advising departments and agencies on chemical safety issues;

- co-ordinating with other EU Member States to ensure economies of scale and maximum political leverage in advance of the forthcoming chemicals legislation coming into force;

- providing advice to the public about chemicals in products;

- acting as the UK focal point to interact with the European Commission's proposed 'central entity'; and

- co-ordinating UK input to relevant international programmes on chemicals safety.

4.108 While for a short period it might be necessary for the constituent parts of the unit to remain located in their original organisations, they ought quickly to be brought together within a host organisation to achieve the benefits of collegiate working. The choice of host organisation is not critical, though it must already have chemicals responsibility and expertise to an extent that would allow it to take full ownership of the objectives of the unit.

4.109 The Health and Safety Executive might not be ready to take on this role for the reasons mentioned (4.106), and in any case, the balance of policy attention on chemicals is currently driven more by environmental and consumer safety concerns than by occupational safety. The remits of the Food Standards Agency and the other agencies might prove a little narrow to take on the range of responsibilities needed for this role, though they ought to benefit from, and therefore contribute to, the operation of the unit.

4.110 The Environment Agency has a small but expert chemicals team that plays a key role in the operation of European legislation. It also has extensive environmental monitoring expertise and regulatory responsibility for many of the pathways through which chemicals enter the environment. As an England and Wales body it would need to maintain strong links with organisations in Scotland and Northern Ireland, but it already has those links to a large extent.

4.111 Another option might be the Pesticides Safety Directorate. The Directorate has extensive expertise in the assessment and management of chemical risks, including environmental safety. Its expertise, suitably augmented by the transfer of personnel from other bodies, would be applicable to a wider range of synthetic chemicals. It is an agency of the Department for Environment, Food and Rural Affairs, but already has UK-wide responsibilities. On balance, though, we conclude that the greater independence of the Environmental Agency, coupled with its broader responsibilities for environmental monitoring, make the Agency a more suitable host. **We recommend that the government establish a chemicals safety co-ordination unit, with the responsibilities set out above, by transferring resources (staff and budgets) from existing organisations dealing with chemicals safety to the Environment Agency.**

4.112 The responsibilities of the unit will be derived from European Community legislation and have a UK-wide application. It will be necessary for departments and the devolved administrations to consider the case for separate units in Wales, Scotland and Northern Ireland, but given the need for a high level of technical expertise it would be sensible to avoid over-duplication of investment, and to establish a single unit acting as a cross-border resource. It is critically important that the unit liaises with and seeks advice from other expert organisations in the wider research community, including bodies such as the National Environmental Research Council's British Geological Survey and Centre for Ecology and Hydrology, and Centre for Environment, Fisheries, Aquaculture and Science. The unit should take on responsibility for co-ordinating all aspects of chemicals safety, including those chemicals that are covered by separate legislation, such as pesticides. The forthcoming consolidation of directives (3.7) will provide a further stimulus for this.

4.113 The unit will need a source of independent advice, and access to ways of determining public views on the subjects with which it deals. We have recommended (4.45) a new role for the Chemicals Stakeholder Forum, to provide advice to the unit in connection with the assessment and management programme. We recommended statutory underpinning, and a change of name to the Chemicals Standards Forum. This reconstituted Forum would, however, be able to provide stakeholder views, and to collate public views, on a much wider range of chemicals topics covering many of the responsibilities of the unit. **We recommend that the Chemicals Standards Forum be mandated to provide advice to the unit on any topic within the unit's remit, and that the unit be required to take such advice into account in making regulatory decisions about chemicals, or in advising Ministers or government departments on chemicals policy.**

RESEARCH

4.114 The proposals we have made for a chemicals assessment and management programme earlier in this chapter (4.8-4.39) are based on the observation that it is not feasible, with current technologies, to carry out extensive checking for potentially harmful properties in such a large number of chemicals within a reasonably short time. Our proposals are founded instead on taking decisions largely on the basis of a small number of properties of the chemical, and then undertaking a fuller investigation and risk management of those chemicals that exhibit potentially hazardous properties. Despite the uncertainties inherent in such a limited approach, we see no better way forward in the short term, but the Royal Commission takes the view that this is not an acceptable long-term position.

4.115 The properties of most concern in this context relate to the physiological effects of a chemical on biological organisms including humans, and on unexpected physical effects on the environment. This includes the more established measures of toxicity, such as acute and chronic lethal and sub-lethal doses, oncological properties (carcinogenicity, mutagenicity and reprotoxicity), emerging concerns (such as the potential to disrupt the endocrine or immune systems), damage to the atmosphere (for example, potential to deplete the ozone layer), or effects which have not yet come to light but which might cause concern for future generations. Testing of even a single chemical for all of these effects using conventional techniques, would be a daunting and expensive prospect, and, axiomatically, testing for effects that have not yet been conceived of is not feasible.

4.116 We have heard no reasons why the sorting system that we describe above could not be geared towards the identification of a full range of adverse physiological effects. The emphasis should be on permitting modern computational techniques to play a much more significant role, both for sorting and for further investigation of chemicals. It could apply equally to reviewing existing chemicals that have already been sorted and to new chemicals subject to the provisions of the Notification of New Substances Regulations.

4.117 **We recommend that the chemicals safety co-ordination unit commissions and co-ordinates a programme of research to evaluate and keep under review rapid**

screening techniques to assess the environmental safety of synthetic chemicals. The chemicals industry, co-operating internationally, should play a central role in this work, including the provision of resources.

4.118 For the longer term, the most satisfactory way of handing over our chemical inheritance to future generations would be in conjunction with a complete and coherent understanding of the way chemicals behave in the environment and affect biological organisms. This full knowledge is not realistic. But inter-generational equity dictates that it is unreasonable to continue to release large numbers of synthetic chemicals into the environment without a much better understanding of the long-term implications of this activity. What is certainly needed is a means of ensuring that the cutting edge of science is applied to these issues. So far, such research funding from government or the industry has not matched that spent on innovation or the development of new chemical products.

4.119 There are several emerging areas of science that may prove helpful in moving towards this goal. In particular we have been considering the role of genomics (appendix H). Research into these areas is already under way for medical reasons. **We encourage the chemicals industry to augment genomics research significantly, in a direction that will lead towards an understanding of the way that synthetic chemicals interact with biological organisms.** This work will be of relevance internationally and is likely to lead to improved ways of managing the risks from chemicals in products. An international research initiative would seem to be the most cost-effective way of implementing this recommendation.

4.120 In parallel to this there needs to be a drive towards a better understanding of the behaviour of chemicals in the environment. Already sufficient is known to permit the use of reasonably sophisticated monitoring techniques, and we take the view that the challenges here are less demanding than those of understanding the effects of chemicals. Nevertheless, use of environmental monitoring results in the way that we have recommended (4.91-4.101) will augment this work.

4.121 **We recommend that the chemicals safety co-ordination unit publish its strategic approach to research, setting out the steps it will take to ensure that it will be possible to predict with adequate confidence the fate and effects of synthetic chemicals released into the environment.** It should report progress at 5-yearly intervals.

EUROPEAN

4.122 Because of the European basis for much of the legislation relating to chemicals, and particularly when REACH comes into effect, there will need to be some system of co-ordination across the EU. The European Commission's Chemicals White Paper proposes a 'central entity', which will co-ordinate Member States' activities and commission work from the competent authorities.

4.123 In European institutions, there is a tendency towards bureaucracy. One objective, both of the proposals we have made in this chapter and of REACH, is to greatly speed up the process of securing adequate information about, and risk management of, chemicals in the environment. Unless the bureaucratic overheads are minimised to a level considerably below those currently applied to the Existing Substances Regulation and other chemicals legislation, progress towards this objective will not be made. The key to avoiding this situation is subsidiarity – maximum responsibility should be left with the competent authorities of the Member States, and the central entity should co-ordinate activities to the minimum extent consistent with ensuring common standards across the EU.

4.124 A further objective of our recommendations is to bring the cutting edge of science to bear on the challenge of ensuring that we understand the effects that synthetic chemicals are having on our environment. This requires the research we recommend above (4.114-4.121), and there are huge efficiencies to be gained if this research were to be shared between governments and industry, and co-ordinated across Europe and other countries with developed chemicals industries. To some extent this is a role presently played by the OECD. The central entity ought to adopt, as one of its primary tasks, co-ordination of the European contribution to this international effort.

4.125 **We recommend that the government argue for a European central entity that takes on, as a main objective, the co-ordination of research into chemicals assessment and risk management.**

THE NEED FOR PRECAUTION

4.126 This chapter has outlined our proposals for improving the statutory procedures for assessing and managing the risks from chemicals. The approach we recommend will mean that all chemicals are examined, and some are selected for further study and risk management measures, very much more quickly than either current arrangements or the proposed new European scheme, REACH. However, the inherent uncertainties in the methods used to assess hazard and risk, and the limitations in our understanding of environment processes, mean that this should not be the only approach to dealing with chemicals. In the next chapter we go on to examine the scope for more precautionary approaches, including non-statutory ones, based around the concept of substitution. .

This chapter argues for a different approach to chemicals assessment and management. All chemicals on the market should be examined and some evaluated using modern approaches to screening. Reconnaissance monitoring should be tightly integrated into the process. The UK's efforts should be focused through one office and led by the Environment Agency.

Chapter 5

TOWARDS ENVIRONMENTALLY SUSTAINABLE PRODUCTS

Regulation of chemicals as and in products needs as much attention as regulation of processes and facilities. Better information provision is needed. Substitution, the replacement of more hazardous chemicals or processes by those that are less hazardous, should be the core goal of policies on chemicals. How might chemicals innovation be stimulated towards this end? What approaches are available to reduce emissions of chemicals used as products?

BRINGING PRODUCTS INTO FOCUS

5.1 We have noted from this study (in chapter 1) and from previous reports of the Royal Commission that the development of contemporary environmental legislation and policy, both nationally and at the European level, has focused heavily on the regulation of emissions (including waste) from processes and facilities. In comparison, regulation of chemical products and their behaviour and effects in the environment is poorly developed, and is not co-ordinated with other regulatory regimes.

5.2 It is true that complex chemicals legislation has been developed in the last twenty years, but this has largely been focussed on the regulation of substances and preparations and we have identified in previous chapters major problems with this legislation, especially in relation to existing chemicals. To take one example, pollution inventories of the type being developed by the Environment Agency (5.86) are concerned with emissions from processes, but there has been little comparable effort in the development of product registers. This is despite emerging evidence that the diffuse pollution from chemicals contained in finished articles is considerable (5.19-5.24). This chapter considers the building blocks that are needed to ensure that the direction of innovation is towards the more environmentally sustainable use of chemicals in products.

5.3 The existing legislation has brought substantial environmental benefits, but a more sustained effort is now needed from government to develop a consistent framework in order to bring about the more environmentally sustainable development and use of products. This will involve legal initiatives, but we do not feel that it is possible to rely upon regulation as the main tool for change to the same extent as has happened with processes. Instead we recommend a combination of fiscal incentives, producer responsibility concepts, legal liability principles and voluntary schemes to improve the framework in which chemicals are managed. These findings have been echoed by the National Society for Clean Air,[1] which noted in its 'Smarter Regulation' report that there needs to be a regulatory shift to address more effectively the burden of chemicals in products, which are relatively poorly controlled.

5.4   The regulatory regime proposed in chapter 4 will in time achieve certain standards of safety for existing and new substances, but it alone will not stimulate the systematic evolution of the chemicals industry towards the manufacture and use of less hazardous substances. Chapter 1 identified our concerns about the diffuse release of chemicals from products during the use phase, and we recognise here that, for all but a few cases, testing finished articles for their detailed chemical composition will be unfeasible. Yet there needs to be improved information provision at the use phase, both to provide adequate protection for end-users, and to allow proper application of take-back and other extended producer responsibility initiatives. In addition, substitution of hazardous chemicals by less hazardous substances or processes could be facilitated through a re-design of products and delivery (green chemistry) and through the wider adoption of service-based approaches. This chapter discusses these and other instruments needed to stimulate substitution.

5.5   The chemicals industry is international in nature, and new approaches to improving chemicals safety, including those discussed in chapter 4 and here, will be more effective with better harmonisation. This applies especially to information, and ways are proposed for achieving the more efficient international use of available information about chemicals in products.

5.6   Finally, the chapter discusses the impact of regulatory regimes on innovation, and recommends the development of a framework to measure the direction of innovation, in order to monitor progress in delivering all of our objectives.

SUBSTITUTION

5.7   Substitution, in its strictest sense, is the replacement of one chemical with another. This is commonplace in industry and is normally driven by market forces, for example, switching to lower-cost alternatives. In the context of chemicals risk management, substitution has come to mean the replacement of a hazardous substance with another of lower hazard. The term can also helpfully be extended to the replacement of processes that use hazardous chemicals with processes that do not; the move towards integrated pest management well exemplifies such a shift (box 5A). The term has become somewhat value-laden, with some countries elevating the concept to the status of a principle[2] or even a law.[3] We consider here the role of substitution in chemicals risk management, its pitfalls (problematic examples and high expectations) and, where these can be successfully addressed, possible drivers towards substitution on environmental grounds.

5.8   The considerable inherent uncertainty in our understanding of the way that chemicals interact with the environment means that there will continue to be a risk of serious effects, as a result of the use of chemicals products, that we cannot predict on the basis of our current or foreseeable understanding of these processes. This requires a precautionary approach to chemicals management, and this is best implemented through substitution. When safer replacement chemicals become available, market forces and liability considerations might ensure that they replace older and more hazardous chemicals. It is often the case, however, that established chemicals are cheaper, possibly due, at least partially, to economic obstacles to introducing new chemicals on to the market or to changing established processes.[4] Substitution, where desirable, might therefore need some further incentive, through regulatory or other means.

BOX 5A	**INTEGRATED PEST MANAGEMENT (IPM):**
	NON-CHEMICAL SUBSTITUTION

In recent years there has been growing concern about the impact of modern farming on the environment. These concerns have surrounded the increasing use of pesticides, herbicides, and fertilisers. One result has been moves towards organic farming and Integrated Pest Management (IPM) approaches.

IPM is an ecological approach that gives highest priority to the prevention of pest problems, thereby reducing the need for pesticides. The World Bank suggests that IPM is based on the following principles:[5]

i. relying as much as possible on non-chemical measures to keep pest populations low. The focus is on plant breeding and on cultural practices aimed at keeping the crop healthy and resistant or tolerant to attack;

ii. managing pests, rather than trying to eradicate them; and

iii. selecting and applying pesticides (when they have to be used) in a way that minimises adverse effects on beneficial organisms, humans and the environment.

The cultural control practices include alteration of tilling, crop rotation, removal or provision of alternative hosts or volunteer plants, altering planting and harvest timing, and the planting of trap crops. Other IPM measures have included the release of sterilised insects and the use of semiochemicals (pheromones used to draw insects to traps or disrupt breeding behaviour).

Under an IPM approach, monitoring and forecasting are used to determine when pests have exceeded an economic threshold. When this threshold has been exceeded, pesticides may be used, with preference towards those causing least harm to the beneficial organisms and the agro-ecosystem. Pesticides are not therefore the first course of action.

IPM has also been incorporated into Integrated Crop Management (ICM), where rotations, seed variety selection, soil structure, nutrition and crop protection are considered as part of a site-specific plan. Integrated Farm Management (IFM) goes further and considers all aspects of farming – not only ICM and IPM, but also the management of livestock and wider issues such as the ecosystem and energy efficiency, again on a site-specific basis.

SELECTING THE SUBSTITUTE

5.9   Substitution relies on the availability of a chemical or process that performs the intended function as well as the original, but that offers some other advantage. There have been cases where substitution on environmental grounds has led to occupational safety concerns and *vice versa,* and cases where substitution has replaced one environmental problem with another. Sometimes political pressure to remove a well-characterised but publicly feared chemical will result in its substitution by another chemical about which much less information is available. Box 5B describes two examples of cases in which substitution proved to be unsatisfactory.

BOX 5B   **EXAMPLES OF PROBLEMATIC SUBSTITUTION**

---

1. Refrigerators operate by cyclically compressing and decompressing a chemical with a boiling point near room temperature. Early refrigerators used ammonia, which is toxic. Chlorofluorocarbons (CFCs) are very much less toxic than ammonia, have ideal properties both as refrigerants and as thermal insulators, and were used as such in domestic and commercial refrigeration plant for many years. However, they were discovered to be potent ozone depleters, and have been banned under the Vienna Convention for the Protection of the Ozone Layer and its Montreal Protocol (3.77). Initially, they were replaced by hydrocarbon gases, but these are explosive and caused hazards in the workplace. Another group of chemicals, the hydrofluorocarbons (HFCs), was then phased in, but these turn out to be potent greenhouse gases. This has led to a move back to the use of ammonia.

2. Scab, a sheep parasite, is very infectious and, if untreated, causes considerable commercial loss to farmers. Control measures using chemical agents have been compulsory for many years, normally through the use of sheep-dips. Use of the organochlorine pesticide dieldrin was phased out because of its persistence and propensity to accumulate in the environment. Replacements were based on organophosphate chemicals but subsequently concerns have arisen about their impacts on human health – particularly on farm workers massively exposed to the chemical during dipping operations. Synthetic pyrethroids, such as cypermethrin, are starting to be used as alternatives, but these exhibit very high toxicity to aquatic organisms, and disposal avoiding water contamination presents a serious problem.

5.10   It is crucial to recognise that the substitute need not be another chemical. Changes in practice to reduce or eliminate the need for certain hazardous chemicals may be preferable. The serious damage caused by the successive sheep-dip compounds in the substitution chain described in box 5B might have been avoided (further damage could still be avoided) by changes in animal husbandry to reduce the spread of scab between sheep. Box 5C offers views of other stakeholders on the role of substitution.

BOX 5C   **OTHER VIEWS ON SUBSTITUTION**

CEFIC (the European chemical industry association) considers the substitution principle to be an emerging principle that has so far not been debated at European level and which still lacks a clear and common definition.[6] CEFIC notes that references to the principle tend to be inconsistent, especially concerning the conditions under which it should be applied.

The Royal Society of Chemistry has suggested[7] that because of the need for value judgements on the acceptability of risk to both humans and the environment, stakeholders should have a clear role in establishing the case for substitution.

The European Environment Bureau[8] has expressed concern that, while evidence is needed that substitutes are less harmful than those products that they replace, the extent of the evidence sought by industry would undermine the promotion of substitution as a general principle.

COMPARING SUBSTITUTES

5.11   The Biocides Products Directive[9] introduces a statutory approach to substitution, known as comparative assessment. There are difficulties in defining formal methodologies for comparing different types of hazard, necessary within a statutory framework, which would be resistant to challenge – particularly judicial review in situations where serious distortion of competition might result. At this stage we take the view that it is too early to judge whether or not comparative assessment will deliver an adequate rate of substitution, or whether it should be extended to chemicals more generally. It is worth watching, but we put more emphasis, at this stage, on the full chemicals assessment and management programme that we recommend in chapter 4 coupled with non-statutory approaches that we discuss in this chapter.

5.12   A proper comparison of a chemical with its potential substitutes (other chemicals or other processes) ought to cover the whole life cycle of the product. This can be onerous and contentious, but there will often be discrete activities within each life cycle phase (for example, the use of substances in closed or open systems) that will have different levels of associated risk, and which could be targeted for substitution. Under the current (and proposed future) European Community regulatory systems, evaluation and authorisation is of a particular substance for a particular use.

5.13   There may therefore be activities for which the substance is considered acceptable and no substitution is required, while others may result in unacceptable levels of risk. A Department for Environment, Food and Rural Affairs (Defra) report on the use of economic instruments (5.67-5.68) includes a case study of nonylphenols[10] and points out that for these substances there are over 20 relevant sectors of use, with just seven uses accounting for some 70% of the burden of the substance in the environment. For these seven sectors, marketing and use restrictions are being proposed at the EU level. For the remaining sectors, it has been proposed that risks are managed through the use of activity-based emissions controls and environmental quality standards.

5.14   In addition to consideration of different life cycle impacts of substances, a harmonised set of criteria for comparative assessment would need to be agreed. These could not be based merely on intrinsic hazardous properties, but would need to incorporate release and exposure potentials. Substances can have different potential hazards, so that comparative evaluation would have to cover multiple criteria. Combined with the inherent uncertainties in the science involved, it would be difficult to provide a robust basis for decision-making on substitution, capable of being defended against legal challenge. Substances would need to be evaluated not just against the criteria generating concern but perhaps also against all other relevant authorisation criteria.

5.15   Evaluation of at least some of these problems is undertaken in routine decision-making for chemical risk management measures, and there is, therefore, scope for regulatory mechanisms both to act as drivers of substitution and to inform substitution decisions. But because of the difficulties of agreeing and enforcing comparative assessment regimes in the wider use of a statutory approach to substitution we are unconvinced that regulation alone offers a pragmatic way of driving substitution. Other non-regulatory drivers are needed.

SUBSTITUTION AS A GOAL

5.16   There will continue to be circumstances where it is appropriate for government to use regulatory powers to ban or phase out substances or products that are especially harmful. However, it is desirable that chemical products generally should become less hazardous over time. The substitution principle is a valuable concept to this end. The approach adopted in the Swedish Chemical Products Act of 1990 (3.100) was to seek to impose a general duty of care on manufactures and importers to select and use the substances (or techniques) that fulfil a given function with minimal impacts. The UK Chemicals Strategy (3.89) included the following statement:

> 'Risk reduction strategies should always look at substitution of more hazardous chemicals by safer alternatives. Industry therefore needs to look continuously for ways of reducing the different impacts that chemical production and use have on the environment. This should include systematic replacement of the most hazardous chemicals by less hazardous ones. Where we introduce restrictions on marketing and use of a chemical, we would certainly expect replacements to be less hazardous.'[11]

5.17   This, however, seems not to have been followed up by clear government or industry action. Substitution needs to be driven by measures aimed specifically at stimulating it. This chapter discusses some such measures, including a more concerted focus on the use phase of chemicals in products and improved flows of information through the supply chain, emerging new approaches to the delivery of chemical services, the use of fiscal incentives, producer responsibility concepts, legal liability principles, and voluntary schemes. In many cases these instruments may need to be brought together to form a cohesive and effective risk reduction package for a particular chemical or group of chemicals. What is important is that they should be used in a manner that consistently supports the underlying policy goal of encouraging and ensuring progressive substitution.

5.18   **We recommend that the UK government adopt substitution as a central objective of chemicals policy.**

INFORMATION ABOUT THE USE PHASE

DOMINANCE OF THE USE AND DISPOSAL PHASES OF THE LIFE CYCLE

5.19   Some chemicals are intentionally released into the environment in the use phase of their life cycle. Examples include agrochemicals, some cleaning and laundry products, and some cosmetics and personal care products. Other chemicals will find their way into the environment as a consequence of their use. As a result, users may be exposed directly to the chemicals in these products and, in many cases, individuals other than the immediate user may also be affected via exposure through various environmental pathways.

5.20   A study for the Swedish National Chemicals Inspectorate (KemI) examined the emissions of chemicals from products in a life cycle assessment.[12] The report found that for four of the five substances studied, the majority of emissions occurred during the service life of the product. For several of the substances significant emissions were also identified during waste disposal (most commonly to landfill). The examples given below (5.21-5.24 and Box 5D) suggest that the substances chosen were not unique in this respect and that there are many other substances for which the majority of release will occur via distributed products.

BOX 5D   **THE PAN UK DOMESTIC PESTICIDE USE SURVEY**

The UK Pesticide Action Network (PAN UK) has carried out a survey of members of the public to find out more about the use, storage and disposal of domestic pesticides. The survey took the form of a questionnaire, also available on the Internet[13], which was distributed to community groups and societies, and advertised in specialist media such as gardening and consumer magazines.

PAN found that that in 2001 householders purchased 4,893 tonnes of pesticide active ingredient, an increase of 14% compared with sales in 2000, and of 76% compared with sales in 1998. The results of the survey showed that while 5-10% of householders surveyed took pesticide waste to a specialised facility at their local authority civic amenity site, 20-30% disposed of pesticides inappropriately (down the drain or in the bin), and the remainder stored these chemicals indefinitely (mainly in garden sheds and kitchen cupboards).[14]

5.21   Swedish data from 1990 shown in table 5.1[15] compare emissions of heavy metals from point sources in Sweden with potential emissions from products. While there may be some capacity for recovery, re-use and recycling of these metals, the figures clearly show the potential dominance of diffuse sources of pollution for these substances.

Table 5.1

Heavy metals in products and point source emissions, Sweden, *ca.* 1990

	Emissions from point sources into air and water (tonnes per year)	Content in products put into circulation during the same year (tonnes)	Point-source emissions as a percentage of potential releases via products
Lead	740	30,000	2.5
Cadmium	4.5	170	3.0
Mercury	3.2	14	23.0
Chrome	85	50,000	0.2
Nickel	75	20,000	0.4
Zinc	1,140	52,000	2.2

5.22   Since 1990 California's Air Resources Board[16] has introduced a series of regulations designed to reduce emissions of volatile organic compounds (VOCs), which volatilise readily into the atmosphere and cause unwanted effects such as ozone formation in the lower atmosphere. Petroleum and transport fuels are an important source of VOCs, but the Board estimated that consumer products emit more than all the refineries and petrol stations in the State (consumer products emitted 265 tons of VOCs per day). The State Implementation Plan for air quality commits California to an 85% reduction in emissions of ozone-forming consumer products.

5.23 The VOC emissions from the structure and fittings of three different cars on the Australian market – two locally-made cars that reached the market one to two months after manufacture and one imported car that reached the market four months after manufacture – have been studied.[17] Initial measurements for the imported vehicle were approximately thirty times lower than for the locally-produced vehicles. The study noted that in-car VOC concentrations decayed exponentially, that a reduction in concentration to the Australian indoor air goal for VOCs would be reached after around six months, and that initial concentrations were present at levels found to have caused sensory irritation, and performance and memory impairment in humans.

5.24 Researchers from RIVM (a Dutch public and environmental health research institute) report observational studies of consumers[18] which show that individuals tend to have a consistent way of using a product for a particular activity, but that there is a large variation in product usage between individuals. This implies that there will be a group of individuals with a consistently higher exposure pattern for a particular product. For example, an individual who developed acneforms on his face and back, claimed to be a consequence of watching TV and playing video games for several hours a day, was found to have exceptionally high exposure to the brominated flame retardant pentabromodiphenyl ether[19] and chromosomal abnormalities consistent with chemical exposure. The researchers also noted the lack of observational studies on human behaviour with regard to product use. This information is of particular importance in formulating models to assess end-user exposure.

IMPORTANCE OF KNOWING COMPOSITION FOR WASTE MANAGEMENT AND TAKE-BACK

5.25 The diffuse release of chemicals during the use of a product is, therefore, a growing issue of concern. Of equal significance are the challenges that the chemical content of products poses for their subsequent re-use or management as a waste. The current formulation of the EU's hazardous waste list presents difficulties for those involved in the recovery of waste electrical and electronic equipment (3.175-3.176). The definition of hazardous components provided in the Community legislation[20] does not provide clear examples to distinguish hazardous from non-hazardous components. There are no established criteria for types of electrical and electronic equipment that are likely to contain 'hazardous' materials. This may result in all separately collected electrical and electronic equipment waste being classified as hazardous, and means that manufacturers and authorities involved in the collection, storage and handling of such waste may have to apply for permits to handle hazardous waste.[21] When increased re-use and recovery of materials from electrical and electronic waste is a clear objective, these unnecessary barriers need to be removed. Therefore, action is needed to re-classify the waste equipment where appropriate necessitating better information about substances in the products.

INFORMATION TRANSFER THROUGH THE SUPPLY CHAIN

5.26 Generally speaking, the longer the supply chain for a particular substance, the less that is known about that substance at the end of the chain. This means that by the time chemicals are incorporated into finished products, their presence may be unrecorded. Consequently, the most straightforward way of obtaining information about the constituents of a product might appear to be to analyse them, but the huge number of products on the market, and the large number of chemicals that they might contain, makes this impractical for routine purposes. An improved flow of information would resolve this problem and would permit better user protection and more control over the release and disposal of finished products containing substances of concern. With increased knowledge about the quantities of chemicals in use and the uses to which they are put, chemical producers and retailers would also be in a better position to implement appropriate product policy.

5.27 There are several initiatives under way to address this information blockage. The European Commission's Chemicals White Paper[22] envisages the formation of consortia at the registration phase. Downstream users will be obliged to report use of a substance to its manufacturer in order to ensure that the use in question is covered by the substance registration. The operation of such a scheme will require the transfer of information about use back up the supply chain, and a flow of information about the properties of the substance all the way down the supply chain to end-users.

5.28 The scheme will need to ensure that, while delivering the disclosure required, intellectual property rights are adequately protected. A number of responses to the Chemicals White Paper raised consortia formation as an issue.[23] The concerns relate to the formation of consortia, to the potential for manufacturers to use information from downstream users to their own advantage, and to the possible loss of intellectual property rights. A certain amount of downstream user knowledge rests in the composition of their products. Disclosure of this type of information to those upstream, and to competitors using the same products, could remove competitive advantage.

5.29 Directive EC 91/155[24] requires that a Safety Data Sheet be supplied for professional users of substances and preparations labelled as dangerous under the respective directives. Safety Data Sheets contain specific information about the physico-chemical properties of the product, information on occupational and environmental hygiene, and requirements for safe handling, use and proper disposal. Such information is complex, and expertise may be needed to interpret the Safety Data Sheet. An assessment of the usefulness of Safety Data Sheets in small and medium-sized companies in Austria, Germany and the Netherlands[25] found that the necessary expertise was lacking in most small enterprises, casting doubt on the usefulness of Safety Data Sheets. Under the current legislation, private consumers do not have to be supplied with a Safety Data Sheet for substances not intended to be used in the course of work.

5.30 The Netherlands has drafted framework legislation (as chapter 9 of its Environmental Management Act) covering all aspects of chemicals management as currently listed in the Netherlands Chemical Substances Act.[26] This includes legislation (in preparation) on the transfer of information through the supply chain, which is based on the principle of transferring and having access to information one step up and one step down in the supply chain.

5.31 In the UK, the Chemicals (Hazard Information and Packaging for Supply) (CHIP) Regulations[27] govern the transfer of information down the supply chain. These Regulations require the transfer of classification, packaging and labelling information alongside the supply of substances. The CHIP Regulations are in force through the whole supply chain from manufacturer to consumer. Chemical supply chains are, however, often complex with multiple industrial users and formulators typically involved before an end-product is supplied to a consumer. This is demonstrated in the example in figure 5-I for a compound used in the manufacture of printing inks and in paper pulp dyeing, Rhodamine B.[28]

Figure 5-I

The complexity of chemical supply chains: Rhodamine B

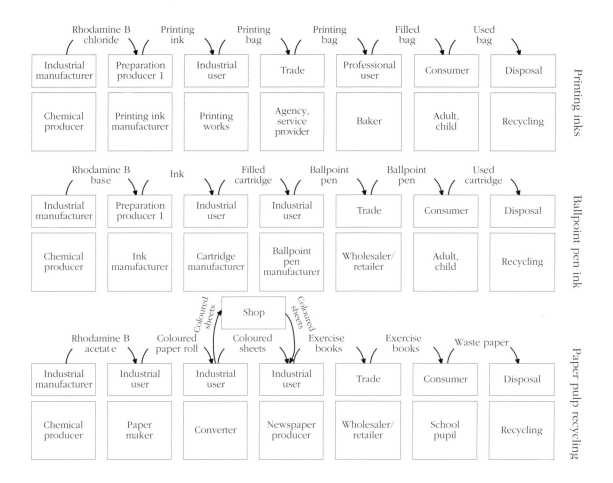

5.32 The project that gave rise to the above example also looked at ways of clarifying the proposed EU REACH system to deliver improved information flows. Many of the concerns identified stem from the lack of clarity in the Chemicals White Paper on expectations for information flow within the supply chain. The study noted loss of flexibility under the proposed system as a result of the need to register new substances or uses as these are introduced. It was thought that this might result in formulators moving outside the EU. The complexities of exposure and risk assessments were identified, with calls to simplify the process through identification of exposure categories, product grouping and the use of appropriate volume thresholds. The work also identified that the European Commission's proposals had not yet sufficiently addressed the disclosure of commercially-sensitive information and that this would need to be considered in the context of the European central entity's registration database (which may be fully open to the public).

5.33 **We recommend that the government carry out work with users to investigate the flow of information up and down the supply chain.**

5.34 **We recommend that the government investigate means of improving the information provided on Safety Data Sheets in order to make them more user-friendly.**

5.35 **We recommend that the government review the role of commercial confidentiality and statutory protection of relevant intellectual property rights.** The objective should be to provide the latter as an incentive to innovation without suppressing relevant information. All information thus made available should be placed on the list of marketed chemicals (4.14).

5.36 **We recommend that the government formulate legislation requiring all companies trading in chemicals to ensure that they receive all available information about any chemical substance or preparation when they obtain it, and supply full information about it when they sell it.**

TESTING FINISHED ARTICLES

5.37 As chapter 3 has shown, current legislation is focused on the regulation of chemical substances as used in finished articles rather than on the articles themselves. The Royal Commission has heard evidence for example, that while the active substances used in domestic aerosol sprays may have been tested (usually through standard oral exposure tests), in relatively few cases is respiratory testing carried out on the finished marketed product. There are no regulatory requirements to test finished household products, that is products not covered by the cosmetics, pesticides or biocides, medicines, or pharmaceuticals or medical devices regulations.[29] Manufacturers are merely required to determine the possible risks to human health and the environment posed by a product using the data available on the toxicity of the individual constituent chemicals of the product and on any possible synergistic effects between these chemicals, in line with the procedures laid down in the CHIP Regulations and administered by the Department of Trade and Industry's Consumer Safety Unit.

5.38 However, as previously emphasised, there may be few test data available for existing chemicals, especially concerning environmental effects and the effects of mixtures of chemicals. Those tests that are carried out on household products are mainly aimed at assessing effects on skin and eyes, or acute and systemic toxic effects induced by a variety of routes of exposure, such as by inhalation, through the skin, or ingestion.[30] We believe that the data made available on existing chemicals in products through the scheme proposed in chapter 4 would fill many outstanding data gaps, and that increased monitoring may provide further evidence of the environmental fate of the chemicals from these products, which would allow more effective enforcement of the CHIP Regulations.

5.39 This lack of information about the chemical content of finished articles has given rise to a number of studies seeking to determine their detailed chemical composition. The Swedish National Chemicals Inspectorate KemI, the Danish Environmental Protection Agency, and the Hamburg Environment Institute have undertaken work in this area, as have several international initiatives. The Hamburg Environment Institute[31] has analysed gaseous emissions from several complex household and office appliances using microwave thermal desorption and highly sensitive gas chromatography. The products analysed included computer mice and mobile phones, leisure products such as swimming armbands, and some interior decoration materials, such as carpet and wallpaper. The study found that over 100 compounds were emitted from the 19 products tested, including known carcinogens, endocrine disrupters, and sensitisers. The results obtained from similar products made in different countries varied considerably.

5.40 The Danish Environmental Protection Agency has begun a programme to investigate the chemical content of finished articles.[32] Results have been reported for chromium in leather products, plant substances in 'natural' cosmetics, and cleaning materials and polishes for metal. Some of these studies (for example, the work on metal polishes) are derived from a review of the ingredients listed on the product labels. Others have chemically analysed the composition and concentrations of the substances present and have then examined the toxicological profiles (where available) for the chemicals identified.

5.41 KemI[33] has tried to develop a methodology for obtaining information about the chemical constituents of products. In a pilot project, a number of products with confounding factors in the information gathering process were chosen, such as wholly imported products or those containing chemical substances not regulated by law. The product groups investigated were newsprint, plastic wrapping intended for processed meat products, trousers made of stretch fabric, jet engines, ceramic flat gaskets, still cameras and costume jewellery necklaces. Attempts were made to determine the chemicals included in these products by a variety of means, including questionnaires, telephone surveys and, in some cases, chemical analysis. It emerged that whilst it was possible to determine the materials used to make the articles, chemical composition was much more difficult to ascertain. It was found to be impossible, in most cases, to determine the concentrations of chemicals in the product groups tested. If a small number of companies were dominant in a particular sector then information was easier to obtain. Where trade-based research and development centres were present, data gathering was simpler.

5.42 This concern about the release of chemicals from diffuse products led to the Falkenberg Conference, held in April 2001 in Sweden under the Swedish Presidency of the EU.[34] The conference sought to investigate products and their constituents as sources of chemical pollution and to look for ways in which negative impacts could be reduced. Concerns were identified about diffuse sources of chemicals and the importance of the disposal phase of a product's life cycle. It was noted that there were also concerns about the relationship between product release and exposure in the target organism, as well as the identification of sensitive target organisms. It was concluded that the most feasible way forward was a management approach based on hazardous properties of groups of chemicals, as individual product assessments seem highly impractical because of the sheer number of products and the resources required to test each one for substances of concern.

5.43 Product registers, such as those in Sweden (box 3A), provide valuable information about the manufacture and import of chemical products, but do not yet go as far as holding information about the use of chemical products in finished articles. The sheer number and volume of finished products on the market makes such a task daunting, with issues around conformity of production and differences between individual manufacturers of the same product.

5.44 Our conclusion from the evidence above is that methodologies for testing the chemical content of finished products remain at an early stage, and that the practicalities and cost involved in any comprehensive programme of finished product testing would outweigh any policy benefits. Nevertheless, as chapter 3 indicates, we wish to see much greater effort in future paid to the enforcement of the new and existing chemicals legislation. In this context, a programme of random tests on the content of chemical products and preparations, both as part of import checks and in the context of concerted campaigns to monitor the presence and diffusion of individual substances of concern, would form an important element. These tests would provide one means of checking that the system recommended in chapter 4 was operating properly, and would serve to establish the presence of unlisted substances, notably in imported products. **We recommend that a programme of random tests on the composition of chemical products, including imported products, be carried out by the relevant authorities as part of their enforcement strategies, and that the results be made public.**

TOWARDS SUSTAINABLE CHEMISTRY

GREEN CHEMISTRY

5.45 'Green chemistry' has been defined as 'the design, manufacture, and use of environmentally benign chemical products and processes that prevent pollution and reduce environmental and human health risks'.[35] It describes a systematic approach to increasing resource productivity, and reducing costs, risks, wastes and emissions by rethinking the chemistry used rather than simply abating emissions. Green chemistry initiatives have addressed three areas in particular:[36]

- the use of alternative synthesis pathways;

- the use of alternative reaction conditions; and

- the design of safer chemicals that are, for example, less toxic than current alternatives, or inherently safer with regard to accident potential.

5.46 To date, green chemistry initiatives have largely focused on developing cleaner processes, particularly through the use of novel catalysts to avoid the use of very toxic chemicals and to reduce hazardous waste production. There has also been attention to using feedstocks from renewable sources, for example, the use of raw materials from plants. As well as their direct application to industry, green chemistry programmes have also been aimed at producing educational material that promotes the concept that chemical process design and engineering should include environmental impact as a primary consideration alongside efficiency and economy. Work in schools and universities to introduce students to the concepts of green chemistry is one way in which future chemists can be encouraged to consider environmental concerns during product development.

5.47 In order to foster green chemistry techniques, several award programmes aimed at encouraging the development of more sustainable chemical processes and products have been established.

Green chemistry awards

5.48 National green chemistry award programmes operate in the US, UK, Germany, Italy, Japan and Australia.

5.49 The most ambitious is the US Presidential Green Chemistry Challenge Awards Programme,[37] which began in 1995. The programme is administered by the US Environmental Protection Agency's Office of Pollution Prevention and Toxics in collaboration with partners from industry, government, academia and other organisations. Each year, nominations are sought in five categories: academic, small business, alternative synthetic pathways, alternative reaction conditions and design of safer chemicals.

5.50   In the UK, there are two annual green chemistry awards to companies for technology, products or services, at least one being to a small or medium-sized enterprise (SME). These awards are sponsored by the CRYSTAL Faraday Partnership in Green Chemical Technology[38] and administered by the Green Chemistry Network.[39]

5.51   The European Environment Agency has investigated the potential development of a European green and sustainable chemistry award.[40] The programme was envisaged to operate along the lines of the US system, covering the three discrete areas of green chemistry identified in 5.45, and providing for separate awards to business, SMEs, academics and educational establishments.

5.52   The Organisation for Economic Co-operation and Development (OECD) has produced a guidance document for Member Countries on establishing research and development programmes in sustainable chemistry.[41] Although OECD does not fund research, it encourages its Members to establish programmes to support green chemistry research. The guidance suggested that there are dual roles for the development process: to provide funding for green chemistry research and development; and for governments to identify incentives and disincentives, and to modify national policies accordingly.

5.53   OECD identified a number of gaps in the way green chemistry is being developed and adopted. These included: the need for better tools to evaluate the long-term benefits of green chemistry technologies; the right regulatory environment to facilitate the uptake of green chemical processes; a balance between intellectual property rights and the wider adoption of new technologies; and for industry leaders to be persuaded of the importance of research and development in green chemistry for the industry overall.

5.54   While the concept of green chemistry can play a valuable role in helping to achieve the policy goal of progressive substitution, we are disappointed that to date most of the effort in the UK has been concerned with novel synthesis routes for existing products rather than its application to new synthesis routes for green products. **We recommend that the government together with the chemical industry continue to promote programmes for the development and promotion of green chemistry but with a new emphasis on its application to product design and use. We commend the establishment of annual green chemistry awards, but again there has been an undue emphasis on processes rather than products. We recommend that specific awards be developed for the application of green chemistry to products and services.**

CHEMICAL MANAGEMENT SERVICES

5.55   Redefinition of a firm as a service provider rather than as a product manufacturer, would mean that function not form, is the source of added value.[42] This 'service approach' relies on a shift from maximisation of the volume of a product sold to a partnership in which material savings are shared between supplier and consumer. In this way, firms can decouple profit from volume sales.

5.56 Within the chemical industry the approach has been adopted as 'chemical management services', which has had particular applications in the vehicle production and electronics sectors. The approach has been most successful where chemical substances are used indirectly (rather than being incorporated into a final product), since in this case, the real value of the chemical is in performing some industrial function (such as cleaning or degreasing). In this way, the chemical management services approach is only applicable to substances and preparations and not to articles. It has been noted[43] that considerable costs are associated with the use of chemicals, from health and safety legislation compliance costs through to public relations and liability costs (particularly heavy in the US (3.146)) and that at least some of these could be overcome by out-sourcing or replacing some of the work done using chemicals.

5.57 Green Alliance launched a UK programme on 'Service Innovation for Sustainability' in 2002,[44] noting that 'Chemical Management Services (CMS) appears to be the most successful service innovation for sustainability and can now be found in 50-80 per cent of the US auto industry [box 5E], 35 per cent of the US electronics industry and 10 per cent of the US aerospace industry'. Green Alliance attributes the adoption of Chemical Management Services to increasing complexity and concern about the environmental and human health effects of chemicals.

BOX 5E	CHEMICAL MANAGEMENT SERVICES: DUPONT CANADA'S AUTOMOTIVE FINISHING SERVICE[45]

In 1996 DuPont Canada established a partnership with Ford Motor Company's Ontario Plant, which produced 280,000 vehicles in 2000. Problems had been identified in the vehicle painting process: it was estimated that 30% of the paint was lost to air emissions and waste water. The two companies entered into a service programme whereby DuPont was paid on the basis of the number of vehicles painted at a guaranteed cost per unit.

Providing the service, rather than selling the paint, encouraged DuPont not only to reduce the cost of producing the paint, but also to improve the efficiency of its use. Ford estimates that losses of volatile organic compounds have been reduced by some 50%, with accompanying cost savings of 35-40%.

5.58 The adoption of the chemical management services model in the US has been most noticeable within the two industries mentioned – electronics and cars – largely as the result of service approaches for lubricants and degreasing solvents. The approach may not be suited to all types of chemicals, and given the development work in the US in the solvent and lubricant fields, these seem most likely to succeed elsewhere.

5.59 The lack of adoption of chemical management services in Europe is explained by Green Alliance as being due to liability regimes, and perhaps regulation, being less onerous here than in the US. There have been no real equivalents of the Tellus Institute and the Chemical Strategies Partnership (two principal organisations in the field in the US) to act as facilitators. And many of the US chemical suppliers and customers who have pioneered the initiatives either do not have significant European subsidiaries or, if they do, give them a great deal of autonomy so that experience is not easily transferred. Green Alliance also suggests that the EU White Paper on chemicals could provide an opportunity for the wider adoption of chemical management services approaches in Europe.

5.60 However, the Austrian Environment Ministry is already planning to promote chemical management services at a European level.[46] In a study involving 15 chemical firms, it was estimated that some 4,000 companies in Austria use 153,000 tonnes of chemicals per year. The study claimed that with chemicals leasing, this amount could be cut by 53,000 tonnes.

5.61 One route to achieving wider adoption of chemical management services would be the dissemination of best practice and results from pilot trials. However, there may be some opposition to this, as it is likely to involve some sharing of confidential information.

5.62 We feel that the greater use of chemical management services could play a useful role in reducing the volume of chemicals employed without reducing their utility, but the evidence suggests that such services are likely to most effective only in certain sectors and for certain types of chemicals. We recognise that the greater take-up in the United Kingdom appears to have been hampered by lack of dissemination of best practice. **We recommend that one function of the chemicals safety co-ordination unit proposed in chapter 4 (4.111) should be to promote the adoption of chemicals management services in appropriate sectors.**

DRIVING CHANGE

5.63 A range of instruments may need to be brought together to form a cohesive and effective package of measures driving towards the substitution of hazardous for less hazardous substances (5.17). The following paragraphs describe instruments most suitable for inclusion in such a package.

ECONOMIC INSTRUMENTS

5.64 There is a strong case for the further implementation of economic instruments to promote sustainable development in the UK. The UK Round Table on Sustainable Development[47] identified that economic instruments are rarely effective alone, and that a complementary package of measures is needed, including regulation, voluntary agreements and public and consumer information, alongside economic measures.

5.65 The European Commission Green Paper on Integrated Product Policy identified that product policy should exert its influence through the market using economic instruments:[48]

> 'Promotion (of environmental quality of goods and services) means using market forces ... Economic instruments probably most effective are those, like taxes and subsidies, that ... internalise external costs ... [including] differentiated taxation ...'

In the case of chemical products, economic instruments would be used to incentivise the development and use of less hazardous alternatives, ultimately resulting in the removal of hazardous substances of concern from the market.

A pesticides tax

5.66   In 2000, research was carried out to investigate the possible use of a tax or a charge scheme as a contribution to pesticide reduction.[49] The project sought to determine the most appropriate basis for applying a tax or charge to pesticides and specifically examined the application of non-banded and banded charges on an *ad valorem* basis, on a per kilogram basis, and a per dose basis. It concluded that a differential tax between pesticides was the most appropriate instrument, with higher rates of tax for more hazardous products. This work showed that products could be taxed on the basis of harm caused. It was determined that, because of difficulties in establishing dose, the instrument should be applied per kilogram of the active substance, and that the banding system should be dynamic to allow categorisation of new products and to reflect the process of scientific review. It was recommended that revenue from the instrument be used to support information dissemination, advice and training. In order to avoid the introduction of the tax, in April 2001 industry and other stakeholders entered into a voluntary agreement on measures to reduce the environmental damage caused by pesticides.

A chemicals charge

5.67   In 2001, as a result of the continuing need to examine the role that alternative approaches to direct regulation could play in managing chemical risks, Defra commissioned research to consider the scope for using economic instruments to manage the risks associated with a wide range of persistent pollutants. The work was carried out in two phases. In the first phase, the potential for the use of economic instruments in controlling 30 chemicals identified according to the Chemicals Stakeholder Forum's persistence, bioaccumulation and toxicity criteria was investigated.[50] The economic instruments considered included emissions or products charges, tradable permit schemes, performance bonds, and deposit-refund schemes. The conclusions from this first phase were that economic instruments could offer important advantages as complementary measures to regulation, particularly as incentive mechanisms to encourage longer-term improvements in environmental performance.

5.68   The second phase of the study[51] examined a set of three case studies on substances of particular concern (nonylphenols and their ethoxylates, three chlorinated solvents and emissions of a series of metals to the marine environment). The research considered that the particular characteristics of each substance (such as the complexity of the whole life cycle and the diffuse nature of the pollution) would influence which instrument was likely to be the most effective in each case. The report concluded that there was greater scope for the use of economic instruments than had been previously thought. However, further work was needed on the risk characterisation of potential substitutes for the substances in question, along with more detailed consideration of the processing and use phases of the life cycle.

5.69   One of the objectives of the chemicals assessment and management programme proposed in chapter 4 is the allocation of selected substances to a category of concern. The appropriate category is determined by the hazardous properties of the substance and its intended uses. We propose that a system of charges be introduced based upon this categorisation of substances. Such an instrument would not only provide a driver for substitution of those substances in the higher categories of concern (box 5F), but also stimulate innovation in the development of less hazardous substances. The charge would be placed solely on products and would therefore be fully compatible with WTO requirements (discussed further in 5.104-5.115).

BOX 5F	NORWEGIAN SOLVENTS TAX[52]

Norway introduced a tax on the sale of the chlorinated solvents trichloroethylene (used mainly in metal cleaning) and perchloroethylene (mainly used in dry cleaning) in 2000. The Norwegian national statistical office has reported subsequent large falls in consumption of these two substances.

Compared with average consumption in the three years 1997-99, trichloroethylene sales fell 83% in 2000 to 81 tonnes. Perchloroethylene sales fell 89% to 26 tonnes. The reduction in sales of perchloroethylene has been driven by efforts to cut leakage and boost recycling (that is, through chemical management approaches) as well as through substitution.

Perchloroethylene (also known as tetrachloroethylene) is a category 3 carcinogen, while trichloroethylene's classification is being upgraded from a category 3 carcinogen to category 2. Reduction in use has been so pronounced that national consumption of all chemicals classified as carcinogenic, mutagenic or reprotoxic fell by 60% between 1999 and 2001.

5.70   **We recommend that the government introduce a charging scheme to stimulate greater substitution. Categories of concern from our proposed testing regime for chemicals should be used to differentiate the levels of the charge.**

LIABILITY

5.71   As we noted in chapter 3, some commentators consider that the tough civil liability system in the US may be a key driver for industry concerned with the production of chemicals and the design of products, and there is some evidence to support this view. Compensation litigation is undoubtedly on the increase in the UK, but key elements of the US system (such as punitive damage awards) are not replicated here, and we do not think it is desirable to recommend or rely upon a civil liability system as the primary tool for encouraging change. It does not follow that complex regulatory systems are always the sole alternative measure.

5.72   On one aspect of civil liability, though, we feel a change in the current law would act as an incentive for the goals we seek. The EC Product Liability Directive and the UK Consumer Protection Act 1987 (3.180) focus liability on the manufacturer or the importer of the product, whereas in the US, liability tends to rest both on the manufacturer and the retailer. **We recommend that wholesalers and retailers, as well as the manufacturer, should be jointly and severally liable under the Consumer Protection Act.** This would help encourage a two-way flow of information down the chain of supply concerning the content and use of products (5.33), and would reinforce the labelling and information recommendations we make in 5.85-5.94. Apportionment of responsibility between manufacturers, wholesalers and retailers would be determined by their own contractual arrangements; the prospect of potential civil liability to consumers would undoubtedly strengthen the information obligations negotiated under those contracts. This recommendation is therefore not only in the interests of consumers, but should not be unwelcome to wholesalers and retailers, in that it will give them greater leverage to obtain fuller information from manufacturers about the extent and nature of chemicals in products supplied to them. In its evidence, the British Retail Consortium suggested that retailers do not have sufficient expertise to police product safety requirements and so decisions on the use of chemicals in products rest higher up the supply chain.[53] However, there are examples of cases where retailers have initiated controls on products. Evidence from Marks and Spencer suggested that they had identified a list of chemicals of concern that they were now seeking to remove from their products.[54] Other retailers (such as Boots and B&Q) are acting in similar ways.

5.73 We accept that, in the light of the judgement of the European Court of Justice in Commission v. France concerning the harmonising effects of the Product Liability Directive,[55] governments may not have the power to introduce changes unilaterally to national legislation. If this is indeed the case, then **we recommend that the government promote the case for change to the Product Liability Directive in Europe.**

5.74 Provisions under the European Community Product Liability Directive are intended to protect human health but, as the Royal Commission on Environmental Pollution, we have an equal if not greater concern to ensure that the environment is properly protected. Equally, we are concerned that the current discussions at European Community level on civil liability for environmental damage have largely been focused on liability for emissions from manufacturing processes or waste disposal, rather than environmental damage caused by the use of products. **We recommend that the government ensure that the issue of liability for environmental damage from the use of products is given proper weight in current discussions on liability regimes at European Community level.**

EXTENDED PRODUCER RESPONSIBILITY

5.75 Previous research[56] has identified the tendency for environmental regulation to shift towards a life cycle basis. Similar trends can be seen in the move towards extending producer responsibility to cover more of the production, use and waste management of a range of industrial products. This is particularly the case for the 'take-back' legislation identified in chapter 3 and earlier in this chapter for waste electrical and electronic equipment and end of life vehicles (3.172-3.176 and 5.25). While the environmental impacts of reverse logistics (collecting and returning the used products) may be justified in these cases, it may not be so for all products. In addition to providing for take-back, extended producer responsibility seeks to influence the design phase of products.

5.76 Some of the information-based initiatives discussed above will allow for improved assessment of environmental impacts at the design stage. The use of extended producer responsibility as a means of promoting substitution will only be successful if manufacturers are required to pay the costs and implement the legislation themselves. As currently implemented, the EU take-back directives do not fully achieve the objectives of extended producer responsibility, as post-consumer materials are not necessarily returned to their actual manufacturers.

5.77 OECD[57] noted that an Integrated Product Policy should include the concept of shared responsibility throughout the production and use chain, and include stakeholder involvement during the process to develop the assessment. OECD also suggested that governments could document and disseminate best practice guidelines but cautioned that before companies embarked on an Integrated Product Policy they would need to be assured that their approach would be acceptable to governments, that it would need to be applied consistently across the industry, and that it would have to be compatible with current or planned legislation.

5.78 We commend the concept of using producer take-back legislation as a way to promote efficient use of resources and encourage innovation in product design in order to reduce reliance on hazardous substances. However, it is important that the principle of take-back is implemented in ways that ensure that liability for post-consumer waste products returns to the original manufacturer or supplier.

5.79 **We recommend that the government investigate further the effect of take-back legislation on product design.**

VOLUNTARY INITIATIVES

5.80 There are some cases where voluntary agreements have been implemented successfully to reduce emissions of chemicals (for example, in Environment Canada's ARET (Accelerated Reduction/Elimination of Toxics) programme, and by the UK Chemicals Stakeholder Forum (5.83)). Voluntary initiatives may be helpful in being seen to develop a more pro-active approach and better dialogue with stakeholders. It has also been argued that voluntary initiatives may also be less costly than formal regulatory measures, as there is more flexibility in determining how to meet them.

5.81 OECD notes, however, that voluntary initiatives tend to work best as part of a package of other measures (including regulation), rather than in their place, and that such initiatives tend to be easier for larger manufacturers to adopt than for SMEs.[58] It can also be difficult to measure the success of voluntary initiatives.

5.82 Given the likely length of time taken to establish formal EU measures, voluntary measures in advance of any legislative action may form an important part of the chemicals management process. Under EU rules, there is a limited scope for unilateral national action, and voluntary measures may, therefore, represent a more realistic option for encompassing individual national requirements for stricter controls on undesirable substances. Voluntary initiatives may still need to be reported to the European Commission under the requirements of the Technical Standards Directive.[59]

5.83 The Chemicals Stakeholder Forum has been successful in recommending that government negotiate a voluntary reduction with industry in the use of nonylphenols, octylphenols and their ethoxylates.[60] These chemicals, used in a wide range of products and processes including industrial cleaning, paints, paper, inks, and textiles, met the Forum's criteria for persistence, bioaccumulation and toxicity, and are suspected endocrine disrupters. A risk management strategy for these substances has been agreed under existing legislation at European Community Member State level, but the Forum felt that this would take too long to implement.

5.84 **We commend the initiative of the Chemicals Stakeholder Forum in promoting voluntary reduction of certain chemicals, but emphasise that in the longer term such a voluntary approach needs to be seen in the context of a more systematic promotion of regulatory and other instruments to encourage substitution.**

INFORMATION AND LABELLING AS A DRIVER OF CHANGE

5.85 In addition to improving the flow of information within the chemical industry supply chain, the provision of information to end-users can act as a driver towards hazardous product substitution. Recognising this, the Copenhagen Chemicals Charter (3.201-3.202) referred to the need for a full 'right to know', and recommended that, in order to deliver this, information needed to be more effectively conveyed to consumers.

5.86 One way in which information about releases of chemicals into the environment has been conveyed to consumers and other end users is through the operation of emissions inventories or Pollutant Release and Transfer Registers. These are operated by several national agencies, including in the US and in the UK. The Environment Agency's Pollution Inventory has been in operation in the UK for a number of years,[61] and the Scottish Environment Protection Agency is establishing a separate inventory for Scotland. The European Commission has also issued a Decision to establish a Europe-wide emissions inventory.[62] These inventories deal solely with process emissions and have also been used to rank production sites according to releases and breaches of permit conditions.

5.87 Another way in which improved information can be conveyed to consumers is through the use of eco-labels. The Nordic Council of Ministers has introduced a voluntary eco-labelling scheme (the Nordic Swan) in the Nordic Countries.[63] Within the scheme, individual product groups have been identified and criteria for granting the label agreed. Assessments are based on impacts over the whole product life cycle and include restrictions on the use of certain chemical products in specific product types (for example, on the use of formaldehyde in fibreboard). Over 1,000 products in more than 40 product groups now carry the label.

5.88 Wider application of eco-labelling on the basis of chemical content criteria is likely to be difficult. Other eco-labels exist (notably the EU Daisy, which covers 19 product groups at present[64]) and producers in the global chemicals market would support standardisation in this area. Developing eco-labelling criteria for a wide range of products on the basis of their chemical content would be a lengthy process. Also, adoption of the schemes is currently only voluntary and they appear to form a small part of consumers' decision-making processes when purchasing.[65]

5.89 Currently, under the Classification (Hazard Information and Packaging) (CHIP) Regulations (3.8), chemical products are labelled to indicate hazards, including those arising from physico-chemical properties of the material, and potential effects on human health and, to some extent, the environment. Standard risk and safety phrases accompany any hazard markings. Information conveyed through these regulations can be complex and require some detailed interpretation (5.29). As currently implemented, the regulations do not require the supply of Safety Data Sheets to private consumers for hazardous substances not intended to be used in the course of work. The regulations do not, therefore, currently represent an effective means of conveying information to consumers.

5.90 Labelling of all chemical products contained within finished articles is likely to be cumbersome and unworkable given the enormous number of finished articles (and variants within any one product) on the market. In evidence to the Royal Commission, Marks and Spencer suggested that within a decade, intelligent bar-code scanning units could be in widespread consumer use in retail outlets.[66] This would provide a mechanism to convey useful information about products including safety information, though it would not, in itself, address the lack of information on constituent substances in finished articles and possible contaminants within those chemical products.

5.91 Some labelling of products could no doubt be improved, but we are not convinced that consumer labelling *per se* is truly a practical or effective method of encouraging substitution or meaningful consumer choice. Nevertheless, we feel that to date insufficient research has been conducted as to the effectiveness of current practice in conveying information about the chemical content of products to consumers, and how this might be improved. Consumers (particularly, say, those with allergies to certain substances) feel entitled to be able to find out whether products contain particular chemicals and these are pressures that are likely to grow. But present arrangements do not make it easy to obtain such information, even for the retailer.

5.92 We have made recommendations concerning improved information requirements about product use (5.33-5.36), which will, taken together with the other initiatives we recommend, encourage a greater flow of information between manufacturers and retailers, and in the longer term help drive substitution towards chemicals of lower concern. One approach to improve the provision of information to consumers would, therefore, be through the use of the marketed substance list (4.14). Regulators, local authorities, emergency response organisations, non-governmental organisations, and the general public could use the list to access information. At present, under the Swedish system (box 3A), general practitioners and other medical advisors are able to request information from the products register on a case-by-case basis when treating patients. Similar arrangements could operate through the list of marketed chemicals we propose here. In common with other product lists and registers, the recommended list would not contain details of the chemical composition of finished articles, but it could be used to provide information about all substances, with more detailed information available from evaluations of substances of concern.

5.93 **We recommend that the government sponsor research with consumers to determine the most effective means of information transfer and the level of detail required on the hazardous substance content of finished articles.**

5.94 **We recommend that the proposed chemicals safety co-ordination unit (4.111) put in place a means of providing information in response to queries from members of the public.**

INTERNATIONAL HARMONISATION

5.95 The chemicals industry and their client industries – the reformulators and users of chemical products – operate within a global network (1.12). Many of the key players are multi-nationals. Chemicals are shipped around the world in enormous quantities, both as chemicals and as components of products. This gives rise to a need for internationally-harmonised controls, especially where chemicals cross borders intentionally in trade or unintentionally as trans-boundary pollutants. Multilateral environmental agreements such as the Rotterdam and Stockholm Conventions (3.75-3.76) are the starting-point for such controls, but it was reinforced at the 2002 World Summit on Sustainable Development (5.97-5.99) that more is needed.

5.96   The international dimension of the trade also gives rise to opportunities. Many countries have developed regulatory regimes for chemicals that require registration and the provision of environmental safety information. We have already referred (4.49) to the need for better availability and transfer of this information as a means of avoiding testing, especially animal testing. This will only work if the information available in one country meets the standards required by statute in another country. Harmonisation of information requirements is, therefore, a necessary prerequisite for making best use of this opportunity.

CONCLUSIONS OF THE WORLD SUMMIT

5.97   The 2002 World Summit on Sustainable Development included recommendations on chemicals in its final action plan. The main relevant recommendation was to:

> 'renew the commitment, as advanced in Agenda 21, 'to sound management of chemicals throughout their life cycle and of hazardous wastes for sustainable development and for the protection of human health and the environment, *inter alia*, aiming to achieve by 2020 that chemicals are used and produced in ways that lead to the minimization of significant adverse effects on human health and the environment, using transparent science-based risk assessment procedures and science-based risk management procedures, taking into account the precautionary approach, as set out in principle 15 of the Rio Declaration on Environment and Development, and support developing countries in strengthening their capacity for the sound management of chemicals and hazardous wastes by providing technical and financial assistance.'[67]

5.98   Under this section of the action plan, there were then a series of follow-up actions, which included actions at all levels to:

- encourage partnerships to promote activities aimed at enhancing environmentally sound management of chemicals and hazardous wastes, implementing multilateral environmental agreements, raising awareness of issues relating to chemicals and hazardous waste, and encouraging the collection and use of additional scientific data;

- encourage development of coherent and integrated information on chemicals, such as through national pollutant release and transfer registers; and

- promote reduction of the risks posed by heavy metals that are harmful to human health and the environment, including through a review of relevant studies, such as the UNEP global assessment of mercury and its compounds.

5.99   These conclusions flow from the Bahia Declaration on Chemicals Safety (3.79), which called for better global co-operation on chemicals safety, and the increased flow of information about the safe use of chemicals. This will require harmonisation of information provision across the global industry. The same basic information about chemicals should be available for chemicals wherever they are manufactured.

5.100 **We recommend that the government maintain pressure on the international community to achieve the goals of the Bahia Declaration leading to full arrangements for the exchange of information on hazardous chemicals regardless of their country of origin.**

5.101 This implies greater standardisation of testing and sharing of information to generate the standard data set with minimum extra costs and with minimum extra use of animals. Given the difficulty of getting such a standard data set even in Europe, this will be a long-term task, but OECD has already made progress and perhaps it should continue to be the lead agency, though there would need to be close co-ordination with UNEP's information function.

5.102 **We recommend that the government continue to support and encourage greater international standardisation of testing and enhanced sharing of information in order to generate the standard data set required above with minimal additional costs and animal test requirements. The government should also consider, together with other like-minded governments, whether to press for this work (and associated resources) to move from OECD to a broader forum, perhaps UNEP.**

5.103 We acknowledge that countries are likely to continue to have different priorities and preferences in relation to the stringency of control standards. This should not be a problem in relation to GATT/WTO agreements, provided controls are non-discriminatory, and are related both to the standardised information set and the science-based procedures that feature strongly in the World Summit conclusions. Doubtless interpretation of the precautionary principle will continue to cause problems, but that is probably inevitable – it is encouraging to see a strong reference to Principle 15 of the 1992 Rio Declaration (which encapsulates the precautionary principle) in both the Stockholm Convention and the World Summit recommendation. Of more concern is the tendency for international negotiations to lead to a low level of control because of the need for agreement across a wide range of issues by a wide range of cultures. This can be avoided if reasonable provision is made to secure assistance in the form of capacity-building for countries that are economically less well-placed to accept potentially costly regulatory provisions.

TRADE ISSUES

5.104 We noted in chapter 3 that trade measures with respect to imported products are legitimate, so long as imports are treated in the same way as domestic products. Production and use legislation rarely bites on manufacture alone. 'Placing on the market' includes importing and any prohibition is likely to be phrased in these terms, so, for example, PCBs cannot be sold in the UK regardless of origin. Prohibition of a particular use, for example, the use of chlorinated hydrocarbons as a cutting oil, would apply regardless of the origin of the product.

5.105 A chemical imported as a chemical product, or as a component of a formulation or preparation is, therefore, likely to be subject to the same regulatory regime as one manufactured domestically. A significant enforcement option, that of checking potential manufacturers, would be lost, but border controls might apply instead.

5.106 When the chemical is a component of a product, it is the product itself, rather than the chemical, which would be subject to regulation. Controls applied to imported products would be subject to scrutiny under WTO rules. Where there is a clear and internationally recognised risk from the product this would not normally cause a problem. But such situations are relatively rare, perhaps because it is not too difficult to legislate against them. Difficulties are more likely to arise where there is a disagreement about whether or not the presence of a particular constituent chemical, present in an imported product but not in one made domestically, is of sufficient concern to make the two products materially different and, therefore, subject to discrimination.

5.107 In order to begin to address such concerns, following the publication of the EU Chemicals White Paper, a number of working groups were set up by the European Commission to examine particular issues. One of these working groups was on substances in products. There is continuing debate as to the inclusion of products under the REACH system and the meaning of release of the substance during normal use. The Working Group agreed on the following definition of an article:

> 'An article is a manmade object which during manufacturing has been given a special shape, surface or form which determine its function to a greater degree than does its chemical composition.'[68]

5.108 WWF has suggested that the exemption of imported articles from controls will be a trade barrier against EU-produced products and that the continued use of restricted chemicals in imported products will discourage innovation.[69] WWF also feels that REACH should address substances whether present in articles, preparations or otherwise, and agrees that some form of prioritisation (perhaps based on use and release patterns) would be helpful.

5.109 The European chemical industry association (CEFIC) has proposed that only substances marketed as substances or as constituents of preparations should be subject to REACH.[70] CEFIC argues that inclusion of substances in articles would require the disclosure of much commercially-sensitive information, causing the REACH system to collapse due to the volume of articles to be assessed, and represent a barrier to trade unless applied equally to imported and domestically-produced articles. However, they also recognise that exclusion of substances in articles would ignore those substances released deliberately from articles during the course of normal use. CEFIC further argues that the REACH process will already cover many of the substances included in articles since they are marketed in the EU as substances or preparations prior to being included in articles. The need is to cover those situations where all or part of the manufacturing process has taken place outside of the EU using unregistered substances.

5.110 The European Commission Working Group on Substances in Products also felt that substances and preparations in articles were covered by REACH, and that the real need was to address articles where the whole manufacturing process has been carried out outside the European Community and which may contain untested and unregistered substances. It proposed a general obligation on importers and manufacturers of articles containing unregistered dangerous substances released during normal use to register such articles. The Working Group identified the need for effective enforcement and sanctions in order to provide sufficient disincentive for importers, but identified the lack of resources in Member States in this area as an issue.

5.111 Understanding of the application of GATT to market-based policies has come from experience with the WTO dispute resolution panel. Although pre-dating the finalisation of the Uruguay round of trade negotiations, Resources for the Future[71] suggested that the superfund tax dispute resolution is important in this respect. To raise revenue for clean-up operations, the Superfund Act[72] imposed a tax on certain chemical products used in production processes. Not only were border adjustments allowed on these intermediate products themselves, but a tax was also imposed on imported final products according to the content of feedstock chemicals used in production, assessed by weight. The European Commission objected, but the WTO ruled that the border tax adjustment could stand.[73] Important to its findings were that:

i.   the tax was designed to raise revenue, not create incentives, and was imposed on like products;

ii. the polluter pays principle is irrelevant anyway for the GATT; and

iii. the inputs were taxed based on use, not value, and constituted part of the final product[74]

5.112 Thus, polluting materials that are physically incorporated into the final products can be made subject to the importing country's taxes as long as such taxes are imposed equitably on both imported goods and 'like' domestic goods. The pollution rationale might well matter in the case of a regulatory standard.

5.113 We agree with the findings of the European Commission Working Group (5.110) and **recommend that the government press for a provision that all foreign manufacturers and importers who wish to import into the EU should be obliged to register the substances and preparations containing dangerous chemicals, and list what products these have been incorporated into, in precisely the same way as European manufacturers will be required to do.**

5.114 We are concerned by the finding of the Working Group about lack of resources and **recommend that the government increase the resources available to customs authorities or agencies responsible for chemicals regulation, to identify and, where appropriate, restrict the import of products containing unregistered chemical substances.**

5.115 The recent Canada-France asbestos dispute did not relate to an explicit French import ban and the WTO Appellate Body's interpretation of the relevant GATT rules was in favour of the French restriction. (3.156). **We recommend that in appropriate cases both the UK and the EU make use of the powers already available under WTO rules to restrict the marketing or use of dangerous substances or products containing them even at the risk of challenges by overseas suppliers that such measures are indirectly discriminatory.**

REGULATION AND INNOVATION

5.116 In chapter 1 we noted the importance of the chemicals industry to the UK economy (1.9). We also noted the poor reputation of the chemicals industry (1.1-1.4). Even without the changes being proposed to the regulatory system at EC level, the chemicals industry is changing as a result of market forces. The European Commission's Chemicals White Paper and Defra's response to it refer to the need to maintain the competitiveness of the chemicals industry through the proposed changes to the regulatory regime.

THE EFFECT OF REGULATION

5.117 We have heard in evidence that EU regulatory pressure has caused a disproportionate reduction in innovation in the European chemicals industry, compared to that under other regimes (notably the US). It was further suggested to us that this has manifested itself in new chemical development being shifted to other parts of OECD or exported from OECD altogether.[75] Our comparison of regulatory regimes (3.138-3.152) pointed out the importance of both factors determining the rate of innovation and the effectiveness of the regimes in adequately protecting the environment and human health.

5.118 There are conflicting views on how and in what ways regulation can affect the innovation process. Regulation might reduce innovation and competitiveness, but it is also possible that it may actually stimulate them, especially when regulations are of an aspirational or technology-forcing nature.

5.119 In order to examine these issues, we appointed an independent consultant to report on the impact of product notification regulations on innovation in the chemical industry. The full report is available on the Royal Commission's website.[76]

5.120 The report drew an important distinction between the *rate* and *direction* of innovation. The number of innovations quantifies the rate, while the direction is related to the quality of innovations produced. Innovation is not, therefore, a homogeneous concept and it may be that while the rate is high, the direction is socially undesirable. There are several widely used indicators of the rate of innovation (for instance patent/substance notification counts) but no standardised measures of its quality or direction. The report drew attention to deficiencies in several of the major studies carried out in this area over the past few years.

5.121 In chapter 3 we showed that the product notification regulations under different regimes had substantial differences in the structure of their testing requirements, cost of notification, level of exemption, and government intervention. There are fundamental differences between the pre-manufacture notification systems in the US and Japan and the pre-market system in use in the EU, and data indicate that the cost of compliance is higher in the EU.

5.122 The number of chemicals notified in the US and EU since the introduction of the 7th Amendment to the Classification Packaging and Labelling Directive (introducing harmonised risk assessment for new substances) are shown in figure 5-II. The data show that there has been a degree of convergence during the 1990s. However, there are complicating factors that make interpretation of these data difficult. A particular new chemical can be notified both in the EU and in the US either by domestic or foreign firms. Also, different exemption criteria (such as the notification of polymers) used by the different regimes cause further complications. Thus, caution is needed in using notification data as a proxy for innovation counts.

Figure 5-II
New substance notifications in the EU and US since 1994[77]

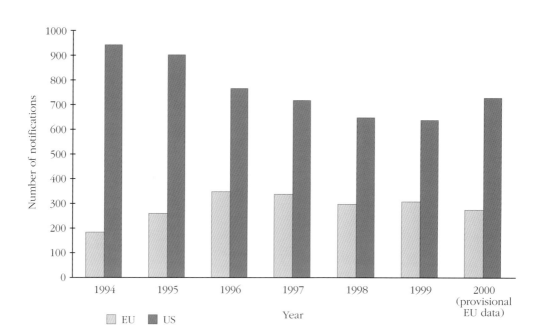

5.123 The main conclusions of our consultant's report were:

i. There is no consensus about whether regulation inhibits or stimulates innovation in industry. It is likely that in most cases regulation both inhibits and stimulates innovation, playing a modulating role. For instance, in many countries the most successful firms and industries are also those that face the highest levels of regulation – pharmaceuticals in the UK, chemicals in Germany, pulp and paper in Sweden, and aerospace and finance in the US. Despite a long tradition of research on the question of how regulation influences innovation in different industries and in different countries, it is far from clear where the balance between inhibition and stimulation falls.

ii. Empirical studies have so far failed to resolve this issue. One problem is lack of agreement about how innovation and regulation – as variables – should be measured, coupled with an absence of appropriate and comparable databases which can be used to measure such variables.

iii. Major methodological problems have been identified in many of the studies reviewed. At present they are of limited value to policy-makers. Some studies draw policy conclusions by looking only at the private costs of regulation and not at the social and environmental benefits. One of the main goals of environmental and social regulation is to screen out new technologies with potentially adverse effects. The extent to which one regulatory system does this more effectively than another is rarely considered.

iv. Even if it were possible to carry out accurate assessments of the overall costs and benefits of different regulatory regimes, their relative rankings would remain largely subjective and involve political judgements that cannot be definitively answered by policy research. Given the different public attitudes towards the regulation of technological risk in the US and Europe, care must be taken when extrapolating from one context to another.

v. It is important to highlight the uncertain, time-lagged costs associated with unexpected problems created by lax regulatory regimes. These costs may not be manifest until far into the future and are impossible to incorporate in cost-benefit analysis today. Slightly greater care in the present may avoid major social and environmental costs in the future.

5.124 Despite these theoretical and methodological difficulties, the available evidence supports two conclusions:

- the introduction of new regulation causes a temporary shock to innovative activity in firms that has a negative effect on the overall rate of innovation. How serious this shock is and how long it persists varies from case to case; and

- there has been a convergence in the rates of notification of new chemicals between the US and Europe over the past decade. There may be several reasons for this, one of which is likely to be that the introduction of the European Community New Substances Directive caused many chemicals that were then still under development to be registered as existing substances, in order to avoid the Directive's registration procedures, thereby reducing EU notifications in subsequent years.

5.125 The convergence in rates of notifications in the EU and US in the 1990s undermines the claim that the European chemicals industry is less innovative than its US counterpart. On several measures, European dominance in the chemicals industry has increased in the past decade. Such vitality would have been unlikely without high levels of innovation.

5.126 The impact of health, safety and environmental regulation needs to be considered within a wider context than short-term changes in the rate of innovation alone. The innovation process for new chemicals is influenced by many factors and it is difficult to isolate the influence of health, safety and environmental regulation alone. Many other private and public policies influence the rate of innovation, such as those related to science, research and development, intellectual property rights and pricing. As these differ between Europe, the US and Japan, one cannot relate differences in innovation directly to differences in health, safety and environmental regulation. The apparent historically lower rates of innovation in the EU, which in any case did not still seem to be operative at the end of the 1990s, were likely to be caused mainly by other factors.

5.127 It seems clear from our consultant's report that claims that new regulation will stifle innovation and growth cannot be substantiated. Nor, though, can they be discounted. It is important to have a better understanding of the interaction between regulation and innovation, particularly given the rather important role of innovation in providing potential substitutes for hazardous chemicals. At the present time, available research does not give firm conclusions on regulation and innovation. We need to understand better the processes of innovation and those features of different regulatory regimes that contribute to effective environmental protection, innovation and competitive advantage.

5.128 In addition to these EU-wide issues relevant to the rate of innovation, it should also be noted that the nature of the chemical industry in the UK is changing (5.130-5.131). These structural changes will also exert an impact on the rate (and possibly the direction) of innovation in this country.

5.129 **Small and medium-sized enterprises (SMEs)** Currently, 96% of all European chemical companies employ fewer than 250 employees, but the SME sector generates over 25% of sales and employment (figure 5-III). OECD[78] suggested that traditionally, chemical regulation has been more targeted towards large continuously-operating processes with little consideration of the different needs of SMEs who more typically operate relatively small batch plant. Given the potential shift in the chemicals industry within the European Community (from large plant manufacturing existing chemicals to smaller 'service-based' industries), the role of SMEs in chemicals regulation is likely to become more important in the future. Existing guidance seems to suggest that when dealing with SMEs, financial instruments may be more effective than regulation.

Figure 5-III

Sales and employment in the SME sector[79]

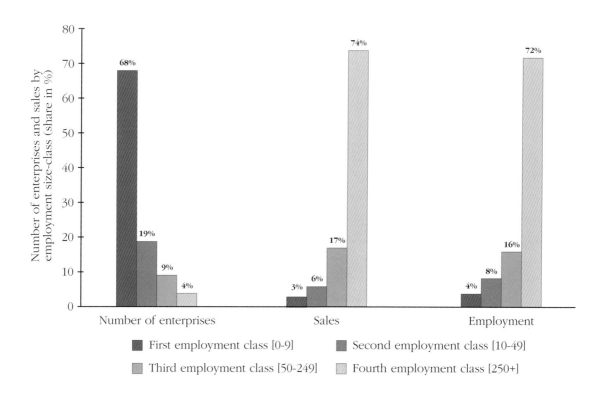

5.130 **Mergers and acquisitions** The Royal Society of Chemistry carried out research into merger and acquisition activity within the UK chemicals industry.[80] Its report noted marked reductions in investment in research and development (R&D) in UK firms (R&D spend down by 16% and R&D staff down by 30% between 1993 and 1997, see also 5.136), as well as a number of takeovers of UK firms working in R&D-intensive areas. Such activity may exert a marked influence on the rates of innovation. Concern was expressed in their report that the current high level of merger and acquisition activity was stifling the longer-term R&D needed to sustain the industry. It was, however, noted that university chemistry departments had adapted well to the changing industry.

5.131 It is likely that issues of industrial structure, research and development, and the dynamism of the SME sector will have a greater effect on the future competitiveness of the UK industry than regulation *per se*.

The Chemicals Innovation and Growth Team

5.132 The Chemicals Innovation and Growth Team (CIGT) was set up by the Department of Trade and Industry in January 2002 to address the key challenges facing the UK chemicals industry through a process of dialogue involving the industry and its stakeholders. The objective of the project was to set out a plan for the future of the chemicals industry to maintain competitiveness and deliver long-term growth. The main recommendation of the CIGT report[81] was the establishment of a Chemistry Leadership Council to formulate strategic policy guidelines and national priorities for the industry, and promulgate them to key stakeholders. It also advocated setting up a Chemicals Innovation Centre, working with relevant government agencies and departments, which would promote the UK as a location of choice for start-ups in chemicals-related technologies and for new ventures within the existing chemicals industry.

5.133 Whilst principally concerned with competitiveness, growth and reputation, the CIGT report did refer to environmental concerns at a number of points. The executive summary noted that public concern is overwhelmingly focussed on the environmental and health impact of the industry's products and processes.

5.134 The report published a survey showing that the unfavourable public impression of the industry was dominated by concern about pollution and the impacts of chemical products on the environment (figure 5-IV).

Figure 5-IV

Reasons for unfavourable public impressions of the chemicals industry[82]

Q: Why do you say your impressions of the chemicals industry are unfavourable?

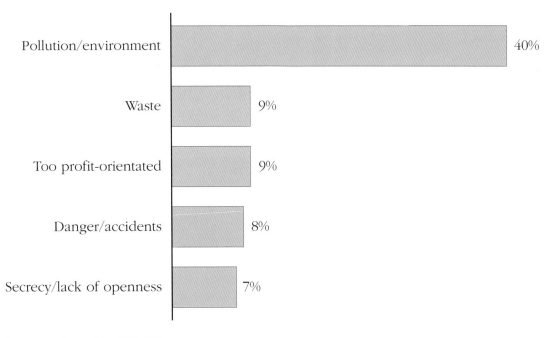

Base: All unfavourable (393), 2001

5.135 When discussing specialty chemicals, the report noted that environmental pressures would provide further stimulus for innovation in a number of product areas, including paints and cleaning products.

5.136 The report also pointed to under-investment in R&D by the UK chemicals industry. In 2001, the UK average R&D spend was 2.2% of sales, against an international average of 4.2% of sales. While R&D spending is only a proxy for innovation (because innovation covers much more than R&D), this under-investment has been a persistent finding over a number of years. The UK should be expected to spend above the international average on R&D in real terms, given that specialty and consumer products form a proportionately larger part of the UK chemicals industry.

5.137 Partly in order to address concerns about the reputation of the industry, the CIGT report contained a number of recommendations on the possibility of self-regulation, over and above legally-enforced regulation. The report recognised that dialogue with stakeholders needs to be further developed. Alongside the development of new standards and the delivery of operational excellence, the report acknowledged that having as complete a picture as possible of the use and impact of the chemicals it produces would assist the industry in developing dialogue with stakeholders. There seems, however, to be little in the report directly to address public concerns about the environmental and health impacts of the industry's products and processes.

5.138 The Royal Commission would welcome the establishment of a Chemistry Leadership Council and Chemicals Innovation Centre. **We recommend that the Chemistry Leadership Council and Chemicals Innovation Centre should take a positive attitude to new regulations designed to address public concerns about the industry, by improving the information about and social management of existing chemicals, and working to ensure that the new regulations act to stimulate innovation in a socially beneficial direction.**

> *This chapter has made recommendations about information flows in the supply chain, economic instruments, the promotion of green chemistry and extended producer responsibility, and other measures to stimulate substitution. This direction of evolution for the chemicals industry can enhance its market appeal as well as the safety of its products.*

Chapter 6
SUMMARY AND CONCLUSIONS

6.1   Development of chemical products during the past hundred years has made important contributions to the quality of life and the economy. But the manufacture and use of chemicals has created risks to the natural environment and human health, many of which are poorly characterised. There is a long history of serious environmental concerns associated with chemicals that were originally thought to be beneficial: for example, organochlorine pesticides, such as DDT; industrial chemicals, such as PCBs; and now a wide range of suspected endocrine disruptors. Public confidence in the chemicals industry is low, due to concerns over its environmental impacts and particularly over the long-term effects of exposure to synthetic chemicals.

6.2   Despite efforts over the years by the UK and other governments to manage these risks, major doubts persist about the effectiveness of present policies in protecting the health of ecosystems and humans from unintended long-term effects. The UK government's recent chemicals strategy and the European Commission's White Paper on chemicals are reflections of these concerns.

6.3   In this report, we examine scientific understanding of the fate and effects of chemicals in the environment, and the degree of uncertainty associated with that understanding. We investigate the way that regulatory systems across the world attempt to manage the risks from chemicals, how they deal with this uncertainty, and how they address public concerns about the process. We identify shortcomings, and recommend ways in which these shortcomings might be addressed.

6.4   Our study deals with synthetic chemicals – by which we mean chemicals that are manufactured by industry, regardless of whether or not they also occur in nature, as well as naturally occurring chemicals that have been extracted and concentrated by industry. The regulatory regime that controls emissions from chemical processes is reasonably well established, and we have focused our attention on the regulation of chemicals which are traded, or incorporated into products, or are substances that derive from such activities. Chemicals that are released into the environment during use or disposal of products create more diffuse sources of pollution than those released accidentally during the production process. Their effects are thus more pervasive and more difficult to detect and correlate with adverse effects on the environment and human health.

THE NATURE OF THE PROBLEM

6.5   All chemicals have some potential to be harmful, and some have properties and patterns of use that allow them to reach compartments of the environment that are vulnerable. For many years it has been widely recognised that some societal mechanism is needed to ensure that the harm caused by such chemicals is contained within acceptable limits. Substantial problems face those who wish to manage the risks from chemicals.

6.6   Firstly, there is the large number of chemicals. Depending on the definition used, there are between 30,000 and 100,000 chemicals on the market in some shape or form in greater than laboratory scale quantities (with several hundred new substances added every year). Of these, less than 5% fall into categories that are approved for specific uses such as food additives, pesticides, biocides or pharmaceuticals. The rest can be used unless specifically regulated against. They are used in a multitude of ways: many are the building block chemicals of other products; others are incorporated into formulations or products that are then used in industries or sold to the public. They may consist of pure individual chemicals, or more commonly as complex mixtures. The supply chain between the manufacturer and public end-use can be long and complicated, and the flow of information along the supply chain is complicated.

6.7   A second problem is the distinct lack of reliable data for the vast majority of these chemicals. Extensive national, EU and international legislation and agreements prescribe requirements for testing and assessing chemicals for their potential to cause harm in the environment, but only a small proportion of chemicals on the market have been the subject of risk assessment. A number of national initiatives and the recent European Commission White Paper on chemicals have put forward proposals to deal with the backlog of chemicals waiting to be assessed. The proposals will increase the data available for assessing chemicals only very slowly and at huge costs in terms of both money and animals used for testing. But we remain far from convinced that the proposed solutions (essentially, more of the presently ineffective approaches) are either practical or adequate.

6.8   Thirdly, major problems arise from limitations and uncertainties in the hazard evaluation procedures and risk assessment process itself, and the continuing debate on costs and benefits of individual risk management proposals. In our Twenty-first Report, *Setting Environmental Standards*, we proposed a conceptual framework for environmental policy that involves several complementary and inter-related components, including scientific evidence, risk assessment and economic appraisal. We recognised that all components would be characterised by uncertainty or indeterminacy and might be influenced by different interests and beliefs. We pointed out that it was essential for uncertainties and different premises to be explicit in the policy process, and a key recommendation of the Twenty-first Report was that peoples' values should be integrated into each critical stage of decision-making, including framing the problem under consideration. Much of the evidence that the Commission has received for this study of chemicals has indicated areas of ignorance and uncertainty in data reliability, the validity of risk assessment assumptions and basic understanding of environmental processes and effects. Mechanisms for incorporating peoples' values into the resolution of these uncertainties are rarely to be found.

6.9   In seeking solutions to these shortcomings, the Commission was aware that this area, in common with many others in the environmental field, is one where most decisions are taken at a European, rather than a national level. Because of the global nature of the chemicals industry and the importance of trade in chemicals many decisions are taken at a supranational level – through the machinery of OECD or UNEP. Solutions to the failure of the regulatory system to deliver chemicals safety and to the challenge of restoring public confidence must, therefore, be ones which can be implemented swiftly and effectively within the UK, but then promulgated through the EU and beyond. Our objective in carrying out this study was to find such solutions.

A FRAGMENTED APPROACH

6.10 We were struck by how fragmented and differentiated the assessment and regulation of chemicals has become. Many different government departments and agencies are involved, and differing regulatory regimes apply, depending on the use to which the chemical is put or the effects that it might have. Linkages between environmental monitoring programmes and environmental risk assessments are rare. Initiatives to reduce industry's reliance on particularly hazardous chemicals are beginning to emerge, but they are quite separate from the overall control and management of chemicals in products. We are convinced that a more integrated and comprehensive approach is long overdue, and we have set out to recommend one.

REDUCING THE HAZARD

6.11 Given the inherent uncertainties about the way chemicals interact with the environment, it makes sense to assume that the continuing use of large numbers of synthetic chemicals will lead to serious effects, which we cannot predict on the basis of our current or foreseeable understanding of these processes. A sensible approach to this uncertainty would be one of precaution – to reduce the hazard wherever we have an opportunity to do so.

6.12 The substitution of hazardous chemicals with ones of lower hazard or a non-chemical alternative, underpins many of the recommendations in this report. We recognise that substitution cannot be achieved systematically through prescription, but will need to be achieved progressively through a range of measures. Our report therefore recommends that the government adopts substitution as a core goal of its chemicals policy, and many of our recommendations will help government drive towards such a goal. They include: better provision of information about chemicals that are on the market, and their hazards; the use of assessment and monitoring programmes to inform substitution decisions; a much improved flow of hazard information along the supply chain, underpinned by legislation such as that being prepared in the Netherlands; and a government-sponsored programme of testing chemical products, as part of a regime to enforce our proposed scheme of chemicals registration management.

6.13 We believe that economic instruments could also play an important role in driving substitution. Our proposed evaluation regime for chemicals will provide the information necessary to design and implement a chemicals charge which will encourage industry to move away from more hazardous chemicals whenever opportunities present themselves, and at the same time avoid perverse effects through a hazard banding system. Complementary to a charge, we recommend a greater emphasis on current initiatives to facilitate the move towards less hazardous products and processes through the development and promotion of green chemistry and chemical management services.

6.14 Additionally we feel that a more rigorous approach towards substitution might be adopted by the chemicals industry if there were clearer rights of redress, through civil liability, for those who can demonstrate that they have been harmed by chemicals, and we recommend changes to UK and European law to this end.

DEALING WITH THE BACKLOG

6.15   We propose a chemicals assessment and monitoring programme that will help the government to tackle the large backlog of untested chemicals on the market. It is unacceptable that after more than a century of chemicals production, and decades of legislation attempting to deliver environmental safety from these chemicals, we still do not have a good understanding of their fate and effects in the environment; nor do we even have much information from which such an understanding might be derived. We have little faith that either the present regulatory system or the proposals coming forward to improve them will provide better answers in the future. We believe that only a substantial paradigm shift will begin to rectify this situation and we believe that such a shift needs to be made now.

6.16   There are two main reasons for the current high levels of uncertainty about the environmental effects of chemicals. The first is fundamental: our understanding of environmental processes and the way that chemicals interact with the physical and biological environment is far from complete. Furthermore, because of the complex and fluctuating nature of the environments into which chemicals are released, providing descriptions of behaviour that will encompass all relevant vulnerable situations is extremely problematic. It is likely that over coming decades a concerted research effort will gradually improve this understanding and reduce this sort of uncertainty though it is unlikely ever to be eliminated. For now it has to be regarded as inherent to the process and not rectifiable, and hence our recommendations for a precautionary approach based on substitution.

6.17   The second reason certainly is rectifiable. The lack of adequate information about the hazards presented by most of the chemicals currently on the market is a serious failure, which must be addressed as a matter of urgency. The REACH process described in the European Commission's White Paper, will, we believe, be cumbersome and time consuming. The infeasibility of carrying on with traditional approaches for hazard and risk assessment and not exploiting fully new technologies and advances in computational assessment techniques are serious failings. However, we applaud the goal, in REACH, of examining all chemicals on the market and selecting a few for further attention, and we believe that authorisation for use is the right way of regulating chemicals in products. Where REACH fails is that it has been insufficiently radical in its approach to the actual process of assessing the hazards and risks from chemicals.

6.18   The alternative process we recommend falls into four interlinked steps – listing, sorting, evaluation and action. Two features span the whole process: the integration of environmental monitoring and the incorporation of public values.

6.19   In the present system, the links between environmental monitoring and risk assessment are rudimentary, and proposals such as REACH appear to do little to put that right. We recommend that monitoring must be an integral part of the whole process of assessing both the potential and actual environmental impacts of chemicals that are on the market. We have advocated the adoption of a reconnaissance monitoring approach, through tighter integration of chemical and biological surveillance, the intelligent use of new sophisticated techniques to provide the data needed for detecting unexpected adverse effects, and the use of opportunities for less formal monitoring that already exist through voluntary schemes and the activities of amateur observers. Those responsible for overseeing the regulatory control of chemicals must have clearly defined routes through which they can influence environmental and monitoring programmes to deliver the required information, and that information must be integrated into the assessment process at all stages.

6.20 The second linking feature is the incorporation of a broad range of opinion into the key stages of design and implementation of the chemicals assessment and monitoring programme. This is important to ensure that the assessment processes properly address public concerns, and do not overlook the importance of incorporating a range of different perspectives into the design of the process and its subsequent implementation. This will require a fully transparent process, with information about chemicals being placed routinely in the public domain, and machinery in place to obtain the views of a broad range of people. We make recommendations on how this might be achieved.

LISTING

6.21 We see no reason why all the chemicals currently on the UK market should not be identified by a suitable regulatory agency and listed on the Internet. We have heard opinion that this would be too complicated, but it has been achieved in other countries on both sides of the Atlantic, and we are unconvinced by any argument that it would be somehow more difficult in the UK than elsewhere. The existence of a list is essential and enforcement of chemicals legislation becomes extremely difficult if it is not in the public domain. There is evidence that enforcement in this area is very poor. Open public access to the list would be an important first stage in improving transparency of the process, and the list would be a factor in the design or re-alignment of environmental monitoring programmes.

6.22 As information is gathered about chemicals that are on the list, and the decisions taken about whether or not to restrict the chemical to certain approved uses, the information and the decisions should be added to the list. A simple, Internet-based database is all that is required. It could be readily augmented with links to other Internet sites with more information about the chemicals listed on the site, in a similar fashion to the Environment Agency's Pollution Inventory.

SORTING

6.23 It is not realistic to expect a comprehensive risk assessment to be carried out on all the tens of thousands of chemicals currently on the market. This would involve detailed analyses of the pathways and fates of chemicals once released into the environment, as well as comprehensive and expensive testing of the effects on living organisms and the environment. We recommend quite a different approach.

6.24 A system that identifies chemicals of concern for further investigation is essential. It should be based on simple criteria that reflect both exposure and hazard and that can be applied quickly to all these chemicals. Two such criteria in wide use that reflect exposure are persistence (the resistance of a chemical to degradation by environmental processes) and bioaccumulation (its tendency to concentrate in the fatty tissues of organisms).

6.25 Information about persistence, bioaccumulation and toxicity is available for many chemicals and these data should be first brought together, exploiting advanced methods of searching available literature and databases. This should be augmented by a system based on the advanced computational techniques, pioneered in the pharmaceutical industry, to identify molecules with particular physiological properties. It is not unusual in the pharmaceutical industry to screen a hundred thousand chemicals in one pass. To some extent these techniques are already used by the US EPA for the pre-manufacture assessment of new chemicals. Information about hazard, reflecting the way a chemical interacts with organisms through various aspects of its toxicity, is also relevant, but more difficult to assess using conventional approaches.

6.26 Securing full European and international acceptance of such an approach might not be straightforward, but it is for the UK to take a lead here, and to demonstrate that, by using such fast and efficient techniques, very large numbers of chemicals can be screened very quickly. Adoption of such an approach would turn the daunting task of assessing the 30,000 chemicals or so on the UK market into a rather straightforward operation. Exposure analysis in risk assessments already involves an element of computer-based modelling, and a sorting process that is both fast and comprehensive is feasible.

6.27 We recognise that such an approach will not resolve the fundamental uncertainties that we referred to above. It would, however, mean that very soon every chemical on the market will have been looked at, systematically, at least once. Some of these chemicals would be selected, against the carefully chosen criteria, for further evaluation (4.31-4.33). Those not selected would remain under review – that is, they would be re-evaluated in the light of any information arising either from the environmental monitoring that we have recommended, from improvements in the screening technology, or from new insights into the properties and behaviour.

EVALUATION

6.28 The sorting process will select a number of chemicals for further evaluation. We make a number of recommendations about the testing and assessment approaches used during this evaluation. Firstly there should be rapid identification of any chemicals that look so dangerous, on the basis of the sorting data, that immediate action is required without further investigation. We recommend the way that criteria might be selected to identify such chemicals, and give examples, and we emphasise again that the selection of such criteria should be made in the light of open debate. This is not a decision to be made solely by experts.

6.29 It is likely that for most of the chemicals requiring further evaluation, it will be necessary to gather further information on properties of the chemical and the uses to which it will be put. Determining its properties might require further testing, although we advocate the use of computational techniques wherever available, and the development of new computational techniques where they do not yet exist. Even in the absence of such an approach, testing regimes should be designed to avoid, wherever possible, the use of animals. To this end we have recommended that all practicable steps should be taken to avoid the use of higher organisms as test animals, and decisions to move to such tests should be on a case-by-case basis following transparent deliberation.

6.30 The evaluation stage should result either in the assignment of a chemical to one of three categories, high, medium or low concern, or in a decision that the chemical is not, after all, of immediate concern. A key benefit of this categorisation process is that it will usefully inform the development of the chemicals charge that we propose.

ACTION

6.31 One of the main criticisms that we have heard about the present regulatory regime for chemicals is the length of time taken from the first indication that a chemical is harmful to action to curtail that harm – typically several years. This must be improved, but regulatory change will be needed. REACH, when it comes into force, will introduce approval for use for chemicals identified as hazardous – this seems to us to be the correct way forward – but it needs to be introduced more quickly than is planned for REACH.

6.32 We envisage that chemicals placed in the category of high concern will face severe restrictions on their use, including a total ban on the production or importation of the chemical in some cases. They will also attract the highest level of the charge that we propose to drive substitution. Chemicals in the medium category may also be restricted to certain uses and attract a lower charge, and those in the low concern category might not need to be restricted – but would still attract a charge, though in the lowest band.

6.33 Information about the category to which a chemical has been assigned must be made available throughout the supply chain, including the public, so that customers can take it into account in making purchasing decisions and assessing their potential liabilities if they choose to use chemicals with a particular hazard rating. Thus, the chemicals assessment and management process will provide both regulatory control over the chemicals of particular concern and a driver for the process of substitution that we have recommended. This should become the central goal of the government's chemicals policy.

REGULATION AND ADMINISTRATION

6.34 We have argued that a policy of substitution is not best driven solely by regulation, and we have, therefore, recommended a package of measures that are, on the whole, non-regulatory. However, some regulatory change will be necessary, and the chemicals assessment and management programme that we have recommended will, in particular, not work effectively without a considerable degree of regulatory underpinning.

6.35 Regulation flowing from chemicals policy usually needs to be accepted and endorsed at EU level, and this has been a major obstacle to the adoption of new regulatory policies in individual Member States, including the UK. We believe that the length of time that it will take for REACH to have any effect, and the widespread criticisms of its efficiency and effectiveness, mean that it is inappropriate for the government simply to wait for the new European Union regime to come into force. There is now a good opportunity for the UK, jointly with like-minded Member States, to come forward with coherent proposals for new legislation, possibly interim legislation pending further development of the REACH proposals, within the European Union. We have identified the areas that require regulatory underpinning, and we have recommended that the government start negotiations with certain other Member States now to secure statutory underpinning for much faster assessment and management of the risk from chemicals.

6.36 We also recommend new administrative arrangements, to provide a much more coherent framework for the assessment and management of chemical risks. We have recommended that a new body be formed, preferably as part of the Environment Agency, with a specific remit to oversee the implementation of a new programme for the assessment and management of chemical risks in the way that we have described above. Responsibilities of this new body would include (*inter alia*) putting in place and co-ordinating the assessment and management scheme we have recommended, including: publication of the list of chemicals; preliminary sorting using available information and computational techniques; securing information from industry and assessment of the hazards posed by those chemicals selected for further evaluation; overseeing reconnaissance monitoring; and ensuring appropriate enforcement of restrictions on use of chemicals products.

6.37 The body, which we have called the *chemicals safety co-ordination unit*, would be advised by an independent committee, which would be mandated to seek the broadest possible range of opinion in formulating its advice. The unit would also be responsible for sponsoring the research that we see as necessary to take forward longer-term improvements in our understanding of the fate and effects of chemicals and new techniques for assessing chemicals. Primarily, though, its remit would be to drive forward progress towards the goal of substitution, by imposing restriction on use where necessary, securing appropriate levels of a charge on chemical products, providing information, encouraging innovation in the chemicals industry and sponsoring business-related initiatives such as green chemistry.

6.38 The provision of a unit of this sort is unlikely to be fiscally neutral, but we observe that:

- resources for the unit will be drawn from the existing Departments and agencies with chemicals responsibilities;

- our proposals for integrating environmental monitoring into the process do not necessarily imply a large increase in monitoring effort. However, to the extent that it does require some increase, this will be offset, at least partially, by a reduced need for full risk assessments; and

- any residual increased costs of administration or monitoring should be paid for by industry through fees for the assessment of their chemicals, and further offset by the revenue raised through the chemicals charge that we have proposed.

OUR VISION FOR THE FUTURE

6.39 As a consequence of our recommendations, we expect to see considerable changes in the way that chemicals are assessed, managed, monitored and used, over the next ten years. This includes the early formation of a chemicals safety co-ordination unit to provide a coherent framework and leadership for the implementation of chemicals policy, and give a clear strategic drive towards substitution. All chemicals currently on the UK market should be listed by the end of 2004, and examined, using the sorting process that we have recommended, by early 2006. All the chemicals selected by that process as being potentially harmful should be fully evaluated by 2009. A government strategy should be in place within the next two or three years to achieve a steady, measurable reduction in the use of hazardous chemicals. And a comprehensive programme of research should be promoted, jointly by industry and government, to expand the new approaches to chemicals assessment that we have identified. We must aim to reduce uncertainty in our understanding of the behaviour and fate of chemicals and their interaction with the physical and biological environment.

Chapter 7

RECOMMENDATIONS

*We bring together here the recommendations that appear (**in bold type**) elsewhere in this report.*

A NEW APPROACH

Current approaches to assessing and managing risks of chemicals in the environment are cumbersome, unsound and rely heavily on animal testing. A new paradigm is needed. We recommend a system comprising four steps: listing of marketed chemicals; sorting to select chemicals of concern; evaluation of selected chemicals; and risk management action. Thus in step 3, following public deliberation, chemicals would be assigned to one of three categories of concern (high/medium/low) or a 'no concern' category (whereby the chemical continues in use without further testing but is kept under review). In step 4 the appropriate risk management regime would be applied to those chemicals of concern.

STEP 1: A LIST OF MARKETED CHEMICALS

1. **The government should compile and publish a list of all chemicals currently marketed in the UK** (4.14).

STEP 2: SORTING TO SELECT CHEMICALS OF CONCERN

2. **The government should put in place now sorting procedures** for dealing with the backlog of untested chemicals to select a more manageable number that can be studied in greater detail. The sorting procedures should be informed by data already available and be **based extensively on computational approaches to hazard assessments, using the US EPA and Environment Canada procedures as models where applicable** (4.17).

3. **The government should publish all necessary toxicity, persistence and bioaccumulation data on the Internet for all chemicals on the UK market, using the list we recommend in 4.14** (4.22).

4. **New legislation should prohibit the marketing of any chemical for which these basic environmental safety data have not been registered on the list** (4.21).

Choosing the criteria

5. A key prerequisite in the sorting procedures is to define the standards on the basis of which a conclusion can be drawn that a chemical is 'of concern' (4.25). **The standards should be reviewed regularly, through an inclusive process taking into account public views, and adjusted accordingly** (4.26).

6. Once standards are defined, sorting of chemicals to identify those of concern becomes an automatic process. The resulting **putative list of selected chemicals should be shared with other countries and their observations used to inform the process** (4.27).

7. **The government should carry out the sorting process on the listed chemicals within three years, and annotate the list to show those exceeding the sorting criteria** (4.28).

8. **Chemicals found in unexpected environmental compartments or at unexpected concentrations, or associated with unusual biological phenomena, should be selected for further investigation** (4.30).

STEP 3: EVALUATION OF SELECTED CHEMICALS

9. **Chemicals selected by the sorting process or identified through environmental monitoring as 'of concern' should be categorised according to their degree of potential risk on the basis of agreed criteria, to determine the level of risk management and charge to which they should be subject** (4.34).

10. **All new chemicals should be considered as potentially harmful and evaluated with chemicals of concern** (4.31). This would reflect the fact that they have not yet been released into the environment and we know little about them. The investigation of all in this category of concern would be overseen by the agency.

11. **We recommend that the government should ensure that 90% of the chemicals selected by sorting have been evaluated and categorised within three years of selection (4.24)** (4.35).

12. **In evaluating chemicals, all practicable steps should be taken to avoid the use of higher animals as test organisms, and decisions to move to such tests should be made on a case by case basis following transparent discussion** (4.70).

13. **We endorse the recommendation in the 2002 report by the House of Lords Select Committee on Animals in Scientific Procedures, that the government should be developing a strategy to fund the development and validation of replacements for animal tests (*in vitro* and *in silico*), possibly via a centre for the 3 Rs** (4.71).

14. The phase-out of animal tests for risk assessment of substances used in cosmetics and the international drive for acceptance of data derived from *in vitro* studies for cosmetic ingredients, using validated alternative methods as an initiative to gain regulatory acceptance of alternative methods on a global scale is welcomed. **The government should press for wider application of this approach, using screening tests, existing data and computational techniques, together with in vitro studies, to describe the hazards of chemicals in all but exceptional cases** (4.64).

STEP 4: RISK MANAGEMENT ACTION

15. **Where synthetic chemicals are found in elevated concentrations in biological fluids such as breast milk and tissues of humans, marine mammals or top predators, regulatory steps should be taken to remove them from the market immediately** (4.38).

16. There will be some chemicals for which risk management action should be taken as a matter of urgency. The proposed **chemicals safety co-ordination unit, (4.107-4.111), guided by a statutory advisory committee (4.45) and within a wider deliberative process (4.26), should indicate at an early stage, the criteria that will trigger a higher level of concern** (4.39).

17. **The government should open discussions with other Member States with similar national approaches to chemicals management, and seek EU legislation to underpin a satisfactory listing, sorting and management scheme for chemicals** (4.44).

ADMINISTRATIVE ARRANGEMENTS

Current administrative arrangements for chemicals safety are complex and fragmented. We propose the establishment of a chemicals safety co-ordination unit to be placed in the Environment Agency. The unit would be charged with co-ordinating a national chemicals management programme, including responsibility for the new assessment scheme and monitoring activities we recommend. It would be formed from experts in chemicals policy, regulation and science already in government departments, thus minimising any additional costs.

18. **The government should establish a chemicals safety co-ordination unit, by transferring resources (staff and budgets) from existing organisations dealing with chemicals safety to the Environment Agency** (4.111).

19. **The Chemicals Standards Forum should be mandated to provide advice to the unit on any topic within the unit's remit, and that the unit should be required to take such advice into account in making regulatory decisions about chemicals, or in advising Ministers or government departments on chemicals policy** (4.113).

20. **As part of the UK implementation of this statutory development, the Chemicals Stakeholder Forum should be reconstituted as a statutory advisory body to the chemicals safety co-ordination unit to enable it better to carry out the risk management role proposed in 4.29-4.35, and this should be reflected in a change of name to the 'Chemicals Standards Forum'** (4.45).

21. We foresee reluctance on the part of some authorities to move from the traditional and slow testing protocols (chapter 2) to the much more rapid, and in many ways simpler, computer-based systems we propose (chapter 4). Therefore we recommend **that the UK government, jointly with like-minded Member States, should press for an EU-wide initiative to demonstrate and promulgate the effectiveness of these techniques, and to secure their international acceptance through OECD** (4.46).

INTERNATIONAL HARMONISATION

22. **The government should maintain pressure on the international community to achieve the goals of the Bahia Declaration leading to full arrangements for the exchange of information on hazardous chemicals regardless of their country of origin** (5.100).

23. **The government should continue to support and encourage greater international standardisation of testing and enhanced sharing of information in order to generate the required standard data set with minimal additional costs and animal test requirements. The government should also consider, together with other like-minded governments, whether to press for this work (and associated resources) to move from the OECD to a broader forum, perhaps UNEP** (5.102).

24. **The government should press for a provision that all foreign manufacturers and importers who wish to import into the EU should be obliged to register the substances and preparations containing dangerous chemicals, and list what products these have been incorporated into, in precisely the same way as European manufacturers will be required to do** (5.113).

25. **The government should increase the resources available to customs authorities or agencies responsible for chemicals regulation, to identify and, where appropriate, restrict the import of products containing unregistered chemical substances** (5.114).

26. **In appropriate cases both the UK and the EU should make use of the powers already available under WTO rules to restrict the marketing or use of dangerous substances or products containing them even at the risk of challenges by overseas suppliers that such measures are indirectly discriminatory** (5.115).

RESEARCH

27. **The chemicals safety co-ordination unit should commission and coordinate a programme of research to evaluate and keep under review rapid screening techniques to assess the environmental safety of synthetic chemicals. The chemicals industry, cooperating internationally, should play a central role in this work, including the provision of resources** (4.117).

28. **The chemicals industry should be encouraged to augment genomics research significantly, in a direction that will lead towards an understanding of the way that synthetic chemicals interact with biological organisms** (4.119).

29. **The chemicals safety co-ordination unit should publish its strategic approach to research setting out the steps it will take to ensure that it will be possible to predict with adequate confidence the fate and effects of synthetic chemicals released into the environment.** It should report progress at 5-yearly intervals (4.121).

30. **The government should argue for a European central entity that takes on, as a main objective, the co-ordination of research into chemicals assessment and risk management** (4.125).

INTEGRATING ENVIRONMENTAL MONITORING

Some of the most severe problems caused by chemicals in the environment have been detected by observation rather than assessment techniques. For this reason and as a key part of the review process, the new approach we advocate would integrate an expanded and better organised monitoring programme with the assessment procedures.

31. **The chemicals safety co-ordination unit, in co-ordinating monitoring as recommended, should direct effort towards reconnaissance monitoring and environmental epidemiology, using an integrated approach to detecting the presence or possible effects of chemicals in the environment as part of its risk management programme. Responsibility for carrying out publicly-funded monitoring should remain with the expert bodies** (4.97).

32. **Following the introduction of reconnaissance monitoring as recommended, the regulatory approval of chemicals should include requirements for post-approval monitoring by (or at the expense of) the producer or importer** (4.101).

33. **Environmental epidemiological studies of human and animal populations should be used by the chemicals safety co-ordination unit to identify chemicals, and combinations of chemicals, with the potential to damage animal and human health** (4.95).

34. **Monitoring activity related to the fate and effects of chemicals in the environment should be co-ordinated by the proposed chemicals safety co-ordination unit (4.111). However, the monitoring activity itself should continue to be carried out by the relevant expert organisations as at present** (4.93).

35. **The chemicals safety co-ordination unit (or other relevant agency) should assess the feasibility of a 'yellow card' scheme for use by the public to report unusual environmental events that might be related to chemical exposure** (4.86).

TOWARDS ENVIRONMENTALLY SUSTAINABLE PRODUCTS

Substitution of hazardous substances with others of lower hazard should be a central objective of chemicals policy. This can be achieved by design, manufacture and use of environmentally benign chemical products and processes ('green chemistry') or by indirect approaches such as replacing processes which use chemicals with processes that achieve similar effects without the involvement of chemicals. Implementing substitution policies requires reliable information on product composition, use patterns and comparative properties together with surveillance regimes.

SUBSTITUTION

36. **The UK government should adopt substitution as a central objective of chemicals policy** (5.18).

INFORMATION TRANSFER THROUGH THE SUPPLY CHAIN

37. **The government should carry out work with users to investigate the flow of information up and down the supply chain** (5.33).

38. **The government should investigate means of improving the information provided on Safety Data Sheets in order to make them more user-friendly** (5.34).

39. **The government should review the role of commercial confidentiality and statutory protection of relevant intellectual property rights** (5.35).

40. **The government should formulate legislation requiring all companies trading in chemicals to ensure that they receive all available information about any chemical substance or preparation when they obtain it, and supply full information about it when they sell it** (5.36).

41. **A programme of random tests on the composition of chemical products, including imported products, should be carried out by the relevant authorities as part of their enforcement strategies, and the results made public** (5.44).

TOWARDS SUSTAINABLE CHEMISTRY

42. **The government together with the chemical industry should continue to promote programmes for the development and promotion of Green Chemistry but with a new emphasis on its application to product design and use. We commend the establishment of annual green chemistry awards, but again there has been an undue emphasis on processes rather than products. We recommend that specific awards be developed for the application of green chemistry to products and services** (5.54).

43. **One function of the chemicals safety co-ordination unit proposed in chapter 4 (4.111) should be to promote the adoption of chemicals management services in appropriate sectors** (5.62).

DRIVING CHANGE

To effect the changes we advocate will require a suite of strong 'drivers'. These should include a charging scheme to encourage substitution of chemicals in categories of high concern; greater product liability and extended producer liability; enhanced labelling and information for consumers; together with voluntary initiatives. Given that much chemical business and regulation is international the UK government should work closely with other like-minded administrations, particularly in the EU, to achieve the goals identified in this report.

A CHEMICALS CHARGE

44. **The government should introduce a charging scheme to stimulate greater substitution. Categories of concern from our proposed testing regime for chemicals should be used to differentiate the levels of the charge** (5.70).

LIABILITY

45. **Wholesalers and retailers, as well as the manufacturer, should be jointly and severally liable under the Consumer Protection Act** (5.72).

46. **The government should promote the case for change to the Product Liability Directive in Europe** (5.73).

47. **The government should ensure that the issue of liability for environmental damage from the use of products is given proper weight in current discussions on liability regimes at European Community level** (5.74).

48. **The government should fund a joint scientific/legal study in order to anticipate the moral, legal and practical challenges to traditional civil liability concepts posed by increasing knowledge of genetic susceptibilities to specific chemicals** (3.195).

EXTENDED PRODUCER RESPONSIBILITY

49 As currently implemented, the EU take-back directives do not fully achieve the objectives of extended producer responsibility, as post-consumer materials are not necessarily returned to their actual manufacturers. We commend the concept of using producer take-back legislation as a way to promote resource productivity and innovation via substitution in product design. However, it is important that the principle of take-back is implemented in ways that ensure that liability for post-consumer waste products returns to the original manufacturer or supplier. **The government should investigate further the effect of take-back legislation on product design** (5.79).

VOLUNTARY INITIATIVES

50. **We commend the initiative of the Chemicals Stakeholder Forum in promoting voluntary reduction of certain chemicals, but emphasise that in the longer term such a voluntary approach needs to be seen in the context of a more systematic promotion of regulatory and other instruments to encourage substitution** (5.84).

51. **The government should sponsor research with consumers to determine the most effective means of information transfer and the level of detail required on the hazardous substance content of finished articles** (5.93).

INFORMATION AND LABELLING

52. **The proposed chemicals safety co-ordination unit (4.111) should put in place a means of providing information in response to queries from members of the public** (5.94).

REGULATION AND INNOVATION

53. **The Chemistry Leadership Council and the Chemicals Innovation Centre should take a positive attitude to new regulations designed to address public concerns about the industry, by improving the information about and social management of existing chemicals, and by working to ensure that the new regulations act to stimulate innovation in a socially beneficial direction** (5.138).

54. **The UK government should argue strongly for adherence to the EU model** (commercial confidentiality is the exception not the rule) **despite pressure to the contrary from the US** (3.141).

ALL OF WHICH WE HUMBLY SUBMIT FOR
YOUR MAJESTY'S GRACIOUS CONSIDERATION

Tom Blundell *Chairman*

Brian Follett

Roland Clift

Paul Ekins

John Flemming

Ian Graham-Bryce

Stephen Holgate

Brian Hoskins

Richard Macrory

Cheryl Miller

Susan Owens

Jane Plant

Janet Sprent

John Speirs

Peter Hinchcliffe   *Secretary*

Georgina Burney

Andrew Deacon   } *Assistant Secretaries*

Jonathan Wentworth

176

REFERENCES

Chapter 1

1. In this report, 'synthetic chemicals' includes manufactured chemicals that do not exist in nature, manufactured chemicals that can also be found in nature, and human-made concentrations of naturally occurring chemicals.

2. Chemicals Innovation and Growth Team (CIGT) (2002). *Enhancing the Competitiveness of the UK Chemicals Industry.* Department of Trade and Industry, London.

3. CIGT (2002).

4. Carson, R. (1962). *Silent Spring.* Houghton Mifflin Company, Boston.

5. Hickey, J.J. and Hunt, I.B. (1960). Initial songbird mortality following Dutch elm disease control program. *Journal of Wildlife Management,* **24**, 259.

6. Edwards, C.A. (1973). *Environmental Pollution by Pesticides.* Plenum Press, London and New York; Hickey, J.J. and Anderson, D.W. (1968). Chlorinated hydrocarbons and eggshell changes in raptorial and fish eating birds. *Science,* **162**, 271-273; Newton, I. and Haas, M.B. (1984). The return of the sparrowhawk. *British Birds,* **77**, 47-70; Ratcliffe, D. (1980). *The Peregrine Falcon.* Calton, Poyser.

7. Chanin, P. and Jeffries, D. (1978). The decline of the otter *Lutra lutra L.* in Britain: an analysis of hunting records and discussion of causes. *Biological Journal of the Linneaus Society,* **10**, 305-328.

8. Harrington, L.A. and Macdonald, D.W. (2002). *A Review of the Effects of Pesticides on Wild Terrestrial Mammals in Britain.* Wildlife Conservation Research Unit; Stringer, R. and Johnston, P. (2001). *Chlorine and the environment – an overview of the chlorine industry.* Kluwer Academic Publishers, Dordrecht, The Netherlands.

9. Molina, M.J. and Rowland, F.S. (1974). Stratospheric sink for chlorofluoromethanes: chlorine catalysed destruction of ozone. *Nature,* **249**, 810-814.

10. Farman, J.C., Gardiner, B.G. and Shanklin, J.D. (1985). Large losses of total ozone in Antarctica reveal seasonal ClO and NOx interaction. *Nature,* **315**, 207-210.

11. Guy, W.S. and Taves, D.R. (1976). *Organic Fluorocompounds in Human Plasma: Prevalence and Characterisation.* American Chemical Society, ACS Symposium Series No. 28. Washington.

12. Giesy, J.P. and Kannan, K. (2001). Global distribution of perfluorooctane sulfonate in wildlife. *Environmental Science and Technology,* **35**, 1339-1342; Kannan, K., Koistinen, J., Beckmen, K., Evans, T., Gorzelany, J.F., Hansen, K.J., Jones, P.D., Helle, E., Nyman, M. and Giesy, J.P. (2001a). Accumulation of perfluorooctane sulphonate in marine mammals. *Environmental Science and Technology,* **35**, 1593-1598; Kannan, K., Franson, J.C., Bowerman, W.W., Hansen, K.J., Jones, P.D. and Giesy, J.P. (2001b). Perfluorooctane sulphonate in fish-eating water birds including bald eagles and albatrosses. *Environmental Science and Technology,* **35**, 3065-3070; Kannan, K., Newsted, J., Halbrook, R.S. and Giesy, J.P. (2002a). Perfluorooctane sulfonate and related fluorinated hydrocarbons in mink and river otters from the United States. *Environmental Science and Technology,* **36**, 2566-2571;

Kannan, K., Corsolini, S., Falandysz, J., Oehme, G., Focardi, S. and Giesy, J.P. (2002b). Perfluorooctane sulfonate and related fluorinated hydrocarbons in marine mammals, fishes, and birds from coasts of the Baltic and the Mediterranean seas. *Environmental Science and Technology*, **36**, 3210-3216.

13. Bryan, G.W. and Gibbs, P.E. (1991). Impact of low concentrations of tributyltin (TBT) on marine organisms: a review. In: *Metal Ecotoxicology: Concepts and Applications*. Ed. M.C. Newman and A.W. McIntosh. Lewis Publishers Inc., Boston. See pages 323-361;

Bryan, G.W., Gibbs, P.E., Burt, G.R. and Hummerstone, L.G. (1987). The effects of tributyltin (TBT) accumulation on adult dog-whelks, *Nucella lapillus*: long-term field and laboratory experiments. *Journal of the Marine Biological Association of the United Kingdom*, **67**, 525-544;

Gibbs, P.E. and Bryan, G.W. (1986). Reproductive failure in populations of the dog-whelk, *Nucella lapillus*, caused by imposex induced by tributyltin from antifouling paints. *Journal of the Marine Biological Association of the United Kingdom*, **66**, 767-777.

14. De Wit, C.A. (2002). An overview of brominated flame retardants in the environment. *Chemosphere*, **46**(5), 583-624;

Rahman, F., Langford, K.H., Scrimshaw, M.D. and Lester, J.N. (2001). Polybrominated diphenyl ether (PBDE) flame retardants. *Science of the Total Environment*, **275**(1-3), 1-17.

15. Meironyte, D., Noren, K. and Bergman, A. (1999). Analysis of polybrominated diphenyl ethers in Swedish human milk. A time related study, 1972-1997. *Journal of Toxicology and Environmental Health Part A*, **58**(6), 329-341.

16. AMAP (2002). *Arctic Pollution 2002*. Arctic Monitoring and Assessment Programme (AMAP). Oslo.

17. Though by no means all chemicals found in nature are rendered harmless by these mechanisms.

18. CIGT (2002).

19. ICCA (2002). *The ICCA chemical sector report to UNEP for the World Summit on Sustainable Development,* September *2002*.

20. UK Chemical Industry Association (CIA) and the American Chemistry Council (ACC) (1999). *Main world chemical markets by geographic area – 1996-2010*.

21. Evidence to the Commission from the British Union for the Abolition of Vivisection, October 2002.

22. Haigh, N. (1995). *Legislation for the Control of Chemicals*. A report prepared for the Department of the Environment. Institute for European Environmental Policy, London.

23. Department of the Environment, Transport and the Regions (1999). *Sustainable Production and Use of Chemicals – a Strategic Approach. The Government's Chemicals Strategy.* December 1999.

24. *Commission White Paper of 27 February 2001 on the strategy for a future chemicals policy.* COM(2001)88.

25. TNO (2001). *Emissions of hazardous substances from finished products*. TNO Report MEP-R2001/121, TNO, The Netherlands.

26. Twenty-first Report, figure 8-I, page 118.

27. Twenty-first Report, paragraph 2.79.

28. Twenty-first Report paragraph 4.58.

29. Principle 15 of the 1992 Rio Declaration on the Environment and Development.

Chapter 2

1.   Department of the Environment, Transport and the Regions (DETR) (2000). *Guidelines for Environmental Risk Assessment and Management.* Produced jointly with the Environment Agency and the Institute for Environment and Health. July 2000. The Stationery Office, London.

2.   United Nations Environment Programme (UNEP)/International Programme on Chemical Safety (IPCS) (1999). *Chemical Risk Assessment. Training Module No. 3.* Prepared by the Edinburgh Centre for Toxicology. WHO/PCS/99.2.

3.   ECVAM (2002). *Alternative (Non-animal) Methods for Chemicals Testing: Current Status and Future Prospects.* Eds. A. Worth and M. Balls.

4.   Sun, B., Griffin, B., Ayala-del-Rio, H.L., Hasham, S.A. and Tiedje, J.M. (2002). Microbial dehalorespiration with 1,1,1-trichloroethane. *Science*, **298**(1), 1023-1025;
      Urbance, J.W., Cole, J., Saxman, P. and Tiedje, J.M. (2003). BSD: the Biodegradative Strain Database. *Nucleic Acids Research*, **31**(1), 152-155.

5.   *Dosis sola facit venenum* – Dosage alone makes the poison. Paracelsus (Theophrastus Philippus Aureolus Bombastus von Hohenheim) (1494-1542).

6.   English Nature (2002). *Policy mechanisms for the control of diffuse agricultural pollution, with particular reference to grant aid.* Research Report No. 455. English Nature and the Environment Agency.

7.   Preston, C.D., Telfer, M.G., Arnold, H.R., Carey, P.D., Cooper, J.M., Dines, T.D., Hill, M.O., Pearman, D.A., Roy, D.B. and Smart, S.M. (2002). *The Changing Flora of the UK.* Department for Environment, Food and Rural Affairs (Defra), London.

8.   English Nature (2002).

9.   English Nature (2002);
      Plantlife (2002). *Junk Food for Plants.*

10.   Commission Regulation 1488/94 laying down the principles of the assessment of risks. *Official Journal* **L 161**, 29.06.94.

11.   *Technical Guidance Document in support of Commission Directive 93/67/EEC on Risk Assessment for New Notified Substances and Commission regulation (EC) No 1488/94 on Risk Assessment for Existing Substances* (1996). Luxembourg: Office for Official Publications of the European Communities.

12.   Commission Directive 93/67/EEC of 20.7.1993 laying down the principles for assessment of risks to man and the environment of substances notified in accordance with Council Directive 67/548/EEC *Official Journal* **L 227**, 08.09.1993.

13.   Definitions from the Twenty-first Report, see paragraph 2.38.

14.   Based on graph from the nickel development institute website: http://www.nidi.org/index.cfm/ci_id/100.htm.

15.   IGHRC Working Group (2003). *Uncertainty Factors: Human Health Risk Assessment by UK Government.*

16.   IGHRC Working Group (2003).

17.   Evidence from Professor Finn Bro-Rasmussen, February 2002.

18.   World Health Organization (WHO) (1999). *Principles for the Assessments of Risks to Human Health from Exposure to Chemicals.* IPCS Environmental Health Criteria Document No. 170. WHO, Geneva.

19. Dybing, E., Doe, J., Groten, J., Kleiner, J., O'Brien, J., Renwick, A.G., Schlatter, J., Steinberg, P., Tritischer, A., Walker, R. and Younes, M. (2002). Hazard characterisation of chemicals in food and diet: dose response, mechanisms and extrapolation issues. *Food and Chemical Toxicology*, **40**, 237-282.

20. Barlow, S.M., Greig, J.B., Bridges, J.W., Carere, A., Carpy, A.J.M., Galli, C.L., Keiner, J., Knudson, I., Koeter, H.B.W.M., Levy, L.S., Madsen, C., Mayer, S., Narbonne, J.F., Pfannkuch, F., Prodanchuk, M.G., Smith, M.R. and Steinberg, P. (2002). Hazard identification by methods of animal-based toxicology. *Food and Chemical Toxicology*, **40**, 145-191.

21. Committee on Toxicity of Chemicals in Food, Consumer Products and the Environment (2002). *Risk Assessment of Mixtures of Pesticides and Similar Substances*. FSA/0691/0902. Food Standards Agency. September 2002.

22. Cassee, F.R., Groton, J.P., van Bladeren, P.J. and Feron, V.J. (1998). Toxicological evaluation and risk assessment of chemical mixtures. *Critical Reviews in Toxicology*, **28**(1), 73-101.

23. Harrington, L.A. and Macdonald, D.W. (2002). *A Review of the Effects of Pesticides on Wild Terrestrial Mammals in Britain*. Wildlife Conservation Research Unit;

    Hodgson, E. (1999). Induction and inhibition of pesticide-metabolising enzymes: roles in synergism of pesticides and pesticide action. *Toxicology and Industrial Health*, **15**(1/2), 6-11;

    Johnston, G., Collett, G., Walker, C., Dawson, A., Boyd, I. and Osborn, D. (1989). Enhancement of malathion toxicity to hybrid red-legged partridge following exposure to prochloraz. *Pesticide Biochemistry and Physiology*, **35**, 107-108;

    Thompson, H.M. (1996). Interactions between pesticides: a review of reported effects and their implications for wildlife risk assessment. *Ecotoxicology*, **5**, 59-81;

    Thompson, H.M., Hart, A.D.M., Thomas, M.R. and Langton, S.D. (1995). *Pesticide mixtures: scale of usage in the UK and implications for wildlife risk assessment*. 5th SETAC–Europe Congress 1995. Copenhagen, 25-28 June 1995.

24. Lehmann, E.J. and Fitzhurgh, O.G. (1954). 100-Fold margin of safety. *Quarterly Bulletin of the Association of Food and Drug Officials*, **18**, 33-35.

25. Renwick, A.G. and Lazarus, N.R. (1998). Human variability and noncancer risk assessment – an analysis – an analysis of the default uncertainty factor. *Regulatory Toxicology and Pharmacology*, **27**, 3-20.

26. Subdivision proposed by Renwick (Renwick, A.G. (1993). Data-derived safety factors for the evaluation of food additives and environmental contaminants. *Food Additives and Contaminants*, **10**, 275-305) and modified by IPCS (IGHRC (2003)).

27. IGHRC Working Group (2003).

28. Evidence from Professor Finn Bro-Rasmussen, February 2002.

29. IPCS (2001). *Guidance document for the use of data in development of chemical-specific adjustment factors (CSAFs) for interspecies differences and human variability in dose/concentration response assessments*. Document number WHO/PCS/oi.4. Available at: http://www.ipcsharmonise.org.

30. IPCS (2001);

    WHO (1994). *Assessing Human Health Risks of Chemicals: Derivation of Guidance Values for Health-based Exposure Limits*. IPCS Environmental Health Criteria Document No. 170. WHO, Geneva;

    WHO (1999).

31. IPCS (2001).

32. Evidence from the Department of Health, January 2002.

33. Brown, D. (1998). Environmental risk assessment and management of chemicals. In: Hester, R.E. and Harrison, R.M. (Eds.) (1998). *Risk Assessment and Risk Management.* Issues in Environmental Science and Technology No. 9. Royal Society of Chemistry, Cambridge. Pages 91-111.

34. Van Leeuwen, C.J., Bro-Rasmussen, F., Feijtel, T.C.J., Arndt, R., Bussian, B.M., Calamari, D., Glynn, P., Grandy, N.J., Hansen, B., Van Hemmen, J.J., Hurst, P., King, N., Koch, R., Müller, M., Solbé, J.F., Speijers, G.A.B. and Vermeire, T. (1996). Risk assessment and management of new and existing chemicals. *Environmental Toxicology and Pharmacology,* **2**, 243-299.

35. Evidence from Finn Bro-Rasmussen, February 2002.

36. Evidence from Finn Bro-Rasmussen, February 2002.

37. Pennington, D. (2001). *Indicators for Ecotoxicity in LCIA (Life Cycle Impact Assessment).* Presented at the SETAC North America Conference, Baltimore, November 2001.

38. European Commission. Technical Guidance Document in support of Commission Directive 93/67/EEC on Risk Assessment for New Notified Substances and Commission Regulation (EC) No1488/94 on Risk Assessment for Existing Substances. Part I. Office for Official Publications of the European Communities, Luxembourg. 1996.

39. Tipping, E., Smith, E.J., Hughes, S., Lawlor, A.J., Lofts, S., Simon, B.M., Stevens, P.A., Stidson, R. and Vincent, C.D. (2001). *Metals in Ombrotrophic Peats across Scotland.* Scottish Natural Heritage Research, Survey and Monitoring Report No. 129.

40. Yang, H., Rose, N.L., Boyle, J.F. and Battarbee, R.W. (2001). Storage and distribution of trace metals and spheroidal carbonaceous particles (SCPs) from atmospheric deposition in the catchment peats of Lochnagar, Scotland. *Environmental Pollution,* **115**, 231-238.

41. Harada, M. (1995). Minamata disease: methylmercury poisoning in Japan caused by environmental pollution. *Critical Reviews in Toxicology,* **25**:1-24.

42. Scheifler, R., Schwartz, C., Echevarria, G., de Vaufleury, A., Badot, P-M. and Morel, J-L. (2003). 'Nonavailable' Soil Cadmium Is Bioavailable to Snails: Evidence from Isotopic Dilution Experiments. *Environmental Science and Technology,* **37**, 81-86.

43. European Commission. Part I. 1996.

44. Figure from the website of the Japanese National Institute of Resources and Environment: http://www.nire.go.jp/eco_tec_e/hyouka_e.htm

45. Mackay, D. (1991). *Multimedia Environmental Models: the Fugacity Approach.* Lewis, Boca Raton, Florida;
    Mackay, D. (1994). Fate models. In: *Handbook of Ecotoxicology.* Ed. P. Calow. Blackwell Scientific Publications, Oxford. Pages 348-367;
    Mackay, D. and Paterson, S. (1991). Evaluating the multimedia fate of organic chemicals: a level III fugacity model. *Environmental Science and Technology,* **25**, 427-436;
    Mackay, D. and Paterson, S. (1993). Mathematical models of transport and fate. In: *Ecological Risk Assessment.* Ed. G.W. Suter. Lewis, Chelsea, Michigan. Pages 129-151;
    Mackay, D., Paterson, S. and Shiu, W.Y. (1992). Generic models for evaluating the regional fate of chemicals. *Chemosphere,* **24**, 695-717.

46. ECETOC (1993). *Environmental Hazard Assessment of Substances.* Technical Report No. 51. ECETOC, Brussels;
    UNEP/IPCS (1999);
    Wright, D.A. and Welbourn, P. (2002). *Environmental Toxicology.* Cambridge University Press, Cambridge.

47. *Commission White Paper of 27 February 2001 on the strategy for a future chemicals policy.* COM(2001)88.

48. European Environment Agency/European Science Foundation (EEA/ESF) (2002). *Chemicals in the European Environment: a survey of monitoring and exposure information.*

49. EEA/ESF (2002).

50. EEA/ESF (2002).

51. European Commission. Technical Guidance Document in support of Commission Directive 93/67/EEC on Risk Assessment for New Notified Substances and Commission Regulation (EC) No1488/94 on Risk Assessment for Existing Substances. Part II. Office for Official Publications of the European Communities, Luxembourg. 1996.

52. European Commission. Part II. 1996

53. European Commission. Part II. 1996

54. Regulatory Impact Unit (2003). *Better Policy Making: A Guide To Regulatory Impact Assessment.* Reference No. 255288/0103/D24. At website: http://www.cabinet- office.gov.uk/ regulation/scrutiny/ria-guidance.pdf

55. Organisation for Economic Co-operation and Development (OECD) (1999). *Guidance for Conducting Retrospective Studies on Socio-Economic Analysis.* OECD Environmental Health and Safety Publications, No, 11. OECD, Paris;

    OECD (2000a). *Framework for Integrating Socio-Economic Analysis in Chemical Risk Management Decision-Making.* ENV/JM/MONO(2000)5. OECD, Paris;

    OECD (2002). *Technical Guidance Document on the Use of Socio-Economic Analysis in Chemical Risk Management Decision Making.* ENV/JM/MONO(2002)10. OECD, Paris.

56. OECD (2000), page 21.

57. OECD (2000), page 21.

58. OECD (2000), page 74.

59. OECD (2000), page 105.

60. OECD (2000), page 107.

61. European Commission. Part II. 1996.

62. Defra (2002). *INF/02/25 Monitoring chemicals in the environment.* Paper prepared for the Chemicals Stakeholder Forum by Defra. Available at Defra website: http://www.defra.gov.uk/ environment/chemicals/csf/10122002/pdf/csf-inf-02-25.pdf.

63. UNEP/IPCS (1999).

64. Kenny, A.J., Thomas, K., Peeler, E., Osborn, D., Waldock, M., Matthiessen, P., Shore, R., Wright, J. and Feist, S. (2002). *Assessing the potential of environmental monitoring for detecting and responding to damage caused by the use of chemicals.* Report for the Royal Commission on Environmental Pollution by the Centre for Environment, Fisheries and Aquaculture Science (CEFAS) and the Centre for Ecology and Hydrology (CEH).

65. EEA/ESF (2002).

66. Pesticides in the Environment Working Group (PEWG) (2000). *Report on the monitoring of pesticides in the environment.* Environment Agency.

67. Personal Communication, Steve Killeen, Environment Agency, March 2003.

68. Environment Agency (2002). *Managing Chemicals for a better environment. The Environment Agency's Strategy.* Consultation Document. June 2002.

69. Defra (2002).

70. OECD (2000b). *High Production Volume Chemicals Covered by Environmental Monitoring Programmes and the Needs of Exposure/Risk Assessors.* Task Force on Environmental Exposure Assessments. OECD, Paris.

71. European Environment Agency (1999). *Environment in the European Union at the turn of the century*. Environmental Assessment Report No. 2.

72. EEA/ESF (2002).

73. EEA/ESF (2002).

74. Evidence from the Environment Agency, October 2002.

75. Kenny *et al*. (2002).

76. PEWG (2000).

77. PEWG (2000).

78. Evidence from English Nature, March 2002.

79. Evidence from English Nature, March 2002;
    Environment Agency (2002). *Review of Human Pharmaceuticals in the Environment*. Technical Report No. P390;
    Hallingsorenson, B., Nielsen, S.N., Lanzky, P.F., Ingerslev, F., Lutzhoft, H.C.H. and Jorgensen, S.E. (1998). Occurrence, fate and effects of pharmaceutical substances in the environment – a review. *Chemosphere*, **36**(2), 357-393;
    Hirsch, R., Ternes, T., Haberer, K. and Kratz, K.L. (1999). Occurrence of antibiotics in the aquatic environment. *The Science of the Total Environment*, **225**, 109-118.

80. PEWG (2000).

81. Environment Agency (2002).

82. Scientific Committee on Toxicity, Ecotoxicity and the Environment (SCTEE) (2001). *Opinion on: Draft CPMP Discussion Paper on Environmental Risk Assessment of Medicinal Products for Human Use*. C2/JCD/csteeop/CPMPpaperRAssessHumPharm12062001/D(01).

83. Flaherty, C.M., Kashian, D.R. and Dodson, S.I. (2002). *Ecological Effects of Pharmaceuticals on Daphnia*. Ecological Society of America Annual Meeting. Available at: http://199.245.200.45/pweb/document/?SOCIETY=esa&YEAR=2002&ID=17084.

84. SCTEE (2001).

85. Webb, S.F. (2000). *Risk assessment approaches for pharmaceuticals*. Presented at International Seminar: Pharmaceuticals in the Environment. Technological Institute, Section on Environmental Technology. Brussels, 2000.

86. Environment Agency (2002).

87. Kolpin, D.W., Furlong, E.T., Meyer, M.T., Thurman, E.M., Zaugg, S.D., Barber, L.B. and Buxton, H.T. (2002). Pharmaceuticals, Hormones, and Other Organic Wastewater Contaminants in U.S. Streams, 1999-2000: A National Reconnaissance, *Environmental Science and Technology*, **36**(6), 1202-1211.

88. The European Agency for the Evaluation of Medicinal Products (2001). *Discussion Paper on Environmental Risk Assessment of non-Genetically Modified Organism (non-GMO) containing Medicinal Products for Human Use*.

89. European Environment Agency (2003). *Europe's environment: the third assessment*. Environmental Assessment report No. 10.

90. WHO (1996). *Environment and Health 1 Overview and Main European Issues*. WHO, European Centre for Environment and Health, and European Environment Agency.

91. Institute for Environment and Health (1999). *Risk assessment strategies in relation to population subgroups*. Report of a workshop organised by the Risk Assessment and Toxicology Steering Committee.

92. Dybing *et al*. (2002)..

93. Van den Brandt *et al*. (2002).

94. Parkin, R. (2001). *Strategies for Incorporating Susceptibility in Risk Assessment.* 8th International Inhalation Symposium (INIS). Monograph Heinrich U, Mohr.

95. Parkin (2001).

96. Stern, A.H. and Korn, L.R. (2001). How useful is linear regression analysis in detecting the existence of dose response relationships in large-scale epidemiologic studies when only a fraction of the population is sensitive? The case of methylmercury. *Regulatory Toxicology and Pharmacology, 33*(1), 29-36.

97. Department of Health and Human Services, Centers for Disease Control and Prevention (2003). *Second National Report on Human Exposure to Environmental Chemicals.* NCEH Publication No. 02-0716.

98. Bornschein, S., Hausteiner, C., Drzezga, A., Bartenstein, P., Schwaiger, M., Forstl, H. and Zilker, T. (2002a). PET in patients with clear-cut multiple chemical sensitivity (MCS). *Nuklearmedizin, 41*(6),233-239.

99. Caccappolo-van Vliet, E., Kelly-McNeil, K., Natelson, B., Kipen, H. and Fiedler, N. (2002). Anxiety sensitivity and depression in multiple chemical sensitivities and asthma. *Journal of Occupational and Environmental Medicine, 44*(10), 890-901.

100. Bornschein, S., Hausteiner, C., Zilker, T. and Forstl, H. (2002b). Psychiatric and somatic disorders and multiple chemical sensitivity (MCS) in 264 'environmental patients'. *Psychological Medicine, 32*(8),1387-1394.

101. Greene, G.J. and Kipen, H.M. (2002). The vomeronasal organ and chemical sensitivity: a hypothesis. *Environmental Health Perspectives., 110*(Supplement 4), 655-661.

102. Johansson, A., Lowhagen, O., Millqvist, E. and Bende, M. (2002). Capsaicin inhalation test for identification of sensory hyperreactivity. *Respiritory Medicine, 96*(9),731-735.

103. Bornschein *et al.* (2002b).

104. See US EPA website: http://www.epa.gov/heasd/edrb/nhexas.htm.

105. Evidence from the Food Standards Agency, February 2002;
Evidence from the Food Standards Agency, September 2002;
Evidence from the Foods Standards Agency, October 2002;
Food Standards Agency website: http://www.food.gov.uk/science/surveillance.

106. At University of Leeds website: http://www.leeds.ac.uk/miru/research_programme.htm;
Evidence from the Foods Standards Agency, October 2002.

107. Twenty-first Report, see paragraph 2.28 and boxes 2B and 2C.

108. EEA/ESF (2001). *Chemicals in soil, food, and consumer products, with emphasis on specified human exposure assessment.* EEA, Copenhagen.

109. Van den Brandt *et al.* (2002).

110. Information supplied by Mr Steve Killeen, Environment Agency, March 2003.

111. Neven, B. and Schubert, R. (1998). *Comparison of Regulatory Requirements for the Notification of New Chemical Substances in the European Union, the USA and Japan.* Institute for Prospective Technological Studies. EUR 18119 EN.

112. Risk Policy Analysts (RPA) and Statistics Sweden (2002). *Assessment of the Impacts of New Regulations in the Chemicals Sector.*

Chapter 3

1. The European Union (EU) has no legal personality and it is the European Community (EC) that is the signatory to international conventions.

2. A comprehensive account of European Union chemicals legislation and its policy background is found in *The Manual of Environmental Policy: The EU and Britain*, Release 22, January 2003. Maney Publishing, Leeds.

3. Council Directive 67/548/EEC of 27 June 1967 on the approximation of laws, regulations and administrative provisions relating to the classification, packaging and labelling of dangerous substances. *Official Journal*, **L196**, 16.08.1967.

4. Council Regulation (EEC) No. 793/93 of 23 March 1993 on the evaluation and control of the risks of existing substances. *Official Journal*, **L84**, 05.04.1993.

5. Council Directive 76/769/EEC of 27 July 1976 on the approximation of the laws, regulations and administrative provisions of the Member States relating to restrictions on the marketing and use of certain dangerous substances and preparations. *Official Journal*, **L262**, 27.09.1976.

6. Directive 1999/45/EC of the European Parliament and of the Council of 31 May 1999 concerning the approximation of the laws, regulations and administrative provisions of the Member States relating to the classification, packaging and labelling of dangerous preparations. *Official Journal*, **L200**, 30.07.1999.

7. Council Directive 79/831/EEC of 18 September 1979 amending for the sixth time Directive 67/548/EEC on the approximation of the laws, regulations and administrative provisions relating to the classification, packaging and labelling of dangerous substances. *Official Journal*, **L259**, 15.10.1979.

8. Council Directive 92/32/EEC of 30 April 1992 amending for the seventh time Directive 67/548/EEC on the approximation of the laws, regulations and administrative provisions relating to the classification, packaging and labelling of dangerous substances. *Official Journal*, **L154**, 05.06.1992.

9. *The Chemicals (Hazard Information and Packaging for Supply) Regulations 2002*. Statutory Instrument 2002 No. 1689. See Schedule 2.

10. Royal Commission on Environmental Pollution (1972). *Second Report – Three Issues in Industrial Pollution*. HMSO, London.

11. In the UK the competent authority is jointly the Health and Safety Executive and the Secretary of State for Environment, Food and Rural Affairs. The Secretary of State's responsibilities are delegated through a Memorandum of Understanding to the Environment Agency.

12. Commission Directive 93/67/EEC of 20.7.1993 laying down the principles for assessment of risks to man and the environment of substances notified in accordance with Council Directive 67/548/EEC. *Official Journal*, **L227**, 08.09.1993.

13. *Technical Guidance Document in support of Commission Directive 93/67/EEC on Risk Assessment for New Notified Substances and Commission Regulation (EC) No. 1488/94 on Risk Assessment for Existing Substances*. Office for Official Publications of the European Communities, Luxembourg. 1996.

14. See European Chemicals Bureau website at: http://ecb.jrc.it/.

15. See Health and Safety Executive website at: http://www.hse.gov.uk/hthdir/noframes/nons/nons7.htm.

16. *Notification of New Chemical Substances in accordance with Directive 67/548/EEC on the Classification, Packaging and Labelling of Dangerous Substances. No-Longer Polymers List.* Document No. CR-99-96-932-EN-C. Office for Official Publications of the European Communities, Luxembourg. September 1996.

17. Commission Directive 2001/59/EC of 6 August 2001 adapting to technical progress for the 28th time Council Directive 67/548/EEC on the approximation of the laws, regulations and administrative provisions relating to the classification, packaging and labelling of dangerous substances. *Official Journal,* **L225**, 21.08.2001.

18. See European Chemicals Bureau website at: http://ecb.jrc.it/Elincs/.

19. Regulations have general effect and are directly applicable in Member States. Directives are addressed to Member States and are binding as to the result, but Members may choose the form and methods for adaptation into their national legal systems.

20. Commission Regulation 1488/94 laying down the principles of the assessment of risks. *Official Journal,* **L161**, 29.06.94.

21. Directive 98/34/EC of the Parliament and of the Council of 22 June 1998 laying down a procedure for the provision of information in the field of technical standards and regulations and (following Directive 98/48/EC) regulations on information society services. *Official Journal,* **L204**, 21.07.98.

22. Council Directive 76/769/EEC of 27 July 1976 on the approximation of the laws, regulations and administrative provisions of the Member States relating to restrictions on the marketing and use of certain dangerous substances and preparations. *Official Journal,* **L262**, 27.09.1976.

23. A full list of marketing and use restrictions can be seen at: http://www.europa.eu.int/scadplus/leg/en/lvb/l21271.htm.

24. Commission Decision 1999/815/EC prohibiting the placing on the market of toys and childcare articles intended to be placed in the mouth by children under three years of age and made of soft PVC containing certain phthalates. *Official Journal,* **L315**, 09.12.1999.

25. Proposal for a Directive of the European Parliament and of the Council amending for the twenty-third time Council Directive 76/769/EEC relating to restrictions on the marketing and use of certain dangerous substances and preparations (substances classified as carcinogens, mutagens or substances toxic to reproduction – c/m/r). COM(2001) 256 Final. *Official Journal,* **C213E**, 31.07.2001.

26. Regulation (EC) No. 2037/2000 of the European Parliament and of the Council of 29 June 2000 on substances that deplete the ozone layer. *Official Journal,* **L244**, 29.09.2000.

27. *Commission White Paper of 27 February 2001 on the strategy for a future chemicals policy.* COM(2001)88.

28. *Results of the Fourth Phase of SLIM.* COM(2000)56 Final.

29. Deloitte & Touche (2002). *Feasibility study on the resource requirements for a Central Entity.* Ref. B4-3040/2001/329289/MAR/C3.

30. Risk Policy Analysts (RPA) and Statistics Sweden (2002). *Assessment of the Impacts of New Regulations in the Chemicals Sector.*

31. Department for Environment, Food and Rural Affairs (Defra) (2002a). *EU Chemicals Policy: Animal Testing and Welfare Issues.* Paper No. CSF/02/30. Chemicals Stakeholder Forum, 7th Meeting, 12 March 2002.

32. House of Lords Select Committee on the European Union (2002). *Reducing the Risk – Regulating Industrial Chemicals.* Session 2001-2. 13th Report.

33. Defra (2002b). *New EU Chemicals Strategy – Position Statement by the UK government and the Devolved Administrations.* December 2002.

34. *United States non-paper on EU chemicals policy.*

35. *Swedish views on: Transparency – to benefit the general public and industry; industry's responsibility for chemical safety – a general clause, basic information requirements and quality assurance issues; and the authorisation system and comments on accelerated risk management.* The Swedish government. November 2002.

36. Notification of New Substances (NONS) Project results were reported in: European Commission (1998). *Three yearly report on the implementation of Directive 67/548/EEC on the classification, packaging and labelling of dangerous substances, as amended by Directive 92/32/EEC.*

37. See CLEEN website at: http://www.cleen-europe.org/index.html.

38. *Communication from the Commission to the Council, the European Parliament and the Economic and Social Committee – Towards a Thematic Strategy on the Use of Pesticides.* COM(2002)349 Final.

39. *EC White Paper on food safety of 12 January 2000.* COM(1999)719 final.

40. Directive 2001/95/EEC of the European Parliament and the Council of 3 December 2001 on general product safety. *Official Journal*, **L115**, 15.01.2001.

41. United Nations Environment Programme (UNEP) (1998). *Rotterdam Convention on the Prior Informed Consent Procedure for Certain Hazardous Chemicals and Pesticides in International Trade.*

42. United Nations Environment Programme (UNEP) (2001). *Stockholm Convention on Persistent Organic Pollutants.*

43. See United Nations Economic Commission for Europe (UNECE) website at: http://www.unece.org/env/lrtap/pops_h1.htm

44. UNEP Ozone Secretariat (2000). *The Montreal Protocol on Substances that Deplete the Ozone Layer as adjusted and/or amended in London 1990, Copenhagen 1992, Vienna 1995, Montreal 1997, Beijing 1999.* UNEP, Nairobi.

45. OSPAR Commission (2002). *Provisional Instruction Manual for the Dynamic Selection and Prioritisation Mechanism for Hazardous Substances (DYNAMEC).* OSPAR Secretariat, London.

46. See OSPAR website at: http://www.ospar.org/eng/html/substances/content.htm.

47. Department for Environment, Transport and the Regions (DETR) (1999). *Sustainable Production and Use of Chemicals – A Strategic Approach. The Government's Chemicals Strategy.* DETR, London.

48. Evidence from the Scottish Executive, February 2002.

49. Advisory Committee on Hazardous Substances (ACHS) (2003). *Sixth Annual Report.* Defra, London. The ACHS noted: 'This is a very simplified chart. In particular, the role of the devolved administrations in Scotland and Wales and the Northern Ireland Office who carry out some of these functions and sometimes have their own advisers are not included nor is the role of local government in controlling pollution. Pesticides, veterinary medicines and biocides are dealt with by their own legislation.'

50. Environment Agency (2002). *Managing Chemicals for a Better Environment – The Environment Agency's Chemicals Strategy.* Consultation Document.

51. *The Chemical Products Act.* Swedish Government Bill SFS 1985:426.

52. Swedish Chemicals Policy Committee, Ministry of Environment (1997). *Towards a Sustainable Chemicals Policy.*

53. Dutch Ministry of Housing, Spatial Planning and the Environment (2001). *Strategy on the Management of Substances.* VROM, The Hague.

54. See the Technical Regulations information system details for the decision at: http://www.europa.eu.int/comm/enterprise/tris/pisa/app/search/ index.cfm?fuseaction=pisa_notif_overview&iYear=2002&inum=292&lang=EN&sNLang=EN.

55. Evidence from the British Chemical Distributors and Traders Association, September 2002; evidence from the Chemical Industries Association, November 2002.

56. *The Toxic Substances Control Act (TSCA) of 1976.* 15 U.S.C. s/s 2601 *et seq.* (1976).

57. See US EPA website at: http://www.epa.gov/opptintr/newchems/assess.htm.

58. See US EPA website at: http://www.epa.gov/opptintr/newchems/chemcat.htm.

59. US General Audit Office (1994). *Toxic Substances Control Act: Legislative Changes Could Make the Act More Effective.* GAO/RCED-94-103.

60. US Environmental Protection Agency (EPA) (1997). *Chemistry Assistance Manual for Pre-Manufacture Notification Submitters.* EPA 744-R-97-003. March 1997.

61. See US EPA website at: http://www.epa.gov/tri/.

62. The Canadian Environmental Protection Act 1999 (CEPA 1999). Sections 73 and 74.

63. Chemicals Evaluation Division, Existing Substances Branch, Environment Canada (2002). *Environment Canada's Guidance for Categorising Organic Substances on the Domestic Substances List Determining Persistence, Bioaccumulation Potential and Inherent Toxicity to Non-Human Organisms.* Draft Report.

64. The EU Committee of the American Chamber of Commerce in Belgium (2001). *EU Committee Position Paper on the European Commission's White Paper on a Strategy for a Future Chemicals Policy.* May 2001.

65. Modified from: Fleischer, M.; Kelm, S. and Palm, D. (2000). *The impact of EU regulation on innovation of European industry: regulation and innovation in the chemical industry.* Institute for Prospective Technological Studies. EUR 19735 EN.

66. US EPA (1994). *US EPA/EC Joint Project on the Evaluation of (Quantitative) Structure Activity Relationships.* EPA 743-R-94-001.

67. See the Dow Chemicals website at: http://www.dow.com/environment/reports/ 1999/speech4.html.

68. Neven, B. and Schubert, R. (1998). *Comparison of Regulatory Requirements for the Notification of New Chemical Substances in the European Union, the USA and Japan.* Institute for Prospective Technological Studies. EUR 18119 EN.

69. Neven and Schubert (1998).

70. Neven and Schubert (1998).

71. Evidence from the Chemical Industries Association, November 2002.

72. Nordbeck, R. and Faust, M. (2002). *European chemicals regulation and its effect on innovation: an assessment of the EU 's White Paper on the Strategy for a future Chemicals Policy.* UFZ Discussion Paper 4/2002.

73. *European Communities – Measures Affecting Asbestos and Asbestos-Containing Products, Appellate Body Report and Panel Report.* Action by the Dispute Settlement Body, WT/DS135/12, adopted by the Dispute Settlement Body, 5 April 2001.

74. A summary of the case is available at the World Trade Organization (WTO) website: http://www.wto.org/english/tratop_e/envir_e/edis04_e.htm.

75. *United States – Import Prohibition of Certain Shrimp and Shrimp Products, Appellate Body Report and Panel Report pursuant to Article 21.5 of the DSU.* Action by the Dispute Settlement Body, WT/DS58/23, adopted by the Dispute Settlement Body, 21 November 2001.

76. Directive 2000/60/EC of the European Parliament and of the Council of 23 October 2000, establishing a framework for Community action in the field of water policy. *Official Journal*, **L327**, 22.12.2001.

77. Decision 2455/2001/EC of the European Parliament and of the Council of 20 November 2001, establishing the list of priority substances in the field of water policy and amending Directive 2000/60/EC. *Official Journal*, **L331**, 15.12.2001.

78. Council Directive 91/689/EEC of 12 December 1991 on hazardous waste. *Official Journal*, **L377**, 31.12.1991.

79. European Commission (2001). *Green Paper on Integrated Product Policy*. COM(2001)68.

80. Directive 2000/53/EC of the European Parliament and of the Council of 18 September 2000 on end-of-life vehicles. *Official Journal*, **L269**, 21.10.2000.

81. Proposals for a Directive of the European Parliament and of the Council on waste electrical and electronic equipment. COM(2000)347 Final. *Official Journal*, **C365**, 19.12.2000.

82. Proposal for a Directive of the European Parliament and the Council on the restriction of the use of certain hazardous substances in electrical and electronic equipment. COM(2000)347 Final. *Official Journal*, **C365**, 19.12.2000.

83. Information obtained during the Commission visit to the US, June 2002.

84. Council Directive 85/374/EEC of 25 July 1985 on the approximation of the laws, regulations and administrative provisions of the Member States concerning liability for defective products. *Official Journal*, **L210**, 07.08.1985.

85. The Consumer Protection Act 1987 (c.43).

86. Japanese Product Liability Law 1994 (No. 85).

87. Hamilton *et al.* v. Beretta U.S.A. Corp. *et al.*, 2001 96 N.Y. 2d 222.

88. *First Commission report of 13 December 1995 on the application of the Council Directive on the approximation of the laws, regulations and administrative provisions of the Member States concerning liability for defective products.* COM(95)617 Final.

89. *Report from the Commission of 31 January 2001 on the application of Directive 85/374 on liability for defective products.* COM(2000)893 Final.

90. A & Others v. National Blood Authority (2001). 3 AU E.R. 289.

91. E.C. Commission v. United Kingdom (Re: the Product Liability Directive) (1997). 3 C.M.L.R. 923.

92. Fairchild v. Glenhaven Funeral Services Ltd. (2002). 3 WLR 89 HL.

93. Sindall v. Abbott Laboratories, 707 P.2d 924, California, 1980.

94. Communication from the Commission to the Council and Parliament and the Economic and Social Committee: Green Paper on Remedying Environmental Damage. COM(93)47 Final.

95. Proposal for a Directive of the European Parliament and of the Council of 23 January 2002 on environmental liability with regard to the prevention and remedying of environmental damage. COM(2002)17 Final.

96. See the Chemical Industries Association website at: http://www.cia.org.uk industry/confidence3.htm

97. See for example evidence from the Royal Society, February 2002.

98. European Chemicals Bureau (1999). *Public Availability of Data on EU High Production Volume Chemicals*. EUR 18996EN.

99. Evidence from the Chemical Industries Association, February 2002;
    evidence from the Department of Health, January 2002;
    evidence from the Environment Agency, February 2002.

Chapter 4

1. Royal Commission on Environmental Pollution (1998). *Twenty-first Report – Setting Environmental Standards.* Cm 4053. The Stationery Office, London. See chapter 7.

2. Department for Environment, Transport and the Regions (DETR) (1999). *Sustainable Production and Use of Chemicals – A Strategic Approach. The Government's Chemicals Strategy.* DETR, London.

3. Evidence from Greenpeace, February 2002.

4. UK Chemicals Stakeholder Forum. First Annual Report 2000-2001. Prepared by Defra. Available from Defra Publications.

5. Twenty-first Report, see chapter 7.

6. *The Chemicals (Hazard Information and Packaging for Supply) Regulations 2002.* Statutory Instrument 2002 No.1689.

7. Directive 98/34/EC of the Parliament and of the Council of 22 June 1998 laying down a procedure for the provision of information in the field of technical standards and regulations and (following Directive 98/48/EC) regulations on information society services. *Official Journal,* **L204**, 21.07.98.

8. See ECVAM Scientific Information Service website at: http://ecvam-sis.jrc.it/.

9. OSPAR Commission (2002). Provisional Instruction Manual for the Dynamic Selection and Prioritisation Mechanism for Hazardous Substances (DYNAMEC). OSPAR Secretariat, London; Chemicals Evaluation Division, Existing Substances Branch, Environment Canada (2002). *Environment Canada's Guidance for Categorising Organic Substances on the Domestic Substances List Determining Persistence, Bioaccumulation Potential and Inherent Toxicity to Non-Human Organisms.* Draft Report.

10. Presentation to the Commission by Dr Nigel Rogers, January 2003.

11. Barlow, S.M., Greig, J.B., Bridges, J.W., Carere, A., Carpy, A.J.M., Galli, C.L., Keiner, J., Knudson, I., Koeter, H.B.W.M., Levy, L.S., Madsen, C., Mayer, S., Narbonne, J.F., Pfannkuch, F., Prodanchuk, M.G., Smith, M.R. and Steinberg, P. (2002). Hazard identification by methods of animal-based toxicology. *Food and Chemical Toxicology,* **40**, 145-191.

12. Tyle, H., Larsen, H.S., Wedebye, E.B., Sijm, D, Krog, T.P. and Niemelä, J. (2002). Identification of potential PBTs and vPvBs by use of QSARs. Danish EPA publication.

13. Barlow *et al.* (2002).

14. Eisenbrand, G., Pool-Zobel, B., Baker, V., Balls, M., Blaauboer, B.J., Boobis, A., Carere, A., Kevekordes, S., Lhuguenot, J-C., Pieters, R. and Kleiner, J. (2002). Methods of *in vitro* toxicology *Food and Chemical Toxicology,* **40**, 193-236.

15. Government/Research Councils Initiative on Risk Assessment and Toxicology (1999). *Physiologically-based pharmacokinetic modelling: a potential tool for risk assessment.* Published by the Institute for Environmental Health.

16. Borlak, J. and Bosio, A. (2002). The Use of Toxicogenomics. In: *Crucial Issues in Inhalation Research, Mechanistic, Clinical and Epidemiologic.* 8th International Symposium organised by Fraunhofer ITA. Editors Heinrich U. and Mohr U. INIS Monographs. Fraunhofer IRB Verlag.

17. Council Directive 76/768/EEC of 27 July 1976 on the approximation of the laws of the Member States relating to cosmetic products. *Official Journal* **L 262**, 27.09.1976.

18. Barlow *et al.* (2002).

19. On 5 April 2000 the Commission presented a Proposal for a Directive of the European Parliament and of the Council amending for the seventh time Council Directive 76/768/EEC on the approximation of the laws of the Member States relating to cosmetic products. COM(2000) 189 final. *Official Journal* **C 311 E**, 31.10. 2000.

20. The House of Lords Select Committee on Animals in Scientific Procedures (2002). *Report Volume 1*, HL Paper 150-I.

21. The '3 Rs' in this context are 'Reduction', 'Replacement', and 'Refinement' of animal testing.

22. Kenny, A.J., Thomas, K., Peeler, E., Osborn, D., Waldock, M., Matthiessen, P., Shore, R., Wright, J. and Feist, S. (2002). *Assessing the potential of environmental monitoring for detecting and responding to damage caused by the use of chemicals.* Report for the Royal Commission on Environmental Pollution by the Centre for Environment, Fisheries and Aquaculture Science (CEFAS) and the Centre for Ecology and Hydrology (CEH).

23. Evidence from Royal Society of Edinburgh, July 2002.

24. Kenny *et al.* (2002).

25. Fairbrother A. (2001) Putting the impacts of Environmental Contamination into Perspective. In: *Ecotoxicology of Wild Mammals.* Eds. R.F. Shore and B.A. Rattner. John Wiley and Sons Ltd. Chichester;
    Kenny *et al.* (2002).

26. Kenny *et al.* (2002).

27. Shugart, L., Bickman, J., Jackim, E., McMahon, G., Ridley, W., Stein, J. and Steinert, S.S. (1992). DNA Alterations. In: *Biomarkers: Biochemical, Physiological, and Histological Markers of Anthropogenic Stress.* Eds. R.J. Hugget, R.A. Kimerle, P.M. Mehrle Jr. and H.L. Bergman. Lewis Publishers, Chelsea, Michigan. Pages 125-153.

28. Wright, D.A. and Welbourn, P. (2002). *Environmental Toxicology.* Cambridge University Press, Cambridge.

29. Kenny *et al.* (2002).

30. Allen, Y., Balaam, J., Bamber, S., Bates, H., Best, G., Bignell, J., Brown, E., Craft, J., Davies, I.M., Depledge, M., Dyer, R., Feist, S., Hurst, M., Hutchinson, T., Jones, G., Jones, M., Katsiadaki, I., Kirby, M., Leah, R., Matthiessen, P., Megginson, C., Moffat, C.F., Moore, A., Pirie, D., Robertson, F., Robinson, C.D., Scott, A.P., Simpson, M., Smith, A., Stagg, R.M., Struthers, S., Thain, J., Thomas, K., Tolhurst, L., Waldock, M. and Walker, P. (2002) *Endocrine Disruption in the Marine Environment.* CEFAS;
    Kenny *et al.* (2002).

31. Kenny *et al.* (2002);
    DEFRA Aquaculture Link Website, Project Abstract – SHL27 – Assessment of Toxicity Identification Evaluation (TIE) techniques for the elucidation of bivalve shellfish hatchery and nursery production problems – http://www2.defra.gov.uk/research/LINK/publications/Abstracts/Aquaculture/shl27_Abstract.pdf.

32. Kenny *et al.* (2002);
    Hollis, R.P., Kilham, K. and Glover, L.A. (1999) Design and application of a biosensor for monitoring toxicity of compounds to eukaryotes. *Applied and Environmental Microbiology* **66**: 1676-1679;
    Horsburgh, A.M., Mardlin, D.P., Turner, N.L., Henkler, R., Strachan, N., Glover, L.A., Paton, G.I. and Kilham, K. (2002). On-line microbial biosensing and fingerprinting of water pollutants. *Biosensors and Bioelectronics*, **17**: 495-501;
    Sousa, S., Duffy, C., Weitz, H., Glover, LA., Henkler, R., Kilham, K. (1998). Use of a lux bacterial biosensor to identify constraints to remediation of contaminated environmental samples. *Environmental Toxicology and Chemistry,* **17**: 1039-1045.

33. Balaguer, P., Joyeux, A., Denison, M.S., Vincent, R., Gillesby, B.E. and Zacharewski, T. (1996). Assessing the estrogenic and dioxin-like activities of chemicals and complex mixtures using *in vitro* recombinant receptor-reporter gene assays. *Canadian Journal of Physiology and Pharmacology,* **74**: 216-222;

Clark, G.C., Chu, M., Rayfield B., Stone, J. and Cooke, M. (1999). A novel low-cost air sampling device (AmbStack sampler) and detection system (CALUX bioassay) for measuring air emissions of dioxin, furan and PCB on a TEQ basis tested with a model industrial boiler. *Organohalogen Compounds,* **40**: 79-82.

Kenny *et al.* (2002);

Machala, M., Vondráček, J., Bláha, L., and Ciganek M. and Neča J. (2001). Aryl hydrocarbon receptor mediated activity of mutagenic polycyclic aromatic hydrocarbons determined using *in vitro* reporter gene assay. *Mutation Research/Genetic Toxicology and Environmental Mutagenesis,* **497**: 49-62;

Murk, A.J. Legler, J., Denison, M.S., Giesy, J.P., van de Guchte, C. and Brouwer, A. (1996). Chemical-activated luciferase gene expression (CALUX): a novel in vitro bioassay for Ah receptor active compounds in sediments and pore water. *Fundamentals of Applied Toxicology,* **33**, 149-160;

Van Overmeire, I., Clark, G.C., Clark, D.J., Brown, M.D., Chu, W.M., Cooke, W.M., Denison, W.M., Baeyens, S. and Srebrnik, S. Goeyens, L. (2001). Trace Contamination with Dioxin-like Chemicals: Evaluation of Bioassay based TEQ determination for Hazard Assessment and Regulatory responses. *Environmental Science and Policy,* **4**, 345-357;

Van Overmeire, I., Carbonelle, S., Van Loco, J., Roos, P., Brown, D., Chu, M., Clark, G. and Goeyens, L. (2002). Validation of the CALUX bioassay: quantitative screening approach. *Organohalogen Compounds,* **58**, 353-358.

34. Harrington, L.A. and Macdonald, D.W. (2002). *A Review of the Effects of Pesticides on Wild Terrestrial Mammals in Britain.* Wildlife Conservation Research Unit;

Smith, R.H. (1999). Population biology and non-target effects of rodenticides: trying to put the eco into ecotoxicology. In: *Advances in vertebrate pest management* (Eds. D.P. Cowan and C.J. Frear): 354-356. Filander-Verlag, Fürth.

35. Van den Brandt, P., Voorrips, L., Hertz-Picciotto, I., Shuker, D., Boeing, H., Speijers, G., Guittard, C., Kliener, J., Knowles, M., Wolk, A. and Goldbohm, A. (2002). The contribution of epidemiology to risk assessment of chemicals in food and diet. *Food and Chemical Toxicology,* **40**, 387-424.

36. European Environment Agency/European Science Foundation (EEA/ESF) (2002). *Chemicals in the European Environment: a survey of monitoring and exposure information.*

37. Institute for Environment and Health (1996). *The use of biomarkers in environmental exposure assessment.* Report R5.

38. Twenty-first Report, see paragraph 2.32.

39. Institute for Environment and Health (1996).

40. Kenny *et al.* (2002).

41. Reconnaissance monitoring aims to determine what chemicals are present in the environment and whether a change in the health status or function of the ecosystem, the quality of a habitat, the functional integrity of an ecological community or the level of harm to individuals or populations of organisms in the environment is due to chemicals or attributable to some other cause (information supplied by Dr Dan Osborn and Professor Peter Matthiessen, NERC Centre for Ecology and Hydrology).

42. Department for Environment, Transport and the Regions (DETR) (1999). *Sustainable Production and Use of Chemicals – A Strategic Approach. The Government's Chemicals Strategy*. DETR, London.

43. See documents on HSE website
    http://www.hse.gov.uk/aboutus/hsc/meetings/2002/121102/c142.pdf;
    http://www.hse.gov.uk/aboutus/hsc/meetings/2002/121102/c106a.pdf;
    http://www.hse.gov.uk/aboutus/hsc/meetings/2002/121102/c143.pdf;
    http://www.hse.gov.uk/aboutus/hsc/meetings/2002/121102/c143a.pdf.

Chapter 5

1. National Society for Clean Air and Environmental Protection (NSCA) (2001). *Smarter Regulation – The report of the NSCA Commission on industrial regulation and sustainable development*. NSCA, Brighton.

2. Mont, O. (2001). The Swedish Product Choice Principle. *European Environmental Law Review*, December 2001, 351-363.

3. Ministry of the Environment, Norway. Act No. 79 of 11 June 1976 relating to the control of products and consumer services (The Product Control Act), as amended 1 January 2000.

4. Evidence from the Chemical Industries Association, November 2002.

5. World Bank (1993). *Agricultural Pest Management Guidelines and Best Practice*. World Bank Operating Manual B 4.03. April 1993.

6. CEFIC Position Paper – Substitution and Market Economy a need for clarification, March 2002.

7. Evidence from the Royal Society of Chemistry, January 2001.

8. See EEB comments on the White Paper at: http://www.eeb.org/activities/chemicals/main.htm.

9. Directive 98/8/EC of the European Parliament and the Council of 16 February 1998 concerning the placing of biocidal products on the market. *Official Journal*, **L 123**, 24.04.1998.

10. Risk Policy Analysts (RPA) (2002a). *Scope for the Use of Economic Instruments for Selected Persistent Pollutants – Case Studies*. Report for the Department for Environment, Food and Rural Affairs (Defra). RPA, Loddon.

11. Department for Environment, Transport and the Regions (DETR) (1999). *Sustainable Production and Use of Chemicals – A Strategic Approach. The Government's Chemicals Strategy*. DETR, London. See section 3.3.

12. TNO (2001). *Emissions of hazardous substances form finished products*. TNO-MEP – R 2001/121.

13. See the PAN-UK website at: http://www.pan-uk.org/lap/survey.htm.

14. PAN-UK personal communication.

15. Maxson, P.A. (2001). *Chemical releases from products: Emissions during the product life-cycle*. Presentation at the Falkenberg Conference on chemicals in products.

16. See the California Air Resources Board website at: http://www.arb.ca.gov/html/brochure/consprod.htm.

17. Brown, S.K. and Cheng, M. (2000). *Volatile Organic Compounds (VOCs) in New Car Interiors*. Presented at the 15th International Clean Air and Environment Conference, Sydney, 26-30 November 2000.

18. Van Veen, M.P., Van Engelen, J.G.M. and Van Raaij, M.T.M. (2001). Crossing the river stone by stone: Approaches for residential risk assessment for consumers. *Annals of Occupational Hygiene*, **45**, S107-S118.

19. *EU Risk Assessment – Diphenyl Ether Pentabromo Derivative*. Final Report. August 2000.

20. Commission Decision 2000/532/EC of 3 May 2000 replacing Decision 94/3/EC establishing a list of wastes pursuant to Article 1(a) of Council Directive 75/442/EEC on waste and Council Decision 94/904/EC establishing a list of hazardous waste pursuant to Article 1(4) of Council Directive 91/689/EEC on hazardous waste. *Official Journal*, **L226**, 06.09.2000.

21. Personal communication, Hewlett Packard.

22. *Commission White Paper of 27 February 2001 on the strategy for a future chemicals policy*. COM(2001)88.

23. British Chemical Distributors and Traders Association (BCDTA) (2002). *Position Paper – The European Union's White Paper on the future of chemicals policy*. November 2002;
see CEFIC's (the European chemical industry association) Chemicals Policy review website at: http://www.chemicalspolicyreview.org/frameglobal.asp?redirecturl=keymessages.html.

24. Council Directive 91/155/EEC of 5 March 1991, defining and laying down in implementation of Article 10 of Council Directive 88/379/EEC, the detailed arrangements for the system of specific information relating to dangerous preparations (*Official Journal*, **L76**, 22.03.1991), as amended by Directive 93/112/EC (*Official Journal*, **L314**, 16.12.1993), and Directive 2001/58/EC (*Official Journal*, **L212**, 07.08.2001).

25. SAFE Project (1997). *Assessment of the Usefulness of Material Safety Data Sheets (MSDS) for SMEs*. Commission of the European Union, Directorate-General V, Employment, Industrial Relations and Social Affairs, File No SOC 97 201817.

26. Law of 5 December 1985, comprising rules for the protection of persons in environments where hazardous substances and preparations are present (Netherlands Chemical Substances Act).

27. *The Chemicals (Hazard Information and Packaging for Supply) Regulations 2002*. Statutory Instrument 2002 No. 1689.

28. OKO-Institut e.V. (2002). *White Paper for the Reform of Chemicals Policy: From Concept to Implementation – Requirements, Experiences and Perspectives in relation to Information Flow*. Oko Institut, Freiburg.

29. The Boyd Group (2002). *The Use of Animals in Testing Household Products. A Discussion Paper and Statement of Principle*. The Universities Federation for Animal Welfare. Available at: http://www.boyd-group.demon.co.uk.

30. The Boyd Group (2002).

31. Hamburger Umwelt Institute (1997). *Poor Design Practices – gaseous emissions from complex products*.

32. See Danish Environmental Protection Agency website at: http://www.mst.dk/chemi/01080000.htm.

33. KemI (2002). *Chemicals in articles – where is the knowledge?*

34. KemI (2001). *Chemicals in Products as a Source of Environmental Pollution*. Report of the Falkenberg Conference, 5-6 April 2001. KemI, Stockholm.

35. Presentation to the Commission from Professor James Clark, Green Chemistry Network, March 2002.

36. US Environmental Protection Agency (EPA) (2002). *Green Chemistry Program Fact Sheet*. Office of Pollution Prevention and Toxics.

37. See US EPA website at: http://www.epa.gov/greenchemistry/presgcc.html.

38. See CRYSTAL Faraday Partnership in Green Chemical Technology website at: http://www.crystalfaraday.org/.

39. See the Green Chemistry Network website at: http://www.chemsoc.org/networks/gcn/.

40. European Environment Agency (EEA) (2001). *Establishment of a European Green and Sustainable Chemistry Award.* Technical Report No. 53.

41. Organisation for Economic Co-operation and Development (OECD) (2002). *Need for Research and Development Programmes in Sustainable Chemistry.* OECD Environment Directorate. ENV/JM/MONO(2002)12. OECD, Paris.

42. Reiskin, E.D., White, A.L., Kauffman-Johnson, J. and Votta, T. (2000). Servicizing the chemical supply chain. *Journal of Industrial Ecology*, **3**, 19-31.

43. Reiskin *et al.* (2000).

44. Green Alliance (2002). *Service Innovation for Sustainability – a new option for UK environmental policy?*

45. Global Environmental Management Initiative (2001). *Environment: Value to the Top Line.*

46. Austria promotes chemical leasing model. *ENDS Environment Daily*, No. 1326, 11 November 2002 (http://www.environmentdaily.com).

47. UK Round Table on Sustainable Development (2000). *Not too Difficult! Economic Instruments to Promote Sustainable Development within a Modernised Economy.*

48. European Commission (2001). *Green Paper on Integrated Product Policy.* COM(2001)68.

49. ECOTEC (2000). *Design of a Tax or Charge Scheme for Pesticides.* Report for DETR.

50. RPA (2002b). *Scope for the Use of Economic Instruments for Selected Persistent Pollutants.* Report for Defra. RPA, Loddon.

51. RPA (2002a).

52. Source: ENDS Environment Daily 1413, 26/03/03 (http://www.environmentdaily.com).

53. Evidence from the British Retail Consortium and Marks and Spencer, June 2002.

54. Evidence from the British Retail Consortium and Marks and Spencer, June 2002.

55. Judgement of the European Court of Justice, C-52/00, 2002.

56. Clift, R. (2001). Clean technology and industrial ecology. In: *Pollution – Causes, Effects and Control.* Ed. R.M. Harrison. Fourth Edition. Royal Society of Chemistry, Cambridge.

57. OECD (2001). *Environmental Outlook for the Chemicals Industry.* OECD Environmental, Health and Safety Division. OECD, Paris.

58. OECD (2001).

59. Directive 98/34/EC of the Parliament and of the Council of 22 June 1998 laying down a procedure for the provision of information in the field of technical standards and regulations and (following Directive 98/48/EC) regulations on information society services. *Official Journal*, **L204**, 21.07.98.

60. Government seeks voluntary action by industry to reduce the risks from dangerous chemicals. *Defra News Release*, No. 422/02, 18.10.02.

61. See the Environment Agency website at: http://www.environment-agency.gov.uk/business/301397/255244/?version=1&lang=_e.

62. Commission Decision 2000/479/EC of 17 July 2000 on the implementation of a European Pollutant Emission Register (EPER) according to Article 15 of Council Directive 96/61/EC concerning integrated pollution prevention and control (IPPC) (notified under document number C(2000) 2004).

63. See the Nordic Eco-label website at: http://www.ecolabel.no/Engelsk/Criteria.html.

64. See EU Eco-label website at: http://europa.eu.int/comm/environment/ecolabel/.

65. Statistics Sweden have reported that consumption of eco-labelled goods in Sweden rose steadily between 1995 and 1998 but only to reach 2.2% of total private consumption. Statistics Sweden (2001) *Sustainable development indicators for Sweden – A first set 2001*. Statistics Sweden and Swedish Environmental Protection Agency, Stockholm.

66. Evidence from the British Retail Consortium and Marks and Spencer, June 2002.

67. United Nations Department of Economic and Social Affairs, Division for Sustainable Development (2002). *World Summit on Sustainable Development – Plan of Implementation*.

68. European Commission (2002). *Second Meeting of the Working Group on Substances in Products*. SIP/015. 14-15 January 2002.

69. WWF (2002). *Regulating Substances in Imported Articles*. Presentation given by M. Warhurst at the European Environment Bureau Conference, 'European Chemicals Policy Reform – From paralysis to action', Copenhagen, 27 September 2002.

70. CEFIC (2002). *Substances in articles – justification of the approach taken by the industry support team*. 30 January 2002.

71. Resources for the Future (RFF) (2002). Multilateral Trade Agreements and Market-Based Environmental Policies. Discussion Paper 02-28.

72. United States Superfund Amendments and Reauthorization Act of 1986.

73. United States – Taxes on Petroleum and Certain Imported Substances, Report of the [Disputes] Panel, adopted on 17 June 1987 (L/6175 – 34S/136).

74. Interestingly, though, the [Disputes] Panel quoted Article II, Paragraph 2(a), 'in respect of an article from which the imported product has been manufactured or produced in whole or in part,' not the term 'physically incorporated'.

75. Evidence from the Chemical Industries Association, November 2002.

76. Science Policy Research Unit (SPRU) (2002). *A Review of the Impact of Regulation on the Chemical Industry*. Available on the Royal Commission on Environmental Pollution website at: http://www.rcep.org.uk/chemicals.

77. Note: data for the EU are number of substances notified since the 7th Amendment (from http://ecb.jrc.it/new-chemicals/. Data for the US are effective static NOCs (Fleischer, personal communication, 2003).

78. OECD (2001).

79. CEFIC (2002). *Facts and Figures – The European Chemical Industry in a Worldwide Perspective June 2002*.

80. Brophy, J. (1999). *The Impact of Chemicals Industry Mergers, Acquisitions and Restructuring on the UK Chemistry Infrastructure*. Royal Society of Chemistry, London.

81. Chemicals Innovation and Growth Team (CIGT) (2002). *Enhancing the Competitiveness of the UK Chemicals Industry*. Department of Trade and Industry, London.

82. Results of a MORI poll reported in CIGT (2002).

Appendix A

ANNOUNCEMENT OF THE STUDY AND INVITATION TO SUBMIT EVIDENCE

A1 Announcement of the Study

The Commission's study of the long-term effects of chemicals in the environment was announced on 19 October 2000 in the following terms:

ROYAL COMMISSION STUDY ON LONG-TERM EFFECTS OF CHEMICALS IN THE ENVIRONMENT

The Royal Commission has decided to undertake a study of the long-term effects of chemicals in the environment ('effects' include those on both the natural environment and humans exposed via environmental routes) and how those should be controlled.

The most widely supported of the four options for its next study on which the Commission sought views in November 1999 was the long-term effects of chemicals and biological agents. The Commission's decision has taken that into account, together with the view expressed by several respondents that a study that attempted to cover both chemicals and biological agents would be too broad. The new study will begin in the middle of next year, when the Commission will invite the submission of detailed evidence on specific issues. The aim is to publish a report in 2002.

The Commission is now seeking to identify the issues and areas it would be most appropriate for the new study to investigate.

BACKGROUND TO THE NEW STUDY

The developments in the chemical industry during the last 100 years have brought spectacular benefits to mankind, helping to improve health care and increase agricultural yields, not to mention countless products that make our lives easier. On the other hand, the manufacture and use of chemicals can create risks to humans and the natural environment, many of which are poorly characterised. There is a long history of serious environmental concerns associated with chemicals that were originally thought to be purely beneficial: for example organochlorine pesticides, such as DDT; industrial chemicals, such as PCBs; and now a wide range of suspected endocrine-disrupting chemicals.

For many years there has been a large, and rapidly growing, national and international effort to assess the effects of chemicals in the environment. A variety of EU legislation now covers the assessment of new chemicals, high-tonnage existing chemicals, pesticides, biocides, and veterinary medicines. Framework Directives for water and air also cover the effects of chemicals in those media. OECD has an extensive data-gathering programme on high production volume chemicals, and regional organisations, such as the Oslo and Paris Commission and the United Nations Economic Commission for Europe, have developed potentially far-reaching agreements seeking to control the risk of long-term effects of chemicals in the environment. Globally, organisations such as the International Programme on Chemical Safety, the International Register of Potentially Toxic Chemicals and the International Organisation on the Management of Chemicals seek to review the available data on a range of substances.

Despite this huge effort, and related initiatives by the UK and other governments, pollution control agencies and the chemical industry itself, major doubts persist on the effectiveness of present policies in protecting biodiversity, and the health of both humans and ecosystems, from unintended long-term effects. The UK government's recent chemicals strategy[1] and the forthcoming EU review of policy are reflections of this concern.

The Commission is aware that this area, in common with many others in the environmental field, is one where most decisions are taken at a European, rather than a national level. It considers that it is in a good position to provide an authoritative overview of the many facets of the subject, leading to conclusions on the principles that should underpin the process. Most other reviews focus only on particular aspects. The Commission's study should prove timely, both at a national level, where it will provide an input to the work of the new Chemicals Stakeholder Forum (the Commission is already in touch with the Forum), and will be able to review the impact and effectiveness of the government's chemicals strategy, and internationally, at a time when the debate on the effectiveness of chemical assessment and control programmes is likely to be coming to a head. The UK is, in any case, one of the leading players in chemical assessment programmes in the EU and beyond, and positions taken by the UK government are likely to have significant influence at those levels.

BROAD TOPICS TO BE COVERED

In its study the Commission intends to cover the following broad topics:

a. An overview of existing scientific knowledge on the long-term effects of chemicals in the environment, and further research needs;

b. How chemicals are best assessed and potential hazards and risks identified;

c. The principles that should be followed in regulating chemicals, while capitalising on their potential benefits; that is, how identified problems are best addressed, and chemical manufacture, marketing, use, and disposal most efficiently controlled to protect human health and the natural environment.

Each topic covers a wide range of issues, some of which concern more than one topic. The issues include:

1. The biological species, environmental pathways and adverse effects of most concern;

2. Whether the standard test methods adequately determine the environmental behaviour and long-term environmental effects of chemicals;

3. The balance between the desires for toxicity testing and animal welfare;

4. The development and use of predictive methods to fill data gaps;

5. The adequacy of chemical and/or biological monitoring to help evaluate predicted behaviour and discover unforeseen effects;

6. The chemicals that should be assessed most urgently (are those produced in quantities over 1000t/yr the greatest concern?);

7. Dealing with uncertainty and/or lack of data in the assessment process;

8. The speed of the current assessment process;

9. The pros and cons of different approaches to assessment, for example comparative assessment, assessment of groups of substances, hazard- versus risk-based approaches;

10. The operation of the Precautionary Principle in chemical assessment and control;

11. The role of the Substitution Principle in chemical control (including its possible extension to consider non-chemical solutions);

12. The incorporation of people's values into the process;

13. The responsibilities of producers and users of chemicals (assisting assessment and product stewardship);

14. The openness and transparency of the assessment process;

15. The respective roles of, and most effective co-ordination between, i) national and ii) international bodies in the assessment and control of different types of chemical and exposure route;

16. Gaps or deficiencies in the present coverage of regulation, how these should be filled, and the extent to which existing regulatory codes need to be integrated or made more consistent in their approach at both national and international levels;

17. The effectiveness of different types of control and/or mitigation;

18. Tensions between free trade and environmental protection.

Many of these issues, especially those concerning the application of science and its integration with people's values, have been previously addressed by the Commission in its 21st report[2] and its response to the government's consultation on its chemicals strategy[3].

Any long-term biological effects of chemicals in the environment may be included in the study, regardless of whether their use is deliberately targeted at biological systems or not. So, for example, both the use of xenobiotics in agriculture (with the side effect of the development of resistant organisms) and the inadvertent release of micropollutants (for example, dioxins and PCBs) and other endocrine disruptors will be of interest. The scope of the study could cover all organic and inorganic chemicals that either have, or may have, long-term biological effects in the environment, where human activities increase their release. However, the aim will be to assess the overall significance of the effects on human health and the natural environment, rather than catalogue particular effects of particular chemicals.

In the interests of maintaining a suitable focus for the study, the Commission has decided to exclude consideration of radioactive substances and those that cause only indirect effects on biological systems, for example ozone depleting chemicals. Occupational and consumer exposure (except via the food chain) will also be excluded. However, it will keep in mind that there may be lessons to be learned from the approaches used either in those fields, or others such as the assessment and control of biological agents.

References

1. Sustainable Production and Use of Chemicals – A Strategic Approach, DETR, December 1999.
2. Royal Commission on Environmental Pollution, 21st Report: Setting Environmental Standards, October 1998, TSO, ISBN 0-10-140532-4.
3. Response from the Royal Commission on Environmental Pollution to the DETR consultation paper on Sustainable Use and Production of Chemicals, December 1998: Available on the Commission's website at http://www.rcep.org.uk/news/98-5.html.

A2 Invitation to Submit Evidence

After considering the responses to the original announcement, the Commission invited evidence on 24 October 2001 in the following terms:

ROYAL COMMISSION STUDY ON THE LONG-TERM EFFECTS OF CHEMICALS IN THE ENVIRONMENT: ISSUES ON WHICH THE COMMISSION WOULD WELCOME EVIDENCE

BACKGROUND

The central aim of the Study is to analyse the key issues and make recommendations designed to reduce the chance that chemical use will cause long-term damage to the natural environment, or to human health as a result of exposure mediated by the environment. The Commission will be looking at:

- The current level of understanding of the fate and effects of chemicals in the environment and the need and scope for improvement in this knowledge;

- The short-term optimum balance between regulation, financial instruments, market forces, consumer pressures and technological advances, and the respective effects of these approaches on attitudes and behaviour; and

- The longer-term search to find a better way of doing things, for example by encouraging 'green chemistry' (designing chemical products and processes that reduce or eliminate the use and generation of hazardous substances).

Below is a series of underpinning assumptions, followed by a menu of potential guiding principles, and more detailed questions on chemical assessment and control. It is important to note that the statements and questions are not intended to limit the Commission's range of study, but rather focus attention on the areas where Members believe they are most in need of input at this stage.

UNDERPINNING ASSUMPTIONS

The Commission's questions are based on a number of assumptions. Respondents are free to provide evidence that challenges these assumptions, which are:

i. Only a small fraction of industrially produced chemicals have been studied in any depth, and ignorance outweighs knowledge at every point in the risk assessment process;

ii. Worrying trends in both human health and biodiversity may be at least partly attributable to chemicals;

iii. Large numbers of manufactured chemicals released into the environment interact in some way with biological organisms and ecosystems, many by way of specific modes of action, and we know very little about the vast majority of these individual interactions;

iv. Effects from environmental exposure to chemical mixtures will be synergistic in some cases, but we know very little about which these might be, or how important they are;

v. Environmental exposure estimates are subject to large uncertainty and indeterminacy; and

vi. The capacity of the bureaucratic systems for assessment and regulatory decision are as much limiting factors as the lack of data and scientific understanding of the processes.

ISSUES ON WHICH THE COMMISSION WOULD WELCOME EVIDENCE

OPTIONS FOR GUIDING PRINCIPLES FOR THE CONTROL OF CHEMICALS

The Commission would welcome evidence on the merits and likely outcomes of the adoption of the following principles. The principles are not necessarily mutually exclusive, and respondents might like to comment on the best balance between them. They may also wish to comment on the weight to be given in each case to the degree of environmental precaution and the social and economic costs and benefits:

1. Control of chemicals on the basis of risk (the *status quo*);

2. Control on the basis of hazard;

3. Assessment and/or control on the basis of environmental monitoring;

4. The degree of control should be related to the societal need for the chemical;

5. Using the substitution principle (basing decisions on the availability of safer alternatives);

6. Reversing the burden of proof for chemicals and their use in products (as for pesticides);

7. Placing a much stronger onus on the manufacturer/marketer to find out how a chemical is being used and accept liability for any long-term damage caused (top down approach);

8. Increasing the responsibility on downstream users and retailers to prevent long-term damage from chemicals incorporated in products they make or sell (bottom up approach);

9. Requirements to make information available so that all buyers can make informed decisions on products containing chemicals of concern.

SPECIFIC QUESTIONS

10. Risk assessment
    a. Should we be more concerned with assessments that yield false positive or false negative results? (This will depend on your views on how often each outcome occurs, and the seriousness of taking incorrect, or delayed decisions as a consequence.)

    b. Is there evidence that man-made chemicals introduce a qualitatively different risk to that posed by exposure to naturally occurring chemicals?

    c. What should be the role of monitoring of i) biological systems and ii) concentrations of chemicals and how should the results be incorporated into assessments?

    d. Who should be responsible for providing data on chemicals and their lifecycles, and how can we ensure the data are robust?

    e. How valuable are *in vivo* animal tests in the prediction of each type of effect on the natural environment and in humans?

    f. What is the potential for the replacement of *in vivo* tests in i) priority setting and ii) regulatory decisions?

g. How can the uncertainties and indeterminacies inherent in chemical risk assessment be substantially reduced and/or overcome?

11. Current chemical policy

a. Why do chemical control debates take so long?

b. What in practice has been the relative importance in chemical control debates of: hazard assessment; risk assessment; monitoring data; commercial pressures; public opinion; other factors?

c. Regulatory pressure tends to lead to fewer chemicals on the market (e.g. the Plant Protection Product Directive in the EU, and the relative numbers of new chemicals registered in the EU and US). What are the adverse and/or beneficial effects (economic, social and environmental) of such a trend?

d. Are there any gaps or overlaps in either the organisational structure or the current regulatory regimes for chemicals or protection of specific media from chemicals?

12. Roles and responsibilities in chemical control

a. How should responsibilities for the safe use of chemicals be divided between government, chemical producers, product manufacturers, importers, retailers, and users, and what could be their role in efficient and effective chemical stewardship and control?

b. What influence should the following factors have on regulatory decisions – precautionary principle, cost-benefit appraisal, encouragement of innovation, competition, and international trade issues?

c. Under what circumstances could legal liability be applied to encourage responsible behaviour, and on whom should it fall?

d. How should society ensure fair and reasonable public participation in the process of chemical control and how can this be facilitated?

e. How might government encourage the development of more environmentally friendly chemicals and/or more efficient use of chemicals (e.g. green chemistry/non-chemical solutions, chemicals services industry)?

As ever, the challenge is not so much in pointing out the flaws in the current system, as proposing something better.

Appendix B

CONDUCT OF THE STUDY

In order to carry out this study Commission Members sought written and oral evidence, commissioned studies and advice on specific topics and made a number of visits.

EVIDENCE

In parallel with the news releases inviting evidence, which are reproduced in appendix A, the Secretariat wrote direct to a large number of organisations.

The organisations and individuals listed below either submitted evidence or provided information on request for the purposes of the study or otherwise gave assistance. In some cases, indicated by an asterisk, meetings were held with Commission Members or the Secretariat so that oral evidence could be given or particular issues discussed.

GOVERNMENT DEPARTMENTS

Department for Environment, Food and Rural Affairs*
Department of the Environment, Transport and the Regions
Department of Health
Department of Trade and Industry
Ministry of Agriculture Fisheries and Food

DEVOLVED ADMINISTRATIONS

Department of the Environment Northern Ireland
National Assembly for Wales
Scottish Executive

PARLIAMENTARY BODIES

House of Lords Select Committee on the European Union*

EUROPEAN AND INTERNATIONAL BODIES

Conseil Europeen de L'Industrie Chimique
European Centre for Ecotoxicology and Toxicology of Chemicals
European Centre for the Validation of Alternative Methods
European Commission Directorates General for Environment*, Enterprise, Health and Consumer
    Protection, and Research
European Commission Joint Research Centre
European Environment Agency

Organisation for Economic Co-operation and Development*

OTHER ORGANISATIONS

Advisory Committee on Pesticides
Association of the British Pharmaceutical Industry
B&Q PLC
Biotechnology and Biological Sciences Research Council
BP Chemicals Ltd
British Association of Chemical Specialities
British Chemical Distributors and Traders Association*
British Coatings Federation*
British Medical Association
British Plastics Federation
British Retail Consortium*
British Union for the Abolition of Vivisection*
Centre for Environment, Fisheries and Aquaculture Science*
Centre for Reproductive Biology, University of Edinburgh
Chartered Institute of Environmental Health*
Chemical Industries Association*
Committee of Toxicology of Chemicals in Food, Consumer Products and the Environment
Confederation of British Industry
Cosmetics, Toiletries and Perfumery Association*
Council for British Archaeology
Countryside Council for Wales
Danish National Environmental Research Institute
Development Initiative for Chemically Dependent Areas in the UK*
Economic and Social Research Council
Engineering and Physical Sciences Research Council
English Nature*
Environment Agency*
Environment Canada
Food Standards Agency*
Forestry Commission
Friends of the Earth
Green Alliance
Greenpeace UK*
Health and Safety Executive* with the Health and Safety Commission
Institute for Environment and Health
Institution of Environmental Sciences
Institution of Professionals, Managers and Specialists
Joint Nature Conservation Committee
KemI, Swedish National Chemical Inspectorate
London School of Hygiene and Tropical Medicine
Marine Conservation Society
Marks and Spencer PLC*
Ministère de l'aménagement du territoire et de l'environnement, France
National Farmers' Union of Scotland
Natural Environment Research Council
Non-ferrous Alliance

Pesticide Action Network
Pesticide Safety Directorate
Royal Academy of Engineering
Royal College of General Practitioners
Royal College of Veterinary Surgeons
Royal Environmental Health Institute of Scotland
Royal Society for the Prevention of Cruelty to Animals*
Royal Society of Chemistry*
Royal Society of Edinburgh*
Royal Society*
Scottish Environment Protection Agency
Scottish Natural Heritage
Small Area Health Statistics Unit
Soap and Detergent Industry Association
Thomas Swan Ltd
Transport and General Workers Union
UK Agricultural Supply Trade Association
UK Cleaning Products Industry Association
Ulster Farmers Union
Worldwide Fund for Nature*

INDIVIDUALS

Professor John Ashby
Dr Murdoch Baxter
Professor Finn Bro-Rasmussen
Professor Jim Bridges*
Mr Tom Burke*
Dr Peter Carnell
Professor James Clark*
Professor David Coggon*
Professor Robert Combes
Professor John Dearden
Mr Bill Durodié
Mr Steffen Erler
Mr Nigel Haigh
Professor Kevin Jones*
Dr Norman King
Sir John Krebs*
Dr Ragnar Lofstedt
Dr Richard Murray-Smith
Ms Ilga Nielsen
Dr Nigel Rogers*
The Earl of Selborne
Dr David Slater
Professor John Sumpter*
Mr Stephen Tindale*
Dr Henrik Tyle
Professor Gerd Winter

Commissioned studies

The following papers were commissioned in the course of the study:

Chemical Assessment and Control – Interactions Among Industry, Public and Policy Makers. J. Tait, Scottish Universities Policy Research and Advice Network. March 2001.

Literature Review – Studies on People's Values in Relation to Chemicals and their Effects on Humans and the Natural Environment. A. Bruce, C. Lyall and J. Tait, Scottish Universities Policy Research and Advice Network. March 2001.

Assessing the Potential of Environmental Monitoring for Detecting and Responding to Damage Caused by the Use of Chemicals. A. Kenny, K. Thomas, E. Peeler, D.Osborn, M.Waldock, P. Matthiessen, R. Shore, J. Wright and S.Feist, The Centre for Environment, Fisheries and Aquaculture Science and the Centre for Ecology and Hydrology. August 2002.

A Review of the Impact of Regulation on the Chemical Industry. S. Mahdi, P. Nightingale and F. Berkhout, Science Policy Research Unit (University of Sussex). November 2002.

Visits

During the course of the study, Members of the Commission and its Secretariat made a series of visits. The Secretariat is indebted to the British Embassies in Washington DC and Tokyo and the UK Permanent Representation to Brussels, for the assistance received in organising relevant itineraries.

17-19 June 2002 – USA

Discussions with US Environmental Protection Agency, National Science Foundation, National Academy of Sciences, Office of Science and Technology Policy, WWF, Natural Resources Defence Council, Greenpeace, American Chemistry Council, Office of Information and Regulatory Affairs.

17-18 June 2002 – Stockholm

Discussions with KemI, the Ministry of the Envrionment and the Swedish Environmental Protection Agency.

3 July 2002 – Scotland

Visit to Syngenta, Grangemouth.

3-4 September 2002 – The Netherlands

Discussions with VROM (the Dutch Ministry of Housing, Spatial Planning and the Environment),

RIVM (a public and environmental health research institute), the Ministry of Social Affairs and Employment and the Ministry of Economic Affairs.

7 October 2002 – Geneva

Discussions with UNEP Chemicals Programme staff.

8 October 2002 – Brussels

Discussions with European Commission Health and Consumer Protection Directorate General, European Commission Enterprise Directorate General, David Bowe MEP, CEFIC.

16 October 2002 – Derbyshire

Visit to Safepharm Laboratories and discussions with staff.

19 October 2002 – Paris

Discussions with OECD Environment, Health and Safety Division staff.

1-3 December 2002 – Japan

Discussions with staff from the Ministry of Economy Trade and Industry (METI), the Clinical Evaluation and Research Institute (CERI), the Japan Chemical Industry Association (JCIA) and the National Institute for Environmental Studies (NIES).

SECRETARIAT

Other Members of the Secretariat who made a significant contribution to the content of the report at various stages were John Rea, David Lewis and Steve Hollins.

Appendix C

SEMINAR: FRESH APPROACHES TO CHEMICAL USE AND CONTROL – 19 JULY 2001

On 19 July 2001, the Commission hosted a seminar at the Institute of Materials in London to gather views from interested parties on current and possible alternative approaches to the use and control of chemicals in society. Entitled 'Fresh approaches to chemical use and control', the seminar involved around thirty participants and the following programme.

Introduction
Sir Tom Blundell, Chairman of the Royal Commission on Environmental Pollution

Session 1: Staking Out the Field
Chair: Sir Tom Blundell
Chemicals – The environmental implications of their production and use
Dr Peter Hinchcliffe, Department for Environment, Food, and Rural Affairs
Confidence in Chemicals and the White Paper – A Chemical Industry perspective
Dr Judith Hackitt, Chemical Industries Association
A new regulatory approach to chemicals
Dr Michael Warhurst, Friends of the Earth
Discussion

Session 2: Market and regulatory initiatives
Chair: Professor Jane Plant, Member of the Royal Commission on Environmental Pollution
Sustainable chemicals management
Dr Steve Killeen, Environment Agency
Swedish chemical policy
Ms Taina Bäckström, Swedish Chemicals Inspectorate
The retailer's perspective
Mr Mike Barry, Marks and Spencer
Discussion

Session 3: A view from academia
Chair: Sir Brian Follett, Member of the Royal Commission on Environmental Pollution
The true cost of precautionary chemicals regulation
Mr Bill Durodié, Oxford University
Revisiting the science
Professor Peter Calow, Sheffield University
Discussion

Summing up
Dr Ian Graham-Bryce, Member of the Royal Commission on Environmental Pollution

---

In addition to the speakers and Members of the Commission, the other participants were:

Mr Peter Brooke, Department of Trade and Industry

Dr Nick Cartwright, Environment Agency

Mr David Chesneau, BP Chemicals

Dr Paul Harrison, Institute for Environment and Health

Dr Tom Inch, Royal Society of Chemistry

Mr Don McGillivray, Scottish Executive

Mr Brian Murphy, Robinson Brothers

Dr Dan Osborn, Centre for Ecology and Hydrology, Natural Environment Research Council

Dr Barry Phillips, Royal Society for the Prevention of Cruelty to Animals

Dr Ken Pugh, Scottish Environment Protection Agency

Mr Tom Radice, Clerk, House of Lords European Select Committee, sub-committee D

Mr Sean Ryan, Department for Environment, Food, and Rural Affairs

Dr David Santillo, Greenpeace

Ms Elizabeth Salter-Green, Worldwide Fund for Nature

Dr Andy Stirling, Science Policy Research Unit, University of Sussex

Appendix D
EUROPEAN UNION TESTING REQUIREMENTS FOR CHEMICALS

Table D.1

Tonnage thresholds and testing requirements for new and existing substances[1]

Quantity	New Substances	Existing Substances
Less than 10 kg	None	None
10 to 100 kg	'Reduced'	None
Less than 1 tonne	'Reduced'	None
1 to 10 tonnes	Base set	None
10 to 100 tonnes	Lower Level 1	Basic information (Annex 4 of 793/93)
100 to 1000 tonnes	Upper Level 1	Basic information (Annex 4 of 793/93)
Over 1000 tonnes	Level 2	Detailed available information (Annex 3 of 793/93)

There will be exemptions from testing where there is considered to be sufficient justification

Table D.2a

Base set testing requirements for physico-chemical endpoints based on Annexes VII A, B and C of Directive 67/548/EEC

Melting point (melting range)
Boiling point (boiling range)
Relative density
Vapour pressure
Surface tension
Water solubility
Fat solubility
Partition coefficient log $K_{o/w}$
Flash point
Flammability
Explosive properties
Granulometry

Table D.2b

Base set testing requirements for human health end-points based on Annexes VII A, B and C of Directive 67/548/EEC

End-point	EU test method
Acute toxicity	B.1: acute toxicity (oral) – DELETED ON 25/1/01 B.1bis: acute toxicity (oral) fixed dose method B.1tris: acute toxicity (oral) – acute toxic class method B.2: acute toxicity (inhalation) B.3: acute toxicity (dermal)
Irritation	B.4: acute toxicity (skin irritation) B.5: acute toxicity (eye irritation)
Corrosivity	B.40: skin corrosion
Skin and respiratory sensitisation	B.6: skin sensitization No Annex V method for respiratory sensitisation
Repeated dose toxicity	B.7: repeated dose (28 days) toxicity (oral) B.8: repeated dose (28 days) toxicity (inhalation) B.9: repeated dose (28 days) toxicity (dermal)
Mutagenicity and genotoxicity	B.10: mutagenicity (*in vitro* mammalian chromosome aberration test) B11: mutagenicity (*in vivo* mammalian bone-marrow chromosome aberration test) B.12: mutagenicity mammalian erythrocyte micronucleus test B.13/14: mutagenicity – reverse mutation test using bacteria B.15: gene mutation – *Saccharomyces cerevisiae* B.16: mitotic recombination – *Saccharomyces cerevisiae* B.17: mutagenicity – *in vitro* mammalian cell gene mutation test B.18: DNA damage and repair – unscheduled DNA synthesis – mammalian cells *in vitro* B.19: sister chromatid exchange assay *in vitro* B.20: sex-linked recessive lethal test in *Drosophila melanogaster* B.21: *in vitro* mammalian cell transformation test B.22: rodent dominant lethal test B.23: mammalian spermatogonial chromosome aberration test B.24: mouse spot test B.25: mouse heritable translocation B.39: unscheduled DNA synthesis (UDS) test with mammalian liver cells *in vivo*

Table D.2c

Base set testing requirements for ecotoxicological end-points based on Annexes VII A, B and C of Directive 67/548/EEC

End-point	EU test method
Effects on organisms In those cases where biodegradation may be affected by the inhibitory effect of a substance on the bacteria, a test of bacterial inhibition should be carried out prior to undertaking the biodegradation test.	Acute toxicity for fish Acute toxicity for daphnia Growth inhibition test on algae Bacteriological Inhibition
Degradation If the substance is not readily biodegradable then consideration should be given to the need to carry out the following tests: hydrolysis as a function of pH	Biotic Abiotic
Absorption/desorption	Screening test

Table D.3a

Level 1 testing requirements for physico-chemical end-points based on Annex VIII of Directive 67/548/EEC

Further studies on physico-chemical properties dependent upon the results of the studies laid down in Annex VII. Such further studies could include for example the development of analytical methods, which make it possible to observe and detect a substance or its transformation products and studies on thermal decomposition products.

Table D.3b

Level 1 testing requirements for human health end-points based on Annex VIII of Directive 67/548/EEC

End-point	EU test method
Sub-chronic and/or chronic toxicity	B.26: sub-chronic oral toxicity test: 90-day repeated oral dose study using rodent species B.27: sub-chronic oral toxicity test: 90-day repeated oral dose study using non-rodent species B.28: sub-chronic dermal toxicity test: 90-day repeated dermal dose study using rodent species B.29: sub-chronic inhalation toxicity test: 90-day repeated inhalation dose study using rodent species B.30: chronic toxicity test
Developmental toxicity	B.31: teratogenicity test – rodent and non-rodent
Fertility study	B.34: one-generation reproduction toxicity test B.35: two-generation reproduction toxicity test
Additional mutagenicity studies	
Toxicokinetics	B.36: toxicokinetics

Table D.3c

Level 1 testing requirements for ecotoxicological end-points based on Annex VIII of Directive 67/548/EEC

End-point	EU test method
Effects on organisms	Prolonged toxicity study with *Daphnia magna* (21 days) Tests on higher plants Further toxicity studies with fish
Accumulation	Tests for species accumulation; one species preferably fish
Degradation	Supplementary degradation studies, if sufficient degradation has not been proved by the studies laid in Annex VII
Absorption/desorption	Further studies on absorption/desorption dependent upon the investigations laid down in Annex VII

Table D.4a

Level 2 testing requirements for human health end-points based on Annex VIII of Directive 67/548/EEC

End-point	EU test method
Chronic toxicity	B.30: chronic toxicity test
Carcinogenicity	B.21: *in vitro* mammalian cell transformation test B.32: carcinogenicity test B.33: combined chronic toxicity/carcinogenicity test
Developmental toxicity	Using species not used in level 1 study
Developmental toxicity	For peri-natal and post-natal effects
Fertility study	Extended B.35: three-generation reproduction toxicity test
Additional pharmacokinetic studies	To cover, for example, biotransformation
Additional organ or system toxicity	B.7 includes neurotoxicity and immunotoxicity B.37: delayed neurotoxicity of organophosphorus substances following acute exposure B.38: delayed neurotoxicity of organophosphorus substances 28-day repeated dose study

Table D.4b

Level 2 testing requirements for ecotoxicological end-points based on Annex VIII of Directive 67/548/EEC

End-point	EU test method
Effects on organisms	Further toxicity studies with fish Toxicity tests with birds Additional toxicity studies with other organisms
Accumulation	Further tests
Degradation	Further tests
Mobility	Further tests
Absorption/desorption	Further tests

Table D.5

Testing requirements for new chemicals under Directive 67/548/EEC Annex V

Part A: Methods for the determination of physico-chemical properties

 a.1: melting/freezing temperature

 a.2: boiling temperature

 a.3: relative density

 a.4: vapour pressure

 a.5: surface tension

 a.6: water solubility

 a.8: partition coefficient

 a.9: flash-point

 a.10: flammability (solids)

 a.11: flammability (gases)

 a.12: flammability (contact with water)

 a.13: pyrophoric properties of solids and liquids

 a.14: explosive properties

 a.15: auto-ignition temperature (liquids and gases)

 a.16: relative self-ignition temperature for solids

 a.17: oxidizing properties (solids)

 a.18: number-average molecular weight and molecular weight distribution of polymers

 a.19: low molecular weight content of polymers

 a.20: solution/extraction behaviour of polymers in water

Part B: Methods for the determination of toxicity

 b.1bis: acute toxicity (oral) fixed dose method

 b.1tris: acute toxicity (oral) acute toxic class method

 b.2: acute toxicity (inhalation)

 b.3: acute toxicity (dermal)

 b.4: acute toxicity (skin irritation)

 b.5: acute toxicity (eye irritation)

 b.6: skin sensitization

 b.7: repeated dose (28 days) toxicity (oral)

 b.8: repeated dose (28 days) toxicity (inhalation)

 b.9: repeated dose (28 days) toxicity (dermal)

 b.10: mutagenicity – *in vitro* mammalian chromosome aberration test

 b.11: mutagenicity – *in vivo* mammalian bone-marrow chromosome aberration test

 b.12: mutagenicity – mammalian erythrocyte micronucleus test

 b.13/14: mutagenicity – reverse mutation test using bacteria

 b.15: gene mutation – *Saccharomyces cerevisiae*

 b.16: mitotic recombination – *Saccharomyces cerevisiae*

 b.17: mutagenicity – *in vitro* mammalian cell gene mutation test

 b.18: DNA damage and repair – unscheduled DNA synthesis – mammalian cells *in vitro*

 b.19: sister chromatid exchange assay *in vitro*

(continued overlead)

(table D.5 continued)

Part B: Methods for the determination of toxicity (continued)

   b.20: sex-linked recessive lethal test in *Drosophila melanogaster*

   b.21: *in vitro* mammalian cell transformation test

   b.22: rodent dominant lethal test

   b.23: mammalian spermatogonial chromosome aberration test

   b.24: mouse spot test

   b.25: mouse heritable translocation

   b.26: sub-chronic oral toxicity test: repeated dose 90-day toxicity study in rodents

   b.27: sub-chronic oral toxicity test: repeated dose 90-day toxicity study in non-rodents

   b.28: sub-chronic dermal toxicity test: 90-day repeated dermal dose study using rodent species

   b.29: sub-chronic inhalation toxicity test: 90-day repeated inhalation dose study using rodent species

   b.30: chronic toxicity test

   b.31: teratogenicity test – rodent and non-rodent

   b.32: carcinogenicity test

   b.33: combined chronic toxicity/carcinogenicity test

   b.34: one-generation reproduction toxicity test

   b.35: two generation reproduction toxicity test

   b.36: toxicokinetics

   b.37: delayed neurotoxicity of organophosphorus substances following acute exposure

   b.38: delayed neurotoxicity of organophosphorus substances: 28-day repeated dose study

   b.39: unscheduled DNA synthesis (uds) test with mammalian liver cells *in vivo*

   b.40: skin corrosion (*in vitro*)

   b.41: phototoxicity – *in vitro* 3t3 nru phototoxicity test

Part C: Methods for the determination of ecotoxicity

   c.1: acute toxicity for fish

   c.2: acute toxicity for *Daphnia*

   c.3: algal inhibition test

   c.4: biodegradation: determination of the 'ready' biodegradability

   c.4-a: dissolved organic carbon (DOC) die-away test

   c.4-b: modified OECD screening test

   c.4-c: carbon dioxide evolution test

   c.4-d: manometric respirometry test

   c.4-e: closed bottle test

   c.4-f: MITI test

   c.5: degradation: biochemical oxygen demand (BOD)

   c.6: degradation: chemical oxygen demand (COD)

   c.7: degradation: abiotic degradation: hydrolysis as a function of pH

   c.8: toxicity for earthworms: artificial soil test

   c.9: biodegradation: Zahn–Wellens test

   c.10: biodegradation: activated sludge simulation test

Reference

1. RPA (2001) Regulatory Impact Assessment of the EU White Paper: Strategy for a Future Chemicals Policy Final Report (Contract Reference 16/13/33), RPA, Norfolk.

Appendix E

MONITORING THE EFFECTS OF CHEMICALS ON THE ENVIRONMENT

CURRENT MONITORING SCHEMES FOR CHEMICALS IN THE ENVIRONMENT

E.1　An extensive amount of monitoring is carried out at the international level and within the UK. Monitoring by regulatory bodies is highly targeted at particular groups of chemicals (such as pesticides) or environments (such as freshwaters). Of the types of monitoring described in chapter 2 (2.102), the two that are routinely used by regulatory bodies are *general quality assessment* and *compliance monitoring*.

E.2　The aim of general quality assessment monitoring is to determine whether the environment is in good health (for example, that the invertebrate community at a certain location is not too different from that expected at that time of year at that location), or is improving after a period when the effects of chemicals reduced environmental quality. Mainly founded on simple biological and chemical assessments, quality assessment monitoring is beginning to include evaluation of nutrients and general aesthetic qualities. Compliance monitoring, by contrast, is merely the determination of chemical levels in a particular media, usually to enforce regulations to protect the environment and public health.

E.3　The balance of compliance and general quality assessment monitoring varies considerably between the main environmental compartments (freshwater, marine, terrestrial and air). Partly this is for historical scientific and nature conservation reasons, but increasingly this difference is driven by European environmental protection legislation and by international agreements. In general, there is more extensive chemical monitoring in water than on land, and more general quality assessment work in freshwaters than in the marine environment.

FRESHWATERS

E.4　The Environment Agency is responsible for monitoring the state of the freshwater environment (in England and Wales). European Community (EC) directives drive most of the Environment Agency's current monitoring programmes, and those of the Scottish Environment Protection Agency, and the Environment and Heritage Service in Northern Ireland. The Agency's current programmes for freshwaters (rivers and canals) are driven by the Surface Water Abstraction Directive (75/440/EEC, 79/896/EEC), the Quality of Freshwater Needed to Support Fish Life Directive (78/659/EEC), the Dangerous Substances Directives (76/464/EEC, 82/176/EEC, 83/513/EEC, 84/491/EEC, 86/280/EEC, 88/347/EEC and 90/415/EEC) and the Exchange of Information Decision Directive (77/795/EEC).[1]

E.5　In the aquatic environment, the Agency analyses for 82 organic chemical contaminants to meet national and international reporting commitments, and a further 103 compounds for other purposes. In 2001/02, 268,000 water quality samples were analysed by the Agency, 49% to meet statutory international or national commitments, 40% to monitor compliance with discharge permits, and 9% for local investigations and research.[2] These requirements include Environmental Quality Standards (commonly known as EQS), which are concentration limits for every listed dangerous substance under the EC Dangerous Substances Directive (76/464/EEC) and daughter regulations. Environmental Quality Standards must not be exceeded in any controlled watercourse in England and Wales. The Directive assumes that the dangerous substance is not detrimental to aquatic life at any concentration below its Environmental Quality Standards limit. Environmental Quality Standards vary for each substance and can be different for fresh, estuarine or coastal waters. However, it should be noted that although Environment Quality Standards are derived from ecotoxicological data they do not take into account issues such as complex mixtures and bioavailability[3], they also only apply to the water column and there are no equivalent standards for sediments in the UK.[4]

E.6   The core of the Environment Agency's routine monitoring of freshwaters (rivers and canals) is based on general quality assessments. The chemical part of the general quality assessment (GQA) scheme involves the sampling of 7024 sites at a minimum frequency of 12 times per year, and aims to characterise 40,000 km of rivers and canal.[5] Chemical quality is assessed by reference to three variables: dissolved oxygen (DO), biochemical oxygen demand (BOD), and dissolved ammonia. These are evaluated in terms of percentiles, and then combined into one of six GQA scores ranging from very good[6] to bad.[7,8]

E.7   The biological general quality assessment monitors general ecological quality by measuring the diversity of macroinvertebrate communities, and looks for 83 taxonomic groups at about 6,500 sites, twice a year, representing 37,000 km rivers and canals.[9] These data are assessed by the RIVPACS model which compares measured diversity with that expected on the basis of habitat characteristics.[10] The results are then classified into one of six GQA scores ranging from very good (biology similar to that expected for the given location, with high diversity and no dominance by any one species) to bad (biology limited to a small number of very tolerant species present in high numbers).[11]

E.8   In addition, the pilot nutrient general quality assessment programme monitors annual average concentrations of orthophosphate and nitrate in rivers (as indicators of eutrophication potential), and the aesthetic assessment incorporates such issues as litter, foam, colour and odour of rivers. However, a general quality assessment for lakes does not yet exist, although pilot studies have been performed looking at phosphorus, chlorophyll and pH as the determinands.[12] A range of other aquatic biological measurements are also made in freshwaters that are not part of the routine general quality assessment. These include occasional surveys of populations of aquatic plants, certain fish species, birds, water voles, otters and amphibians, although the data cannot be linked directly with pollution.[13] Furthermore, occasional measurements of bioaccumulated organochlorines are made in various aquatic fauna, although not enough to establish temporal trends.[14]

E.9   Further freshwater monitoring requirements will need to be met under the EC Water Framework Directive (table E1), which combines biological classification schemes and chemical monitoring. At present, the Directive has identified a group of 32 substances that will require monitoring using the combined monitoring-based and modelling-based priority-setting procedure (3.163-3.165).

E.10 At present, there is a lack of co-ordination between the chemical and biological measurements made by the Environment Agency, and there is no systematic use of pollution-specific bioassays, biomarkers or toxicity identification evaluations. It would therefore be difficult to show cause and effect between chemicals and environmental impacts under the current monitoring systems. However, the Agency is addressing this in its chemicals strategy (2.106), although the degree to which its monitoring programmes can be altered and still meet EU requirements remains unclear.

MARINE

E.11 The UK is obliged under the OSPAR Convention (the Convention for the Protection of the Marine Environment of the North East Atlantic) to undertake marine monitoring. The UK contribution is carried out under the National Marine Monitoring Programme (NMMP) established by the Marine Pollution Monitoring Management Group (MPMMG) which has representation from all government organisations with statutory obligations for marine environmental protection. The NMMP aims to detect long-term trends in the quality of the marine environment, to ensure consistent standards in monitoring, to establish appropriate protective regulatory measures, to co-ordinate and optimise marine monitoring in the UK, and to provide a high quality key dataset for key variables.[15]

E.12 OSPAR has identified a list of substances for priority action; some of these substances are already covered by well-established monitoring programmes (such as lead, mercury, cadmium, organotins and pentachlorophenol), while for others, there is little information about concentrations in the environment. Substances or groups of substances of most concern are selected on the basis of OSPAR's dynamic selection and prioritisation mechanism (DYNAMEC), which assesses the substances in terms of their persistence, toxicity and bioaccumulation properties (table E1). A series of EC directives have also imposed monitoring requirements for the marine environment, including the Water Framework Directive (E.9) in both coastal and freshwater environments.[16]

E.13 The initial phases of the NMMP established the spatial distribution of contaminants in UK marine waters and defined their biological status. This involved long-term surveys at estuarine, intermediate and offshore sites to determine the distribution of contaminants in a range of matrices. Phase 2 of the NMMP includes a temporal trend monitoring survey using automated *in situ* instrumentation, capable of deployment at a mooring, for monitoring a range of physico-chemical and environmental variables. These marine environmental real-time observation systems (MEROS) have been developed by the Centre for Environment, Fisheries and Aquaculture Science (CEFAS), with funding support from the Department for Environment, Food and Rural Affairs (Defra), for collecting the high-frequency, near real-time data needed for the NMMP. The CEFAS-developed SmartBuoy is one of an array of automated *in situ* instrumentation systems that can be deployed for extended periods at a mooring. SmartBuoy is currently configured to meet the needs of the NMMP by monitoring plant nutrient concentrations and the response of the ecosystem in terms of phytoplankton growth and species composition. Additional physical measurements are also made to ensure that a full interpretation of the time-series data set is possible. Summary data are returned in near real-time (sub-hourly) via satellite telemetry with full data sets recovered during servicing of the buoy.[17]

Table E.1

List of priority substances under the OSPAR Convention and the EC Water Framework Directive.[18]

CAS number	Name of substance	Policy	Policy
15972-60-8	Alachlor	WFD	
120-12-7	anthracene (X)	WFD	
1912-24-9	atrazine (X)	WFD	
71-43-2	benzene	WFD	
na	brominated diphenylethers X	WFD	
na	brominated flame retardants		OSPAR
7440-43-9	cadmium and its compounds X	WFD	OSPAR
85535-84-8	C10-13-chloroalkanes X	WFD	
	short-chained chlorinated paraffins (SCCP)		OSPAR
470-90-6	chlorfenvinphos	WFD	
2921-88-2	chlorpyrifos (X)	WFD	
107-06-2	1,2-dichloroethane	WFD	
75-09-2	dichloromethane	WFD	
	certain phthalates –		
	dibutylphthalate and diethylhexylphthalate		OSPAR
117-81-7	di(2-ethylhexyl)phthalate (DEHP)(X)	WFD	
330-54-1	diuron (X)	WFD	
115-29-7	endosulfan (X)	WFD	OSPAR
959-98-8	(alpha-endosulfan)	WFD	
206-44-0	fluoranthene	WFD	
118-74-1	hexachlorobenzene X	WFD	
87-68-3	hexachlorobutadiene X	WFD	
608-73-1	hexachlorocyclohexane X	WFD	OSPAR
58-89-9	(gamma-isomer, lindane)	WFD	
34123-59-6	isoproturon (X)	WFD	
7439-92-1	lead and its compounds (X)	WFD	OSPAR
7439-97-6	mercury and its compounds X	WFD	OSPAR
91-20-3	naphthalene (X)	WFD	
7440-02-0	nickel and its compounds	WFD	
25154-52-3	nonylphenols X	WFD	OSPAR
104-40-5	(4-(para)-nonylphenol)	WFD	
1806-26-4	octylphenols (X)	WFD	
140-66-9	(para-tert-octylphenol)	WFD	OSPAR
608-93-5	pentachlorobenzene X	WFD	
87-86-5	pentachlorophenol (X)	WFD	OSPAR
na	polyaromatic hydrocarbons X	WFD	OSPAR
50-32-8	(benzo(a)pyrene),	WFD	
205-99-2	(benzo(b)fluoranthene),	WFD	
191-24-2	(benzo(g,h,i)perylene),	WFD	
207-08-9	(benzo(k)fluoranthene),	WFD	
193-39-5	(indeno(1,2,3-cd)pyrene)	WFD	

(continued overleaf)

(table E.1 continued)

CAS number	Name of substance	Policy	Policy
122-34-9	simazine (X)	WFD	
688-73-3	tributyltin compounds X	WFD	
36643-28-4	(tributyltin-cation)	WFD	
12002-48-1	trichlorobenzenes (X)	WFD	OSPAR
120-82-1	(1,2,4-trichlorobenzene)	WFD	OSPAR
108-70-3	1,3,5-trichlorobenzene		OSPAR
67-66-3	trichloromethane (chloroform)	WFD	
1582-09-8	trifluralin (X)	WFD	
98-51-1	4-tert-butyltoluene		OSPAR
115-32-2	dicofol		OSPAR
732-26-3	dodecylphenol		OSPAR
77-47-4	1,3-cyclopentadiene, 1,2,3,4,5,5-hexachloro-		OSPAR
107-46-0	HMDS (disiloxane, hexamethyl-)		OSPAR
72-43-5	methoxychlor		OSPAR
	musk xylene		OSPAR
	organic tin compounds		OSPAR
	polychlorinated biphenyls (PCBs)		OSPAR
	polychlorinated dibenzodioxins (PCDDs)		OSPAR
	polychlorinated dibenzofurans (PCDFs)		OSPAR
79-94-7	tetrabromobisphenol A		OSPAR

Notes:
WFD   Water Framework Directive Priority List of Substances
X   Water Framework Directive Priority Hazardous Substance
(X)   Water Framework Directive potential Priority Hazardous Substance
OSPAR   List of Chemicals for Priority Action (2000 update)

E.14   The NMMP incorporates a number of biological monitoring components, including the use of *in situ* benthic invertebrate community and fish disease surveys, *ex situ* assessments of waters and sediments by means of bioassays using whole organism responses, and *in situ* biomarkers, such as the induction of the P4501A oxidative enzyme in fish, which are diagnostic of exposure to particular pollutant groups (box E1).[19] A comprehensive review of UK estuarine and coastal monitoring results was published in 2002.[20]

E.15   The future strategy for the NMMP is to move from a pollution focus to an environmental management focus involving a whole ecosystem approach; integrate current effort with sister programmes of the Countryside Agencies and the Natural Environment Research Council's organisations; and develop robust indicators of performance to measure overall trend rather than measuring individual contaminants (around 60,000 at present).[21] This strategy is compatible with the future roles and uses of monitoring suggested by the Commission in chapter 4 (4.72-4.101).

BOX E1	BIOMARKERS

Biological changes that result from exposure to chemicals, usually termed biomarkers, may occur at different levels of biological organisation, from the cellular level to the community and ecosystem level. For example, exposure to a chemical can be determined by analysis of tissues and fluids to measure levels of the chemical itself, of its metabolites, or of enzymes and other biological substances or responses affected by the chemical. The determination of such biomarkers provides an index of the internal dose of the substance and hence of external exposure.

In the case of terrestrial biota, the analysis of chemical levels in tissue samples can give the most accurate picture of exposure to chemicals, if they are not rapidly detoxified or eliminated, and can provide direct evidence for the exposure of individual organisms in a population to a chemical. However, for a biomarker to be relevant, information needs to be available on what constitutes its normal range of response under a range of environmental conditions, and whether the biomarker is a good indicator of the health of the major functions of an organism (will it give a suitable assessment of the impact of the chemical on the organism).

At the biochemical level, molecular markers such as DNA modifications or enzyme induction or inhibition can be used as biomarkers to provide a measure of exposure. This class of biomarkers is of particular interest in terms of monitoring populations of organisms for the effects of chemicals, as they can be more sensitive and occur in advance of responses at higher biological levels, which may be more difficult to directly link to a chemical exposure. Examples of molecular markers used for monitoring include the cytochrome P450 monooxygenases (one of the mixed function oxidase phase I detoxifying enzymes), phase II conjugating enzymes (phase II detoxifying enzymes such as glutathione transferase), metallothioneins (small proteins rich in sulphur containing amino acids that bind to metal ions), serum enzymes, and stress proteins (proteins induced in organisms by variety of stressors including heat, salinity, osmotic changes, metal ions, anoxia and xenobiotics).[22]

AIR MONITORING

E.16　The UK is required to monitor and assess a number of substances in relation to air pollution under a number of compound-specific EC Directives. These substances include sulphur dioxide and suspended particulate matter, lead, nitrogen dioxide and ozone. In addition, a number of 'exchange of information decisions' also set reporting requirements. At present these 'decisions' require the reporting of 31 additional compounds, including volatile organic compounds (VOCs) and seven heavy metals (table E.2).[23]

E.17　The EU Council Directive on ambient air quality assessment and management (the Air Framework Directive, 1996) requires that air quality is assessed in Member States relative to limit values for a number of pollutants including lead, cadmium, benzene, polyaromatic hydrocarbons, arsenic and nickel. In addition, the Air Quality Strategy for the UK sets standards and objectives to be achieved for eight key air pollutants between 2003 and 2008.[24]

Table E.2

International agreements on air pollutants[25]

Substance Quality	UNECE POPs Protocol[1]	UNECE Heavy Metals Protocol	UNEP POPs Convention[2]	EC Air Directives[3] (96/62/EC)
aldrin	Y		Y	
arsenic				Y
benzene				Y
cadmium		Y		Y
chlordane	Y		Y	
chlordecone	Y			
dieldrin	Y		Y	
DDT	Y		Y	
endrin	Y		Y	
heptachlor	Y		Y	
hexabromobiphenyl	Y			
hexachlorobenzene	Y		Y	
hexachlorocyclohexanes	Y			
lead		Y		Y
mercury		Y		Y
mirex	Y	Y	Y	
nickel				Y
toxaphene	Y		Y	
PAHs	Y			Y
PCBs	Y		Y	
dioxins	Y		Y	
furans	Y		Y	

Notes:

1 Within the United Nations Economic Commission for Europe (UNECE) Persistent organic Pollutants (POPs) Protocol:

   (i) Polycyclic aromatic hydrocarbons (PAHs): For the purposes of emission inventories, the following four indicator compounds are used: benzo(a)pyrene, benzo(b)fluoranthene, benzo(k)fluoranthene, and indeno(1,2,3-cd)pyrene;

   (ii) Dioxins and furans (PCDD/F): Polychlorinated dibenzo-p-dioxins (PCDD) and polychlorinated dibenzofurans (PCDF) are tricyclic, aromatic compounds formed by two benzene rings which are connected by two oxygen atoms in PCDD and by one oxygen atom in PCDF and the hydrogen atoms of which may be replaced by up to eight chlorine atoms (reported as International Toxic Equivalents);

   (iii) steps are underway to add certain compounds, e.g. dicofol and pentabromodiphenylether and short-chained chlorinated paraffins (SCCPs) to the 16 already included.

2 Within the United Nations Environment Programme (UNEP) POPs Convention:

   (i) Polychlorinated biphenyls means aromatic compounds formed in such a manner that the hydrogen atoms on the biphenyl molecule (two benzene rings bonded together by a single carbon-carbon bond) may be replaced by up to ten chlorine atoms;

   (ii) Polychlorinated dibenzo-p-dioxins and polychlorinated dibenzofurans are tricyclic, aromatic compounds formed by two benzene rings connected by two oxygen atoms in polychlorinated dibenzo-p-dioxins and by one oxygen atom and one carbon-carbon bond in polychlorinated dibenzofurans and the hydrogen atoms of which may be replaced by up to eight chlorine atoms (reported as World Health Organization Toxic Equivalents).

3 Within the EU Framework directive on ambient air quality management and assessment (96/62/EC) the following additional pollutants are to be regulated by daughter directives: sulphur dioxide, nitrogen dioxide, PM_{10}, suspended particulate matter, ozone, carbon monoxide.

E.18 Defra oversees a national network of air monitoring stations across the UK to meet the above requirements, with additional monitoring carried out by local authorities. A range of pollutants is monitored at over 1,500 sites across the UK. These are organised into automatic and non-automatic networks. Automatic networks, placed at 120 sites, produce hourly concentrations for air pollutants such as ozone, nitrogen dioxide, sulphur dioxide, benzene and particulate matter. The non-automatic network provides less frequent measurements for a wider range of pollutants.[26]

E.19 The UK is also a partner in a number of international air monitoring programmes, including:

- the Co-operative Programme for Monitoring and Evaluation of the Long-Range Transmission of Air pollutants in Europe (ECE-EMEP) which aims to provide information on the transport and deposition of pollutants on a European scale through a combination of monitoring and modelling. The substances monitored include VOCs, heavy metals and persistent organic pollutants (POPs);

- the OSPAR Convention's comprehensive atmospheric monitoring programme (CAMP), under which it has been agreed that the North Sea states will seek a 50% reduction in the atmospheric emissions of a group of 17 substances;

- the World Health Organization's global air quality monitoring system (GEMS/AIR), a global programme for urban air quality management that includes over 250 monitoring sites in about 80 cities in 40 countries; and

- EUROTRAC Tropospheric Ozone Research, a scientific research programme in which some research institutes, universities and industry bodies from the UK participate.[27]

E.20 Because of the very large-scale nature of the enhanced greenhouse gas and stratospheric ozone depletion problems much of the monitoring can only be done on a large-scale. Satellite based measurements plus detailed measurements in a few regions can give most of the relevant information. The UK at present does not have a high profile in greenhouse gas monitoring. However, the British Antarctic Survey discovered the ozone hole through its ozone sonde measurements (that had not been seen in analysed satellite data because the analysis procedure had assumed that such low values were due to observational error). Defra has an obligation under the Montreal protocol to contribute to the monitoring of ozone. The Met Office also has a moral pressure from the World Meteorological Organisation to provide data. However, in recent years financial pressure has led to the end of the routine ozone sonde measurements in Lerwick.

Terrestrial

E.21 Periodic surveys and databases concerned with biodiversity and land use could be considered to provide the type of information needed to assess the health of the environment. There are a number of schemes that provide either background data on geochemistry or trend data on aspects of biodiversity including impacts of mining; natural hazards (such as radon); butterfly populations;[28] plant species distribution;[29] long-running surveys of invertebrates (such as the Game Conservancy Trust survey of invertebrate abundance on farmland); common bird populations;[30] and the Biological Records Centre's Surveillance of Species Distribution.[31]

E.22 At present the British Geological Survey is carrying out systematic baseline surveys to international standards of inorganic determinants in a range of media including surface and groundwater, soils and sediments (inshore and offshore) with high-density sampling being carried out in urban centre soils as part of the Natural Environment Research Council's 'State of the Environment Programme'.[32] However, there is no regular monitoring of soils, in the sense of the large spatial monitoring networks that exist for air, freshwater and marine media, although a number of monitoring campaigns have been carried out, looking at specific pollutants such as heavy metals, sponsored by Defra, the Environment Agency and the Natural Environment Research Council.

E.23 In general, there are few direct links between chemical impacts and any spatial or temporal trends in the ecological or broad environmental data sets, even though chemicals may be important factors in some of the trends (for example, indirect effects of pesticides, not historically included in pesticide risk assessments, may have been largely responsible for the declines in certain farmland birds). Some of these terrestrial data sets are very long running (over 100 years of near-continuous data can be assembled). Those phenological records that show how climate change may impact on biodiversity demonstrate the value of this type of quality status monitoring, especially as once change becomes apparent, causes can be identified through combining statistical analysis of the data with information on other environmental variables and knowledge of species sensitivities to a range of pressures.[33]

E.24 There are, however, a limited number of information sources directly concerning the effects of chemicals on terrestrial biota (further discussed in E.29-E.34). These include long-term studies on the effects of pollutants on particular organisms including birds associated with the marine,[34] freshwater and land environments.[35] The National Predatory Bird Monitoring Scheme operated by the Centre for Ecology and Hydrology monitors the levels and impacts of organochlorine pesticides, polychlorinated biphenyls (PCBs), rodenticides and mercury in eggs and tissues from juveniles and grown birds on a national basis. Surprisingly, despite post-approval monitoring requirements, relatively little information on pesticides is available for assessing their indirect or off-target effects on terrestrial species;[36] which is of particular concern to a number of statutory bodies and non-governmental organisations.[37] However, there have been numerous studies of the direct effects of pesticides on invertebrate populations, including long-term experimental studies such as the Boxworth and SCARAB projects.[38]

MULTIMEDIA

E.25 The Environmental Change Network (ECN) is a multi-agency, long-term monitoring programme for identifying and quantifying environmental changes associated with human activities. It aims to distinguish anthropogenic changes from natural variations and trends, and to give early warning of undesirable effects. ECN measurements are collected regularly at a growing number of network sites (currently 11 terrestrial and 42 freshwater) throughout the UK, using standardised protocols. The data cover a wide range of physical, chemical and biological parameters, including climate, air quality, water quality and flow, soil development and chemistry, invertebrates, vertebrates, vegetation, land use and site management practice.[39] Joined-up monitoring data such as this is essential to determine the effects of chemicals on the environment, and to separate out those effects from other confounding factors.

E.26   The Commission also heard evidence from English Nature that there is also a requirement under the Habitats Directive (92/43/EEC) to assess risks from inputs to Special Areas of Conservation and Special Protection Areas, and includes the collation of all existing biological and chemical information concerning the status of the sites, which is being undertaken in conjunction with reviewing discharge consents with the Environment Agency. English Nature are looking at evidence as to whether or not there is a biological impact on the sites which could be linked to pollutants, but were finding problems with attempting to integrate chemical and biological monitoring data, and were frustrated by the limitations of existing monitoring information. Problems include the fact that the Environmental Quality Standards (E.5) for sites were set below the limits of detection.[40]

FUTURE REGULATORY MONITORING REQUIREMENTS

E.27   In the Sixth Environmental Action Programme,[41] the European Commission undertook to review environmental monitoring requirements in the light of three key issues:

- Assessment of the implementation and compliance with legislation.

- State and trends in the environment.

- Evaluation of policies and their effectiveness.

The information currently collected does not effectively meet the three needs above and in a lot of cases it is believed that the wrong data are being requested. The European Commission intends therefore to review reporting requirements by developing a framework directive covering all environmental reporting of data and information for policy purposes, with a series of committees examining in detail the reporting requirements for each media. This should mean that the resources spent on intensive monitoring of chemicals that are no longer a problem will be reduced.[42]

E.28   As part of a consultation on its monitoring strategy, the Environment Agency has stated its intention to take a more strategic approach to monitoring. This will require a combination of investigative monitoring of specific chemicals and indicators of impacts, as well as general surveillance of chemicals and biota to investigate trends.[43] This is a similar use of monitoring – in a reconnaissance or investigatory role to establish where chemical problems exist – to that we propose in chapter 4 (4.94).

THE EFFECTS OF CHEMICALS ON WILD ANIMALS

E.29   The welfare of wild animals is increasingly emerging as an issue for consideration in research and management, yet the impact of chemicals on wild animals and their environment has hitherto received little attention compared to the efforts to determine the effects of chemicals on human health. Nonetheless, environmental epidemiology (studying non-human populations) has provided some powerful inputs to debates on chemicals in the environment, notably with the identification of organochlorine pesticides as one of the primary causes of the decline in the avian raptor population in the 1970s, and the lethal and sub-lethal effects of organochlorine pesticides on wild mammals (the decline in otters in the 20th century has been partially attributed to the organochlorine pesticide dieldrin[44]).

E.30 Pollutants can have both direct and indirect effects on animal populations. The indirect effects are especially significant when they influence food supplies, for example the decline of the grey partridge can be partially attributed to pesticides diminishing the abundance of prey.[45] Direct effects on populations cause mortality or reduce individual fitness, especially by lowering reproductive output. Mortalities have occurred in small mammals (mice, voles and bats) as a result of insecticide application, and behavioural effects, as well as possible reproductive effects, have been related to sub-lethal exposure.[46] The possible effects of chemicals on reproduction are further discussed in E.38-E.45.

E.31 Direct effects are most likely to be caused by pollutants that bioaccumulate (2.75), such as certain metal species and persistent organic pollutants, or by 'secondary poisoning' where predators rely on specialised prey that are controlled pests, such as rodents, molluscs or insect species.[47] Residues of second-generation anticoagulant rodenticides have been detected in weasels, stoats, polecats and birds of prey in the UK.[48] However, there is little toxicological information from which to extrapolate the likelihood of mortality or sub-lethal effects from such observed residue levels.

E.32 Many carnivore species are at the top of the food chain and in theory could be vulnerable to those contaminants which bioaccumulate by dietary exposure. The biological transfer of chemicals into tissues is often enhanced by the lipophilicity of the chemical, by the lipid content of a tissue, and by physiological functions that may predispose organisms to accumulate environmental chemicals.[49] Biological processes such as depuration (clearance), detoxification (box E2) and other biotransformation mechanisms affect the potential for bioaccumulation within an organism.[50] Species at the top of aquatic food chains that consume organisms which bioconcentrate lipophilic compounds provide some of the most convincing evidence for the impact of chemicals on natural populations (table E.3).

BOX E2	**METABOLISM OF ORGANIC CHEMICALS**

Transformation of organic chemicals occurs through two different kinds of enzyme systems, Phase I and Phase II. The enzymes involved are known as the conjugative enzymes. In all mammals, the detoxification of organic pollutants occurs predominantly in the liver, where the highest tissue concentration of Phase I and Phase II detoxification enzymes are found.

Phase I reactions are metabolic processes which break down complex molecules into simple ones (*catabolic*). They involve the addition of a functional group with a net electrical charge (*polarisation*) to the parent compound by controlled enzymatic addition of oxygen (*oxidation*), thereby creating a more reactive intermediate. Monooxygenase enzymes, principally the flavoprotein monooxygenases and the cytochrome P450 monooxygenases (or mixed function oxidase (MFO) system), catalyse these reactions.

Following oxidation by the MFO system, Phase II reactions conjugate the intermediate with water soluble moieties (such as glutathione) by catabolic reactions or by enzyme-mediated synthesis of complex molecules (*biosynthesis*). The products of the reaction can then be excreted in the bile or urine. When detoxification does not occur at a sufficient rate, a toxic effect will be observed, such as acute toxicity, genotoxicity (damage to genetic material), or chronic or long-term effects in the organism.[51]

E.33 In the case of pinnipeds (seals, sealions and walruses), their insulating and energy-rich blubber layer accumulates the fat-soluble chemical contaminants to which they are exposed through the aquatic food chain.[52] Studies have suggested that reproductive abnormalities and immunotoxicity are occurring in populations of pinnipeds as result of exposure to certain chemicals (PCBs and organochlorines), and the immunotoxic effect of these chemicals, in combination with viral infections, has been implicated as the possible cause of mass mortalities.[53] Other chemicals, such as polybrominated diphenyl ethers (PBDEs) and bis(4-chlorphenyl)sulphone (BCPS), have also been found in pinnipeds, but the effects of these chemicals are unknown.[54]

E.34 Of terrestrial carnivorous mammals, those that consume a high percentage of their body weight on a daily basis are at particular risk from chemicals that bioconcentrate. The Soricidae (shrews) are an example of a high-risk group because their daily food intake may equal or exceed their own body weight, and because the insects they consume accumulate some toxicants such as certain heavy metal species. Shrews also consume invertebrates such as worms, that contain large amounts of potentially contaminated soil, further increasing the risk of exposure.[55]

MONITORING DATA AS EVIDENCE

E.35 There are currently only a few well-known examples of chemicals directly affecting animal populations (table E.3), partly because of the difficulty of separating out the impact a chemical may be having on an animal species from other factors (4.77), the difficulties in showing cause and effect, and the paucity of data in this area. The ability of current monitoring schemes to detect adverse trends in wildlife populations is questionable, and the paucity of monitoring data on the effect of chemicals on terrestrial biota is of concern (E.22). In particular, the ability to deduce the effects of chemicals on populations of wild mammals in the UK is unlikely to be practicable until there is an effective mammal-monitoring network in place.[56]

E.36 Biological changes following exposure to chemicals include biochemical changes at the cellular level such as the expression of enzymes, proteins, and other macromolecules associated with detoxification mechanisms (box E2); these molecules can be used as biomarkers (4.78 and box E1). Use of biomarkers has the advantage over monitoring the levels of a chemical in the environment, as they can demonstrate that an organism has been both exposed and affected by that exposure, that is, meaningfully exposed. Any future monitoring network of the effects of chemicals on terrestrial biota will need to develop and incorporate this methodology in order to establish associations between chemicals and effects on populations of organisms.

Table E.3

Some ecological impacts and possible associations with chemicals[57]

Observation/impact	Species	Substance	Association*
Large-scale effects			
Eggshell thinning	guillemot, eagle, osprey, peregrine, falcon	DDT/DDE	5
Reproduction	seal, otter	PCB	4
Skeletal malformation	grey seal	DDT, PCB	4
Pathological changes	seal	PCB, DDT metabolites	3
Reproduction	mink	PCB	5
Reproductive disturbances	osprey	DDT, PCB	5
Reproductive disturbances	eagle	DDT, PCB	2-3
Reproduction (M74 syndrome)	salmon	Chlorinated substances	2
Imposex	molluscs, e.g. dogwhelk	TBT	5
Impairments in wildlife in relation to endocrine-disrupting chemicals (EDCs)			
Sperm quality, cryptorchidism	panther		2-3 (effects observed in inbred population)
Population decrease	mink, otter		2-3
Female reproductive disorders, adrenocortical hyperplasia	seal		4-5 4-5
Eggshell thinning Embryotoxicity & malformations Malformation of reproductive tract Reproductive behaviour	birds		4-5 4-5 2-3 2-3
Microphalli and lowered testosterone levels	alligators		3-4 (effects seen in connection to accidental contamination)
Vitellogenin Masculinisation Lowered testosterone levels Reduced testis size M74 syndrome/EMS	fish		4-5 3-4 2-3 2-3 1-2
Imposex	molluscs		5

* The strength of the association is assessed on the scale: 1 = no observed association, 2 = suspected association, 3 = weak association, 4 = clear association, 5 = significant association.
PCB – polychlorinated biphenyls
TBT – tributyltin compounds

E.37 In order to provide an appropriate timeline for biological changes it would also be necessary to establish an environmental tissue bank (4.88). Sampling techniques (box E3) and timelines are extremely important in the establishment of cause and effect. Further evidence for cause would need to be obtained through use of bioassay techniques. Using monitoring data to establish whether a chemical causes an environmental effect will also require rigorous quality assurance/quality control (QA/QC) procedures to ensure reliability of the data obtained. The recent Defra report on monitoring chemicals in the environment,[58] stated these should include matrix spikes, measurements of precision, spike recovery studies, detection limit determination, method validation, continuing calibration checks, quantification with standard curves with known reproducibility, frequent documentation, adherence to Standard Operating Procedures (SOPs), instrument performance checks, inter-laboratory comparisons when possible, analysis of reference standards, and frequent quality assurance audits conducted externally. The application of QA/QC to biological measurements is equally important. Measurements of a number of environmental chemicals are covered by laboratory accreditation schemes that address these points.

BOX E3   **SAMPLING**

A report on monitoring by Defra for the Chemicals Stakeholder Forum[59] highlighted the following key issues in collecting samples to measure chemical concentrations.

Representativity of the samples Measurement may be made for a number of different reasons, which may influence the choice of sampling locations or, if looking at exposure through biomarkers, which individuals to sample. For example, collecting samples to provide an understanding of the range of concentrations in the environment will mean using a range of different locations to provide information on background, close to source(s) and intermediate concentrations.

Timing of the sampling and frequency Ideally, sampling should be carried out at times most relevant to the end-points being examined. Timing of sampling should address exposures of greatest concern, for example, understanding long-term chronic exposure will require a different monitoring approach to that needed for intermittent short-term exposure. Patterns of contamination also need to be considered, for example, continuous discharge of a variable mixture compared with occasional accidental contamination.

What matrices to sample The choice of matrix is determined by a number of factors such as relevance to route of exposure, ease and practicability of sampling, which analytes are to be assessed and, in some cases, ethical considerations if invasive sampling is needed.

Statistics Statistical relevance must be ensured in the sampling, for example, pooled *vs.* individual samples, numbers of samples from each and different locations/species. Quality control and quality assurance should be indorporated at the sampling stage.

Sample storage and preservation methods Special methods may be needed to avoid contamination with other chemicals commonly found in sampling and laboratory equipment (such as plasticisers) and if samples are to be stored, transported and analysed at a later date.

EFFECTS OF ENDOCRINE DISRUPTERS

E.38 A number of toxic effects of chemicals have become apparent through environmental and health monitoring. Notable among these is the effect of a chemical, or its breakdown products, on hormonal (endocrine) pathways, especially those involved in reproduction and thyroid gland function. An *endocrine disrupter* is an exogenous substance that causes adverse health effects in an intact organism, or its progeny, consequent to endocrine function.[60] The International Programme on Chemical Safety (IPCS) has stated that: 'endocrine disruption is not a toxicological endpoint *per se* as is cancer or allergy, but that it is a descriptor for a functional change that may lead to adverse health effects'.[61]

E.39 The range of chemicals suspected of having endocrine-disrupting potential is diverse. Some of these are naturally occurring (phyto-oestrogens and mammalian oestrogens), others are biocides (such as atrazine or tributyltin), industrial chemicals (bisphenolic, alkylphenolic compounds and phthalate compounds), pharmaceuticals (such as 17β-ethinyl oestradiol or flutamide), or industrial emissions such as dioxins. Endocrine disrupters can act in a number of ways: by binding to a cell receptor to cause a response; by binding to a cell receptor and blocking the natural hormone from producing a response; by stopping the synthesis of the natural hormone or its receptors; or by directly quashing the activity of the genes that the hormone interacts with. Some substances either mimic or block the effect of the female sex hormone, oestrogen, these are referred to as oestrogenic or anti-oestrogenic respectively. Others mimic or block the effects of male hormones called androgens, such as testosterone, and are referred to as androgenic or anti-androgenic respectively. However, most environmental chemicals that have been shown to alter endogenous hormone action do not have intrinsic hormonal activity, that is, they do not mimic or block the action of testosterone or oestrogen. These chemicals affect hormonal pathways by indirect means, for example some chemicals are believed to affect the enzyme aromatase, which converts testosterone to oestradiol.[62]

E.40 Mammalian foetal sex development follows an orderly sequence of events controlled by a set of gonadal-related transcription factors and hormones acting in a co-ordinated fashion. These trophic factors are only required for male development, female being the constitutive sex. Key to normal male development is critical timing and threshold effects of gene expression and hormonal concentrations. The hormonal interplay required for the process of sexual differentiation at six to nine weeks of foetal development provides a unique window of opportunity for chemical substances to disrupt the developmental process, and pre-natal exposure to certain substances may result in testicular dysgenesis syndrome.[63] For example, in rats it has been shown that dibutyl- and diethylhexyl phthalate can cause testicular dysgenesis by affecting the Sertoli cell development and the Leydig cell function; this may be a model for how similar defects arise in humans.[64] As these cells do not have androgen receptors, it would appear that this effect is not a result of anti-androgen activity but of as yet unknown mechanisms.[65]

E.41 The effects of endocrine disrupters are greatest during foetal development and *in utero* effects may not be manifest until adulthood. Animal models have shown that exposure *in utero* to endocrine-active chemicals may lead to cryptorchidism (failure of testicular descent), hypospadias (an abnormality of the development of the penis), and reduced sperm production/fertility.[66] Cases of testicular dysgenesis syndrome inevitably lead to a high testicular cancer risk after puberty. Human male reproductive disorders associated with testicular dysgenesis are increasing in incidence, with 2-4% of children suffering from cryptorchidism and 6-8% of men having abnormally low sperm counts. In the US one in 125 boys are born with hypospadias, and the numbers are increasing with each decade in both Europe and the US.[67] A possible link with endocrine-disrupting substances must be considered, but definitive answers on a link will only be provided by carefully designed epidemiological studies.[68]

E.42   Epidemiological studies in Denmark have suggested that testicular dysgenesis syndrome may be increasing due to adverse environmental influences.[69] However, almost no information is available to indicate that a causal relationship exists between human exposures to environmental compounds with endocrine-like activity and deficits in human reproduction.[70] Significant gaps in the relevant information are a lack of relevant human exposure data for these agents during critical life stages, and a lack of experimental power in epidemiological studies to relate an *in utero* exposure to an event that may not occur until adulthood in the exposed offspring.[71] Studies of environmental endocrine disrupters have illustrated sub-cellular events with clear implications for reproductive performance, yet only in a few instances has it been possible to link or translate biochemical effects of a single compound into significant changes at the population level.[72]

E.43   As the mechanisms of endocrine disruption are complex and not fully understood the design of suitable animal tests or *in vitro* alternatives is not straightforward.[73] At present, there are no standard risk assessment test methods for endocrine disrupters in the EU, although the OECD has a special working group in this area (the Endocrine Disruptor Testing and Assessment (EDTA) task force) to develop test guidelines. The present multi-generational animal tests used by the US EPA, developed to detect teratogenic effects, have been shown to miss low incidence (less than 10%) developmental phenomena (such as malformations of the epididymus following *in utero* exposure to the herbicide linuron), due to culling prior to the appropriate adult stages.[74] Even where laboratory experiments have shown *in vivo* effects and there is supportive epidemiological evidence, as in the case of the herbicide atrazine and its possible detrimental effects on reptiles (which showed feminisation at levels of atrazine as low as 0.1 parts per billion in water), there remain considerable uncertainties due to the complexity of the issues involved and whether low-level effects can be validated. There is still considerable controversy as to whether more recently identified environmental endocrine-disrupting compounds, such as bisphenolic and alkylphenolic substances pose a health risk at the very low dose levels proposed.[75] IPCS has recently produced a global assessment of the current state of the science on endocrine disruption.[76] It found evidence of endocrine disruption in some wildlife species and populations, but could not find firm evidence of direct causal associations between low-level exposure to endocrine-disrupting chemicals and adverse human health effects.

E.44   Cases of endocrine disruption have been reported for shellfish, fish, alligators, turtles, seals, polar bears and fish eating birds[77] (table E.3). Endocrine-disrupting chemicals have also been shown to affect plant–*Rhizobium* signalling and nitrogen-fixing symbiosis.[78] The first widely-reported incidence of imposex caused by chemicals was the effect of tributyltin on dog whelks (*Nucella lapillus*), which caused the occurrence of a penis-like outgrowth behind the right tentacle in females.[79] It has since been shown that this chemical causes imposex in at least 200 species of mollusc in nanogramme per litre concentrations. In the UK, studies of 3,500 wild fish have shown that exposure of fish to sewage effluent has resulted in sexual abnormalities in 16–100% of the fish.[80] It is believed that steroidal oestrogens are primarily responsible for this effect, although the complex mixture of chemicals the fish are exposed to makes it extremely difficult to ascertain what chemicals are responsible. Studies exposing juvenile fish to effluent have shown it is possible to induce female ducts in male fish, although it has not yet been possible to induce the formation of oocytes in the testes of male fish, as is often found in wild fish.[81] Aquatic organisms with gills are uniquely vulnerable to endocrine-disrupting chemicals, as contaminants can directly enter the blood stream and go to potential target organs without first passing through the liver (as they would if ingested). However, the evidence for endocrine-disrupting effects in humans is less compelling, as this relates to the inherently complex task of ascribing a health change in humans to a single chemical exposure, especially when such compounds accumulate in fat over time and can be transmitted (via breast milk) from one generation to another.

E.45 The European Commission adopted a Communication to Council and European Parliament on a Community Strategy for Endocrine Disrupters in December 1999 and has been reporting on progress to date since then. During 2000, a candidate list of 553 man-made substances and nine synthetic/natural hormones were identified. The candidate list was divided into three separate groupings of substances depending on the level of information available, and a priority list of actions was developed in order to further evaluate these substances. The EC White Paper on chemicals envisages that the majority of endocrine-disrupting chemicals would have to undergo authorisation under the REACH system (chapter 3). The health effects of endocrine disrupters would qualify them either to be classified as carcinogenic or as toxic for reproduction and so would trigger their submission for authorisation. However, although there is research on the effect of endocrine-disrupting chemicals at the individual level, no wildlife studies are being undertaken to establish the ecological consequences of these substances. The White Paper also notes that adverse effects on the endocrine system of wildlife species have been causally linked to certain persistent organic pollutants (POPs), which will be subject to authorisation.

References

1. Defra (2002). *INF/02/25 Monitoring chemicals in the environment.* Paper prepared for the Chemicals Stakeholder Forum by Defra. Available at Defra website:
    http://www.defra.gov.uk/environment/chemicals/csf/10122002/pdf/csf-inf-02-25.pdf.
2. Defra (2002).
3. Kenny, A.J., Thomas, K., Peeler, E., Osborn, D., Waldock, M., Matthiessen, P., Shore, R., Wright, J. and Feist, S. (2002). *Assessing the potential of environmental monitoring for detecting and responding to damage caused by the use of chemicals.* Report by the Centre for Environment, Fisheries and Aquaculture Science (CEFAS) for the Royal Commission on Environmental Pollution.
4. Evidence from English Nature, March 2002.
5. Environment Agency (1998). *The State of the Environment of England and Wales: Fresh Waters.* The Stationery Office, London.
6. 10%-ile DO=80% saturation; 90%-ile BOD=2.5mg/l; 90%-ile ammonia=0.25mg N/l.
7. DO<20% saturation; BOD >15mg/l; ammonia>9.0mg N/l.
8. Kenny *et al.* (2002).
9. Environment Agency (2002). *Rivers and Estuaries – a Decade of Improvement.* Environment Agency, Bristol.

10. Moss, D., Wright, J.F., Furse, M.T. and Clarke, R.T. (1999). A comparison of alternative techniques for prediction of the fauna of running-water sites in Great Britain. *Freshwater Biology*, **41**, 167-181;
    Wright, J.F., Furse, M.T. and Armitage, P.D. (1994). Use of macroinvertebrate communities to detect environmental stress in running waters. In: Sutcliffe, D.W. (Ed.). *Water Quality and Stress Indicators in Marine and Freshwater Systems: Linking Levels of Organisation.* Freshwater Biological Association, Cumbria. Pages 15-34;
    Wright, J.F., Moss, D., Clarke, R.T. and Furse, M.T. (1997). Biological assessment of river quality using the new version of RIVPACS (RIVPACS III). In: *Freshwater Quality: Defining the Indefinable?* Eds. P.J. Boon and D.L. Howell. HMSO, Edinburgh. Pages 102-108.

11. Kenny *et al.* (2002).

12. Environment Agency (1998).

13. Environment Agency (1998).

14. Kenny *et al.* (2002).

15. Kenny *et al.* (2002).

16. Kenny *et al.* (2002).

17. See CEFAS website: http://www.cefasdirect.co.uk/monitoring/page-b3.asp.

18. Kenny *et al.* (2002).

19. Kenny *et al.* (2002);
    Wright, D.A. and Welbourn, P. (2002). Environmental Toxicology. Cambridge University Press, Cambridge;

20. Matthiessen, P. and Law, R.J. (2002). Contaminants and their effects on estuarine and coastal organisms in the United Kingdom in the late twentieth century. *Environmental Pollution*, **120**(3), 739-757.

21. See CEFAS website: http://www.cefasdirect.co.uk/monitoring/page-b3.asp.

22. Evidence from the Department of Health, January 2002;
    Kenny *et al.* (2002).
    Wright, D.A. and Welbourn, P. (2002). *Environmental Toxicology.* Cambridge University Press, Cambridge;
    Peakall, D.B. and McBee, K. (2001). Biomarkers for Contaminant Exposure and Effects in Mammals. In: *Ecotoxicology of Wild Mammals.* Eds. R.F. Shore and B.A. Rattner. John Wiley and Sons Ltd., Chichester;
    United Nations Environment Programme (UNEP)/ International Programme on Chemical Safety (IPCS) (1999). *Chemical Risk Asssessment. Training Module No. 3.* Prepared by the Edinburgh Centre for Toxicology. WHO/PCS/99.2.

23. Kenny *et al.* (2002).

24. Kenny *et al.* (2002).

25. Kenny *et al.* (2002).

26. A list of the pollutants along with concentrations measured for both the automatic and non-automatic networks are provided at http://www.airquality.co.uk.

27. Kenny *et al.* (2002).

28. Asher, J., Warren, M., Fox, R., Harding, P., Jeffcoate, G. and Jeffcoate, S. (2001). *The Millennium Atlas of Butterflies in Britain and Ireland.* Oxford University Press, Oxford; see also the Butterfly Monitoring Scheme at the Institute of Terrestrial Ecology, Monkswood website: http://bms.ceh.ac.uk.

29. Preston, C.D., Pearman, D.A. and Dines, T.D. (Eds.) (2002). *New Atlas of the British and Irish Flora.* Oxford University Press, Oxford.

30. Kenny *et al.* (2002).

31. Biological Records Centre website: http://www.brc.ac.uk/brcResearchStrategy.shtm.

32. Defra (2002);
    Kenny *et al.* (2002).

33. Kenny *et al.* (2002).

34. Broughton, R., Osborn, D., Shore, R.F., Weinburg, C.L. and Wadsworth, R.A. (2002). Identifying pollution hotspots from PCB residues in birds of prey. *Environmental Toxicology and Chemistry*, (In Press)

35. Shore, R.F., Osborn, D., Weiburg, C.L., Sparks, T.H., Broughton, R. and Wadsworth, R.A. (2002). *Potential modifications to the bird of prey monitoring scheme.* Second Report. Report No. 320. Joint Nature Conservation Committee, Peterborough.

36. Harrington, L.A. and Macdonald, D.W. (2002). *A review of the effects of pesticides on wild terrestrial mammals in Britain.* Wildlife Conservation Research Unit;
    Pepper, T. and Carter, A. (2000). *Monitoring of Pesticides in the Environment.* Report of the Pesticides in the Environment Working Group. Produced by ADAS. R&D Publication No. 69. Published by the Environment Agency.

37. Evidence from English Nature, September 2002, and from the Royal Society for the Protection of Birds, September 2002.

38. Young, J.E.B., Griffin, M.J., Alford, D.V. and Ogilvy, S.E. (Eds.) (2001). *Reducing Agrochemical Use on the Arable Farm: the TALISMAN and SCARAB Projects.* Defra, London.

39. Centre for Ecology and Hydrology website: http://www.nmw.ac.uk/ite/ite.old/edn2.html

40. Evidence from English Nature, September 2002.

41. Defra (2002);
    Decision No. 1600/2002/EC of the European Parliament and of the Council of 22 July 2002 laying down the Sixth Community Action Programme. Official Journal, L242 of 10/9/2002;
    Communication from the Commission to the Council, the European Parliament, the Economic and Social Committee and the Committee of the Regions. On the Sixth Environment Action Programme of the European Community Environment 2010: Our future, Our choice. Proposals for a decision of the European Parliament and of the Council laying down the Community Environmental Action Programme 2001-2010. Com (2001) 31 final.

42. Defra (2002).

43. Environment Agency. Managing Chemicals for a better environment. The Environment Agency's Strategy. Consultation Document. June 2002.

44. Chanin, P. and Jefferies, D. (1978). The decline of the otter *Lutra lutra L.* in Britian: an anlysis of hunting records and discussion of causes. *Biol. J. Linn. Soc.*, **10**,305-328;
    Harrington and Macdonald (2002).

45. Campbell, L., Avery, M.I., Donald, P., Evans, A.D., Green, R.E. and Wilson, J.D. (1997). *A review of the indirect effects of pesticides in birds.* JNCC Report Series No. 227. Joint Nature Conservancy Council, Peterborough.

46. Harrington and Macdonald (2002).

47. Harrington and Macdonald (2002).

48. Burn, A.J. and Carter, I. (2002). The threats to birds of prey in the UK from second-generation rodenticides. *Aspects of Applied Biology*, **67**, 203-212;
    Harrington and Macdonald (2002).

49. Ross, P.S. and Troisi, G.M. (2001). Pinnipedia. In: *Ecotoxicology of Wild Mammals*. Eds. R.F. Shore and B.A. Rattner. John Wiley and Sons Ltd., Chichester;
    Boese, B.L., Lee, H., Specht, D.T., Pelletier, J. and Randall, R. (1996). Evaluation of PCB and hexachlorobenzene biota-sediment accumulation factors based on ingested sediment in deposit feeding clams. *Environmental Toxicology and Chemistry*, **15**, 1584-1589.

50. Linder, G. and Joermann, J. (2001). Assessing hazard and risk of chemical exposures to wild mammals: Food-chain analysis and its role in ecological risk assessment. In: *Ecotoxicology of Wild Mammals*. Eds. R.F. Shore and B.A. Rattner. John Wiley and Sons Ltd., Chichester.

51. Wright and Welbourn (2002).

52. Ross and Troisi (2001).

53. Ross, P.S. (2002). The role of immunotoxic environmental contaminants in facilitating the emergence of infectious diseases in marine mammals. *Human and Ecological Risk Assessment,* **8**(2), 277-292;
    Ross and Troisi (2001).

54. Andersson, O. and Wartanian, A. (1992). Levels of polychlorinated camphenes (toxaphene), chlordane compounds and polybrominated diphenyl ethers in seals from Swedish waters. *Ambio,* **21**, 550-552;
    Olsson, M. and Bergman, A. (1995). A new persistent contaminant detected in Baltic wildlife: bis (4-chlorophenyl) sulphone. *Ambio,* **24**, 119-123;
    Ross and Troisi (2001).

55. Ringer, R.K. (2001). Summation. In: *Ecotoxicology of Wild Mammals*. Eds. R.F. Shore and B.A. Rattner. John Wiley and Sons Ltd., Chichester.

56. Harrington and Macdonald (2002).

57. Table reproduced from: European Environment Agency (2003). *Kiev Report*. See Chapter 6: Chemicals. Available on website at: http://www.unece.org/env/europe/kiev/chemicals.pdf.

58. Defra (2002).

59. Defra (2002).

60. Environment Agency (1998). *Endocrine disrupting substances in the environment: What should be done?* Environmental Issues Series;
    Royal Society (2000). *Endocrine Disrupting Chemicals (EDCs).*

61. IPCS (2002). *Global assessment of the state of the science of endocrine disruptors.* World Health Organization (WHO), Geneva.

62. Environment Agency (1998);
    Royal Society (2000).

63. Hughes, I. (2003). *Genetic and hormonal control of male fetal sex development: A brief summary.* Abstract from Endocrine Active Chemicals Meeting. Available at: http://www.acmedsci.ac.uk/20030124abstracts.htm;
    Skakkebæk, N.E. (2003). *Human male reproductive disorders that may arise during sexual differentiation.* Abstract from Endocrine Active Chemicals Meeting. Available at:
    http://www.acmedsci.ac.uk/20030124abstracts.htm.

64. Foster, P.M.D. (2003). *A critical look at the evidence for and against of the risk to human reproduction from exposure to endocrine active chemicals.* Abstract from Endocrine Active Chemicals Meeting. Available at:http://www.acmedsci.ac.uk/20030124abstracts.htm;

Foster, P.M.D., Cattley, R.C. and Mylchreest, E. (2000). Effects of di-n-butyl phthalate (DBP) on male reproductive development in the rat: implications for human risk assessment. *Food and Chemical Toxicology*, **38**(S1), S97-S99;

Foster, P.M.D., Mylchreest, E., Gaido, K.W. and Sar, M. (2001). Effects of phthalate esters on the developing reproductive tract of male rats. *Human Reproduction Update*, **7**(3), 231-235;

Gray, E.L., Ostby, J., Furr, J., Price, M., Veeramachaneni, D.N.R. and Parks, L. (2000). Perinatal exposure to the phthalates DEHP, BBP, and DINP, but not DEP, DMP or DOTP, alters sexual differentiation of the male rat. *Toxicological Sciences*, **46**, 235-246;

Mylchreest, E., Sar, M., Wallace, D.G. and Foster, P.M.D. (2002). Fetal testosterone insufficiency and abnormal proliferation of Leydig cells and gonocytes in rats exposed to di(n-butyl)phthalate. *Reproductive Toxicology*, **16**(1),19-28.

65. Sharpe, R., Rivas, A., Hallmark, N., Anderson, R., Bayne, R., McKinnell, C. and Fisher, J. (2003). *Pathways of endocrine disruption during sexual differentiation.* Abstract from Endocrine Active Chemicals Meeting. Available at: http://www.acmedsci.ac.uk/20030124abstracts.htm.

66. Sharpe, R. (2002). Endocrine disruption: separating fact from fiction. *The Endocrinologist*, **65**, 8-9.

67. Wakefield, J. (2002). Boys won't be boys. *New Scientist*, 174 (2349), 42-45.

68. Sharpe *et al.* (2003).

69. McIntyre, B.S., Barlow, N.J., Sar, M., Wallace, D.G. and Foster, P.M.D. (2002). Effects of *in utero* linuron exposure on rat Wolffian duct development. *Reproductive Toxicology*, **16**(2), 131-139.

70. National Research Council (NRC) (2002). *Hormonally Active Agents in the Environment.* National Academy Press, Washington, D.C.

71. Foster (2003);

Sharpe *et al.* (2003).

72. Wright and Welbourn (2002).

73. ECVAM (2002). *Alternative (Non-animal) Methods for Chemicals Testing: Current Status and Future Prospects.* Eds. A. Worth and M. Balls.

74. Foster (2003);

McIntyre *et al.* (2002);

National Toxicology Program (2001). *Report of the Endocrine Disruptor's Low-Dose Peer Review.* Available at National Toxicology Program website: http://ntp-server.niehs.nih.gov/htdocs/liason/LowDoseWebPage.html

75. Ashby, J. (2003). *Mixtures, low dose effects, mechanisms and the regulation of endocrine active chemicals.* Abstract from Endocrine Active Chemicals Meeting. Available at: http://www.acmedsci.ac.uk/20030124abstracts.htm;

Odum, J., Tinwell, H., Jones, K., Van Miller, J.P., Joiner, R.L., Tobin, G., Kawasaki, H., Deghenghi, R. and Ashby, J. (2001). Effect of rodent diets on the sexual development of the rat. *Toxicological Sciences*, **61**(1), 115-127;

Sharpe (2002);

Tinwell, H., Haseman, J., Lefevre, P.A., Wallis, N. and Ashby, J. (2002). Normal sexual development of two strains of rat exposed *in utero* to low doses of Bisphenol A. *Toxicological Sciences*, **68**(2), 339-348.

76. IPCS (2002).

77. BKH (2000). *Towards the establishment of a priority list of substances for further evaluation of their role in endocrine disruption – preparation of a candidate list of substances as a basis for priority setting.* BKH, The Netherlands;

Guillette Jr., L.J., Pickford, D.B., Crain, D.A., Rooney, A.A. and Percival, H.F (1996). Reduction in penis size and plasma testosterone concentrations in juvenile alligators living in a contaminated environment. *General and Comparative Endocrinology*, **101**(1), 32-42; NRC (2002);

Sumpter, J. (2003). *Sexual differentiation disorders in wildlife that arise from environmental chemicals.* Abstract from Endocrine Active Chemicals Meeting. Available at: http://www.acmedsci.ac.uk/20030124abstracts.htm

78. Fox, J.E., Starcevic, M., Kow, K.Y., Burow, M.E. and McLachlan, J.A. (2001). Endocrine disruptors and flavonoid signalling. *Nature*, **413**, 128-129.

79. Gibbs, P.E. and Bryan, G.W. (1986). Reproductive failure in populations of the dog-whelk, *Nucella lapillus*, caused by imposex induced by tributyltin from antifouling paints. *J. Marine Biological Association of the United Kingdom*, **66**, 767-77.

80. Jobling, S., Nolan, M., Tyler, C.R., Brighty, G. and Sumpter, J.P. (1998). Widespread sexual disruption in wild fish. *Environ. Sci. Technol.*, **32**, 2498-2506.

81. Nolan, M., Jobling, S., Brighty, G., Sumpter, J.P. and Tyler, C.R. (2001). A histological description of intersexuality in the roach. *Journal of Fish Biology*, **58**(1), 160-176;

Panter, G.H., Thompson, R.S. and Sumpter, J.P. (1998). Adverse reproductive effects in male fathead minnows (*Pimephales promelas*) exposed to environmentally relevant concentrations of natural oestrogens, oestradiol and oestrone. *Aquatic Toxicology*, **42**(4), 243-253;

Rodgers-Gray, T.P., Jobling, S., Morris, S., Kelly, C., Kirby, S., Janbaksh, A., Harries, J.E., Waldock, M.J., Sumpter, J.P. and Tyler, C.R. (2000). Long-term temporal changes in the estrogenic composition of treated sewage effluent and its biological effects on fish. *Environ. Sci. Technol.*, **34**, 1521-1528.

Appendix F

FURTHER INTERNATIONAL CHEMICALS PROGRAMMES

INTERGOVERNMENTAL FORUM ON CHEMICAL SAFETY (IFCS)

F.1　The Forum was established to co-ordinate national and international efforts to promote chemical safety and to oversee implementation of the programme on environmentally sound management of chemicals set out in Chapter 19 of Agenda 21, adopted by the Earth Summit in 1992. It proposed action programmes in six areas:

- the expansion and acceleration of international chemical risk assessments;

- harmonisation of chemical classification and labelling;

- information exchange on toxic chemicals and chemical risks;

- establishment of risk reduction programmes;

- strengthening of national capabilities and capacities for management of chemicals; and

- stopping illegal international traffic in toxic and dangerous products.

F.2　These programme areas are being taken forward by a range of voluntary, national and regional measures, and when necessary by international agreements.

THE INTER-ORGANIZATION PROGRAMME FOR THE SOUND MANAGEMENT OF CHEMICALS (IOMC)

F.3　This organisation was established as a co-operative undertaking among inter-governmental organisations that, within the framework of their own respective constitutional mandates, work together as partners to promote international work in the environmentally sound management of chemicals. Its mandate is co-ordination, with scientific and technical work carried out through the existing structures of the participating organisations, either individually or jointly.

THE INTERNATIONAL PROGRAMME ON CHEMICAL SAFETY (IPCS)

F.4　IPCS was established in 1980. It is a joint programme of three co-operating organisations – the International Labour Organization, the United Nations Environment Programme (UNEP), and the World Health Organization (WHO) – implementing activities related to chemical safety. IPCS is an inter-sectoral co-ordinated and scientifically-based programme; WHO is its executing agency.

F.5　The two main roles of IPCS are to establish the scientific basis for safe use of chemicals and to strengthen national capabilities and capacities for chemical safety. IPCS areas of activity include:

- evaluation of chemical risks to human health and the environment (including a major initiative on endocrine disrupters);

- methodologies for evaluation of hazards and risks;

- prevention and management of toxic exposures and chemical emergencies; and

- development of the human resources required in the above areas.

F.6   Within the first of these headings (the evaluation of chemical risks to human health and the environment), there are many relevant activities, such as on 'Risk Evaluation of Priority Chemicals'. This programme results in: Environmental Health Criteria Documents (around 230 have been prepared since 1976 on individual chemicals, groups of chemicals, forms of radiation, and biological agents); Health and Safety Guides (HSG); and Concise International Chemical Assessment Documents (40 CICADs have been published since 1998).

F.7   Under methodologies for evaluation of hazards and risks are such initiatives as: principles for methodologies; development and validation of methods; and harmonisation of approaches to risk assessment of chemical exposure (with the Organisation for Economic Co-operation and Development). The objective of this project is to harmonise generic and technical terms used in chemical hazard/risk assessment. Harmonisation of these terms will help facilitate the mutual use and acceptance of the assessment of chemicals between countries and organisations.

GLOBAL INFORMATION NETWORK ON CHEMICALS (GINC)

F.8   GINC is a worldwide information network providing access to major sources of chemical information. Through the Internet, GINC furnishes a structure for the circulation and sharing of chemical information between countries. Currently the pilot phase is being developed to cover the Asia and Pacific region.

THE GLOBAL ENVIRONMENTAL EPIDEMIOLOGY NETWORK (GEENET)

F.9   GEENET was established in 1987 as part of a WHO initiative to create networks of professionals working on the health effects of environmental hazards and human exposure, pollution control technology, and environmental management and planning. Specifically, GEENET aims to increase the national capacity of developing countries to secure environmental health by strengthening education, training and applied research in environmental epidemiology.

UNITED NATIONS ECONOMIC COMMISSION FOR EUROPE (UNECE)

F.10   The UNECE membership consists of all European countries plus the USA and Canada. Its Convention on Long-Range Transboundary Air Pollution has been the primary mechanism for international agreements to reduce acid rain and other long-range atmospheric pollutants. In 1998 two new protocols on Persistent Organic Pollutants (POPs) and Heavy Metals were agreed. These protocols contain a variety of controls on pollutants that can travel by atmospheric transport and global distillation far from their point of release. The controls range from the reporting of releases, through process control and restrictions on marketing and use, to prohibitions of manufacture. Both protocols contain provisions for adding further substances to the existing 16 persistent organic pollutants and 3 metals they cover.

Appendix G
HAZARDOUS WASTE CLASSIFICATION

H1 'Explosive': Substances and preparations which may explode under the effect of flame or which are more sensitive to shocks or friction than dinitrobenzene.

H2 'Oxidizing': Substances and preparations which exhibit highly exothermic reactions when in contact with other substances, particularly flammable substances.

H3-A 'Highly flammable': Liquid substances and preparations having a flash point below 21°C (including extremely flammable liquids), or substances and preparations which may become hot and finally catch fire in contact with air at ambient temperature without any application of energy, or solid substances and preparations which may readily catch fire after brief contact with a source of ignition and which continue to burn or to be consumed after removal of the source of ignition, or gaseous substances and preparations which are flammable in air at normal pressure, or substances and preparations which, in contact with water or damp air, evolve highly flammable gases in dangerous quantities.

H3-B 'Flammable': Liquid substances and preparations having a flash point equal to or greater than 21°C and less than or equal to 55°C.

H4 'Irritant': Non-corrosive substances and preparations which, through immediate, prolonged or repeated contact with the skin or mucous membrane, can cause inflammation.

H5 'Harmful': Substances and preparations which, if they are inhaled or ingested or if they penetrate the skin, may involve limited health risks.

H6 'Toxic': Substances and preparations (including very toxic substances and preparations) which, if they are inhaled or ingested or if they penetrate the skin, may involve serious, acute or chronic health risks and even death.

H7 'Carcinogenic': Substances and preparations which, if they are inhaled or ingested or if they penetrate the skin, may induce cancer or increase its incidence.

H8 'Corrosive': Substances and preparations that may destroy living tissue on contact.

H9 'Infectious': Substances containing viable micro-organisms or their toxins which are known or reliably believed to cause disease in man or other living organisms.

H10 'Teratogenic': Substances and preparations which, if they are inhaled or ingested or if they penetrate the skin, may induce non-hereditary congenital malformations or increase their incidence.

H11 'Mutagenic': Substances and preparations which, if they are inhaled or ingested or if they penetrate the skin, may induce hereditary genetic defects or increase their incidence.

H12: Substances and preparations that release toxic or very toxic gases in contact with water, air or an acid.

H13: Substances and preparations capable by any means, after disposal, of yielding another substance, such as a leachate, which possesses any of the characteristics listed above.

H14 'Ecotoxic': Substances and preparations that present or may present immediate or delayed risks for one or more sectors of the environment.

Attribution of the hazard properties 'irritant', 'harmful', 'toxic' (and 'very toxic'), 'carcinogenic', 'corrosive', 'teratogenic' and 'mutagenic' in the above list is made on the basis of criteria laid down in annexes of the EC Classification, Packaging and Labelling Directive (3.5).

Appendix H

GENOMICS

H.1　The term 'genomics' is used to encompass many different techniques all of which are related to the analysis of the genetic contents of the cell (both the DNA and RNA).[1]

TOXICOGENOMICS

H.2　The application of genomics to toxicology (*toxicogenomics*) could have a huge impact on our ability to characterise compounds with the potential for adverse health effects, by offering a more effective way of identifying toxic hazards, thus forming the basis for more predictive safety evaluation.[2] In addition, it will greatly improve our current understanding of toxic processes.

H.3　Toxicogenomics has concentrated on the liver, as this is the primary site for the metabolism of toxic substances; *transcription profiling* (analysis of the messenger RNA) of cultured hepatocytes has been used for toxicological testing.[3] The use of these techniques to analyse global changes in gene expression may permit the identification of diagnostic gene expression patterns (which can then be used to determine the toxic potential of agents), and of new biomarkers, and will allow enhanced extrapolation between experimental animals, humans, and human *in vitro* models in the context of hazard identification; this would enable the development of more relevant, mechanistically-based *in vitro* systems.[4] In particular, it will be necessary to establish under a defined set of experimental conditions, the characteristic pattern of gene expression elicited by a given toxicant and to compare this with data collected for known toxins acting via the same mechanisms.[5]

DNA MICRO-ARRAYS

H.4　One of the most promising approaches to the study of gene expression profiles and genome composition is the use of DNA/oligonucleotide micro-arrays, which allow the simultaneous semi-quantitative measurement of the transcriptional activity of thousands of genes in a biological sample.[6] As described in box H1, such micro-arrays are generated by immobilising labelled DNA (cDNA), polymerase chain reaction (PCR) products, or cloned DNA/oligonucleotides on a solid support. The genes represented on the array can be chosen to cover specific end-points or pathways, or may include genes that cover a wide range of biological processes. Almost without exception, gene expression changes will occur during toxicity, either as a direct or indirect result of exposure to the chemical. These changes in gene expression are often a more sensitive, characteristic and measurable (at sub-toxic doses) end-point than the toxic effect itself. As the database of 'known toxins' grows for an individual toxic mechanism, it may be possible to develop 'mini-arrays', customised for specific toxic end-point detection, based on pattern recognition.[7]

PROTEOMICS

H.5　The aim of proteomics is to quantify the expression levels of the complete protein complement (the *proteome*) in a cell or tissue at any given time. It expands the scope of biological investigation from studying single proteins to studying all proteins at once in a systematic fashion, using large-scale experimental methodologies combined with statistical analysis of the results.[8]

H.6   Unlike the genome of an organism, which is essentially fixed information underpinning the organism, the proteome is a varying feature subject to changes due to developmental stage, disease state, or exposure to toxins or environmental conditions, and is therefore closer to the biological consequences of altered gene expression. By comparing proteins expressed following exposure of a biological test system to a chemical with those present under untreated conditions, it is possible to identify changes in biochemical pathways via observed alterations in sets of proteins that may be related to the toxicity. Once a large library of proteomic signatures has been compiled for compounds whose toxicities are known, it will be possible to use the library to assess compounds whose toxicities are not known. One of the significant advantages of proteomics is the ability to analyse proteins using high throughput, automated techniques that can be applied to the analysis of tissue samples, cell cultures and also body fluids, suggesting that proteomics has great potential as a screen for new markers of toxicity and exposure.[9]

Gel electrophoresis and mass spectrometry

H.7   Advances in proteomics techniques have made it possible to characterise proteins rapidly using automated techniques. The techniques are based on two-dimensional gel electrophoresis, which combines separation of proteins by isoelectric focusing (IEF) in the first dimension, followed by gel electrophoresis based on molecular weight in the second dimension, in combination with mass spectrometry to analyse the protein. The introduction of the MALDI–TOF (Matrix-Assisted Laser-Desorption/Ionisation Time of Flight) technique has increased the speed and efficiency of using mass spectrometry to carry out protein mass finger-printing. This method involves selectively cutting the proteins with an enzyme, usually trypsin, and comparing the fragments to theoretical peptides, similarly 'digested' by the computer, from databases.[10]

Bio-informatics

H.8   The aim of *bio-informatics* is to derive knowledge from the computer analysis of biological data.[11] This interface between biological and computational sciences is a key requirement for the organisation, analysis and storage of the potentially huge quantities of data generated by the use of genomic and proteomic technologies. The data from different sources require integration so that it is possible to link gene expression with DNA sequence information, and hence detect pathways and sets of genes tightly correlated with specific toxicity end-points.[12]

H.9   These techniques include 'data mining', which aims to identify trends, patterns and probable relationships in large data sets, that would remain hidden from standard statistical analysis, via complex algorithms that derive explanatory and predictive models from the data. In relation to DNA micro-arrays, data mining could be used to identify groups of genes that are regulated in a similar way across many experiments, or groups of treatments that provoke similar transcriptional responses in many genes.[13]

BOX H1   **MICRO-ARRAYS**

Micro-arrays, or biochips, consist of tens of thousands of individual nucleic acid samples arranged in a grid on a solid surface and are used to assess the expression of multiple genes in parallel.

Consider the identification of genes that differ in expression between a normal cell and one exposed to a particular chemical. Messenger RNA (mRNA), the intermediate between genes and their proteins, is extracted from both exposed and non-exposed cells, and labelled DNA (cDNA) pools are synthesised using the enzyme DNA polymerase and different fluorescent dyes for each sample – the normal cell might be labelled green and the chemically-exposed cell red. The two samples are mixed and incubated with the micro-array. If any of the so-called 'probes' on the micro-array have counterparts in the cDNA sample, they will bind to each other (hybridise). This is then detected as a fluorescent signal excited by a laser beam at a defined location on the biochip. Because the chemically-exposed and non-exposed samples are differentially labelled, the two signals can be distinguished and compared. In this way thousands of genes can be analysed at one time. Technology currently allows up to 500,000 genes to be arrayed on a single biochip using technology from the semi-conductor industry.

The recognition of the importance of alternative spliced variants from single genes, and that mRNA expression does not always reflect the production of corresponding proteins, is leading researchers to combine gene expression and proteomics. The development of technologies to increase the throughput of protein interaction studies would aid similar approaches to study toxicology pathways. Micro-array proteomics will be the next technological advance of high-throughput molecular-based analysis. Further developments are in the direction of functional arrays that include antibody arrays, clusters of transfected cells on arrays using reverse gene transfection ('living' arrays), and human nuclear receptor arrays using yeast cells transfected with genes, such as oestrogen or thyroid receptors.

References

1. Eisenbrand, G., Pool-Zobel, B., Baker, V., Balls, M., Blaauboer, B.J., Boobis, A., Carere, A., Kevekordes, S., Lhuguenot, J-C., Pieters, R. and Kleiner, J. (2002). Methods of *in vitro* toxicology. *Food and Chemical Toxicology*, **40**, 193-236.
2. Eisenbrand *et al.* (2002).
3. Borlak, J. and Bosio, A. (2002). The Use of Toxicogenomics. In: *Crucial Issues in Inhalation Research, Mechanistic, Clinical and Epidemiologic*. 8th International Symposium organised by Fraunhofer ITA. Eds. U. Heinrich and U. Mohr. INIS Monographs. Fraunhofer IRB Verlag;
   Kramer, J.A. and Kolaja, K.L. (2002). Toxicogenomics: an opportunity to optimise drug development and safety evaluation. Expert Opin. Drug Saf., **1**, 275-286.
4. Eisenbrand *et al.* (2002).
5. Eisenbrand *et al.* (2002).
6. Eisenbrand *et al.* (2002).
   Watson, A., Mazumder, A., Stewart, M. and Balasubramanian, S. (1998). Technology for microarray analysis of gene expression. *Current Opinions in Biotechnology*, **9**, 609-614;
   Duggan, D.J., Bittner, M., Chen, Y., Meltzer, P. and Trent, J.M., (1999). Expression profiling using cDNA microarrays. *Nature Genetics*, **21**, 10-14;
   Graves, D.J. (1999). Powerful tools for genetic analysis come of age. *Trends in Biotechnology*, **17**, 127-134;
   Terrett, J., Morrison, J., Moyses C. (2001). Technology: methodologies in genomics and proteomics. *International Journal of Pharmaceutical Medicine*, **15**, 85-88.
7. Eisenbrand *et al.* (2002).
8. Nilges, M. and Linge, J.P. *Bioinfomatics – a definition*. On the Institut Pasteur Website: http://www.pasteur.fr/recherche/unites/Binfs/definition/bioinformatics_definition.pdf.

9. Eisenbrand *et al.* (2002).
10. Eisenbrand *et al.* (2002).
11. Nilges, M. and Linge, J.P.
12. Eisenbrand *et al.* (2002).
13. Eisenbrand *et al.* (2002).

Appendix I

COMPARISON OF ROYAL COMMISSION'S PROPOSALS WITH OTHER SCHEMES

I.1   Chapter 3 described the European Commission's proposals for a future chemicals policy and the REACH process at the heart of this policy reform, and introduced the position statement by the government and the devolved administrations (referred to here as the government), which set out their proposals for the operation of the REACH system. Both of these proposals have elements in common with the chemicals assessment and management programme we propose in chapter 4, but there are also some substantial differences.

I.2   Under both REACH and the Royal Commission's proposals for a chemicals assessment and management programme, strict time limits are established for the operation of procedures and decision-making. Penalties (restrictions on market access) are introduced in those cases where data are not forthcoming. We have recommended a 'no data, no market' requirement for the screening step of the assessment scheme.

I.3   The government proposes the adoption of stringent data quality checks at the registration phase of REACH and random spot-checking of data for accuracy. Where data are incomplete or inconsistent, registration will be denied. The White Paper itself proposes a system of spot checks of data and computerised screening for properties raising particular concern at the registration phase. The lack of time limits for risk assessment and management processes (with continued market access) was one of the major shortcomings of the Existing Substances Regulation, with subsequent 'paralysis by analysis' being one of the drivers for the EU chemicals policy review.

REGISTRATION

I.4   REACH would require detailed information and data sharing for registration and the submission of further data following evaluation. There is also the possibility of a pre-registration phase being implemented (to allow consortium formation), meaning that detailed data might need to be submitted at a number of separate stages of the assessment process.

I.5   The Royal Commission's proposals keep data requirements to a minimum at the initial assessment phase by making use of existing data and literature, and by not requiring the submission of use data in this initial phase.

I.6   The government proposes a 'Basic Information Requirement' approach at the registration phase, whereby a basic set of information would be required unless the registrant could justify exemptions, with the authorities retaining the right to request more data. The government also proposes that exposure information be collected at the registration phase, in the form of tonnage and categories of use (based on those identified in the existing European Technical Guidance Documents for new and existing substances legislation).

I.7   The government proposes initial computer-based screening on the basis of hazard properties and likely human and environmental exposures, unlike the Royal Commission's proposals for computer screening that would apply to all chemicals (I.8). The government's proposed screening would be carried out on the basis of the REACH base data set:

a. **For substances in the range 1-10 tonnes per year**, testing for registration purposes should be confined to *in vitro* methods only (and *Daphnia*). Toxicity testing should only be on *Daphnia*, with valid quantitative structure-activity relationships (QSARs) being used to fill any data gaps. For human health, some information on the following end-points is needed: acute toxicity, skin sensitisation, corrosivity, mutagenicity and reproductive toxicity (teratogenicity). Only two of these end-points need to be studied using animal methods.

b. **For substances in the range 10-100 tonnes per year**, additional environmental data should include information on analytical methods for environmental monitoring, pKa data for ionisable compounds, and consideration of the identity of any hydrolysis products. For human health, additional data are needed on repeated dose toxicity and on fertility. This may be obtained from one study (such as OECD Test Guideline 422, the 'Combined Repeat Dose and Reproductive/Developmental Toxicity Screening Test (Repro Tox)'), or by investigating these end-points separately. Validated *in vitro* test methods for endocrine disrupters should be introduced into the basic information package for substances over 10 tonnes (for screening purposes) as soon as they are available.

c. **For substances over 100 tonnes per year**, intelligent information gathering strategies need to be developed for both environment and human health impacts. These should concentrate on end-points of concern and be based on data already acquired and be augmented by existing non-standard information (QSARs or other techniques).

d. **Above 1,000 tonnes per year**, information may well be available from the global International Council of Chemical Associations' initiative or other testing programmes.

I.8   The scale of this degree of testing at the registration phase and differentiation on the basis of tonnage, contrasts markedly with the Royal Commission's proposals for computer (and existing data) based screening of all substances by regulatory authorities on the basis of persistence, bioaccumulation and calculated toxicity.

I.9   Use and exposure assessments have been demonstrated to be difficult (see chapter 5), and costly (Business Impact Assessment of the White Paper), and to raise confidentiality of data issues. Both the White Paper and the government response require exposure data before a chemical is considered to be 'of concern' – a traditional risk-based approach. The Royal Commission's proposed scheme minimises the collection of data considered unnecessary for the first stage of assessment, thereby also minimising the necessity for data sharing.

I.10 The outcome of the registration scheme proposed by the government results in the allocation of the substance to one of three categories: those of no immediate concern, those where accelerated risk management is necessary, and the remainder, which proceed to the next stage of risk assessment.

EVALUATION

I.11 The government proposes that the substance evaluation should proceed on the basis of risk-based rather than tonnage-based thresholds (a risk-contingent scheme). In common with the Royal Commission's scheme, the government position is that these further stages of risk assessment should be focused on collecting data about end-points of concern indicated by the initial screening assessment, rather than mandatory fixed testing schemes based on tonnage thresholds. In order to reduce animal test requirements, the government proposes that testing for mutagenicity (if indicated by positive *in vitro* data), reproductive toxicity or carcinogenicity should be carried out sequentially, since a positive response in one of these categories alone would be sufficient for authorisation of a substance to be required. The evaluation phase of the Royal Commission's scheme would encourage greater data sharing between companies, thereby reducing the number of animals required.

I.12 Under the government proposals, substances in this evaluated group may move to either accelerated risk management (extreme concern) or no immediate concern as a result of this assessment. Under the Royal Commission's proposed scheme, removal of annotation (a move to being of no immediate concern) is possible, but the extreme concern category is reserved for the highest priority substances from the initial screening.

I.13 The government proposals also introduce a further categorisation at this stage, where the substance is identified as having risks, but the authorities require no action as the risks are already adequately controlled. The Royal Commission's scheme evaluates the contribution of certain uses of a chemical at this stage. This exposure evaluation might result in the re-allocation of the substance to a different category of concern, or to being of no concern. This approach would also allow further toxicity and exposure data collection to focus on those areas of most concern, thereby conserving resources.

I.14 REACH has the limitation of leaving many existing substances on the market without any evaluation for a considerable amount of time (up to seven years after implementation). REACH also has the potential for favouring substances that have already 'been through REACH' regardless as to whether they are safe or dangerous. In the worst cases, this could lead to the cessation of the use of certain safe substances and their replacement by substances that have been though REACH but are actually more hazardous. The Royal Commission's scheme would avoid these potential difficulties by providing persistence, bioaccumulation, and (where possible) toxicity information about all substances at the initial screening phase.

AUTHORISATION

I.15 REACH does not allow for a fast-track risk management process. The White Paper acknowledges that transition periods will be needed to allow for data generation to permit the authorisation step. Under the government proposals, substances that are candidates for accelerated risk management will be subjected to targeted or comprehensive risk assessment. Substances that are candidates for authorisation (those that meet the criteria and for which a specific authorisation is sought for restricted use) will be the subject of targeted risk assessment and a socio-economic analysis. This contrasts markedly with the Royal Commission's proposals, which seek to remove from the market immediately synthetic chemicals found in elevated concentrations in biological fluids such as breast milk and tissues of humans, marine mammals or top predators.

I.16   The government supports the European Commission in recommending authorisation for persistent organic pollutants and carcinogenic, mutagenic, and reprotoxic substances, but wishes to add persistent, bioaccumulative and toxic substances, and very persistent and very bioaccumulative substances to the list of substances for authorisation. It also proposes that certain respiratory sensitisers (those identified with the R42 risk phrase under Classification, Packaging and Labelling Regulations (3.8)) are added to the list of substances subject to authorisation. Once suitable assessment criteria have been developed and agreed, they also recommended that endocrine disrupters be added to the list of substances requiring authorisation. The government position is that authorisations should be time-limited, the period of authorisation depending on the level of risk, with the possibility of review in the light of new information about the substance.

I.17   Under the Royal Commission's proposed scheme, no substances are ever considered to be completely safe. New monitoring data and new insight information may result in any substance identified in the first round of assessments as being of no immediate concern being subject at any time to a re-evaluation through the scheme identified in figure 4-I. This applies equally to those substances allocated to one of the intermediate categories of concern. This re-evaluation may occur as a result of new environmental monitoring data, but may equally take place as a result of the identification of new end-points of concern, and the availability of screening or assessment techniques to quantify them. The list of marketed chemicals will serve to identify the status of every substance on the market.

AVAILABILITY OF INFORMATION

I.18   The government foresees a situation at the end of the process where there is a publicly-accessible website (run by the European central entity) listing all manufactured or imported substances and indicating the outcome of the screening and risk assessment process. This is comparable to the Royal Commission's recommendation for a listing of all chemicals on the UK market, along with information on the outcome of the screening and evaluation processes, except that under the Commission's proposal, compilation of the list would initiate the entire assessment and management process. Under REACH, the registration data would be passed to the central entity and would not be available to the public. It is envisaged in the White Paper that Safety Data Sheets and product classification and labelling would be the principal means by which information would be conveyed.

MONITORING

I.19   The Royal Commission's scheme makes much greater use of monitoring than either the government proposals or the REACH system. Chemicals identified as being of no concern under the government proposals do not appear to be subject to any further evaluation and criteria for their possible re-entry into the assessment process and further phases of the system are not set out (except for those triggered by changes in tonnages on the market). The Royal Commission's scheme, however, makes use of monitoring and epidemiological data during risk assessment. Such use of data is not suitably considered in the White Paper.

The White Paper suggests that such data will only be used during decision-making on restrictions and authorisations.

I.20 Under the Royal Commission's scheme, monitoring data and health statistics provide the support mechanism for identifying existing chemicals that are allowed to remain on the market. Some of these substances may provoke concerns that QSARs were not able to identify. As additional new monitoring methods are developed and deployed, the new techniques will be applied to those substances that have been identified during the screening process as being of no concern.

OTHER CONSIDERATIONS

I.21 A key feature of the Royal Commission's proposals, not yet foreseen in REACH or the government's response, is the development of computational techniques and genomics towards a future enhanced understanding of the fate and effects of chemicals in organisms and on the environment. We believe that this should be integral to any future chemicals assessment and management programme.

I.22 A further critical distinction of the Royal Commission's proposals from those of the EU and the government is the systematic linking of information and assessments to instruments for driving substitution. Although both the EU and the UK government have recognised the potential for economic instruments to drive chemicals policies, neither REACH nor the government's response include explicit discussion of how these or other potential drivers of substitution might be incorporated into REACH.

Appendix J

Computational Approaches to the Safety Assessment of Pharmaceuticals

Structure and Toxicity

J.1   In the absence of direct experimental data, clues about likely toxicity for a chemical can be obtained by a variety of computational approaches.

J.2   A necessary preliminary step is to interrogate websites focused on chemical toxicity. These might include monitoring alerts on the FDA web site,[1] or reference to theNational Center for Toxicological Research (FDA), including the Endocrine Disruptor Knowledge Base Web site. But there is also fast growing interest in clever informatics techniques to search for relevant information from the literature. Such approaches are being used widely elsewhere, for example to establish databases that relate genome analyses to already researched functional data. There is a wide variety of at first sight trivial problems, many of them related to nomenclature, that make this area of informatics quite challenging. Examples of this kind of approach are SciFinder (CAS) and ChemIdPlus (TOXNET[2]), which are search engines with ability to search literature using chemical structure.

J.3   Once this information has been collected, much can be achieved by making deductions from the chemical structure using knowledge from other chemicals for which data are available; they are knowledge-based approaches. They rely on the fact that chemical reactions with biological molecules such as proteins and DNA, and chemical interactions with binding sites of receptors or active sites of enzymes, require chemical subgroups with special shape, chemical reactivity or bonding capacity. The methods seek to identify in the chemical being assessed molecular fragments or substructures that have been found in toxic molecules; these are known as toxicophores. This approach was first developed as an 'art' by experienced medicinal chemists working in the development of new medicines. It is exemplified by the Ashby-Tennant super molecule[3], shown in Figure J-I, in which many chemical fragments known to be toxic have been assembled in an hypothetical super-toxic molecule.

J.4   However, the approach has been systematised using new computational methods. Many of these methods are not quantitative but exploit expert systems or rules for predicting whether toxicophores are present in a molecule, for example DEREK (LHASA UK Ltd[4]) Such approaches can be particularly useful for detecting mutagenicity, carcinogenicity and skin sensitisation. There are many other attempts to predict toxicity based on relationship of substructures; for example, M-CASE (Charles River Laboratories[5]) can predict carcinogenicity.[6] Others are more quantitative, for example AB/Tox (Pharma Algorithms Inc[7]) predicts acute toxicity to rodents (data on > 70,000 compounds) or fish (data on 700 compounds) to first identify toxicophores in LD_{50} databases and then uses of algorithms to predict toxicity. Other approaches, such as the widely used Topkat (Accelrys[8]) use chemical descriptors to predict a wide range of toxicity endpoints, including predictions for biodegradation and toxicity to fish and daphnia. Such approaches are obviously most powerful if the compounds are similar to those in the training set.

Figure J-1

A hypothetical toxic molecule containing many chemical fragments known to be associated with toxicity[9]

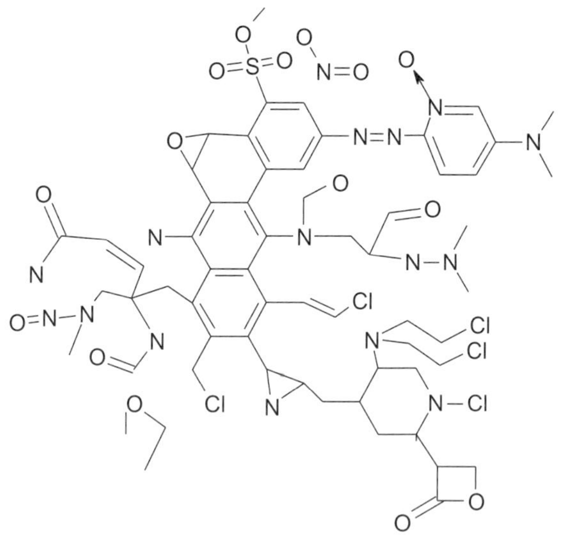

J.5   A few government organisations like the US EPA involved in assessment of chemicals have begun to use structure activity relationships and others like ECVAM are investigating and developing them, but many of the newer methods are encoded in proprietary, and sometimes expensive software developed in new information technology and biotechnology companies. Some of it has not been exploited for assessment of chemicals in the environment, but much of it has the potential to be useful.

References

1. http://www.fda.gov.
2. http://www.toxnet.nlm.nih.gov.
3. Ashby J., Tennan, R.W., Zeiger, E. and Stasiewicz, S. (1989). Classification according to chemical structure, mutagenicity to Salmonella and level of carcinogenicity of a further 42 chemicals tested for carcinogenicity by the U.S. National Toxicology Program. *Mutation Research/Genetic Toxicology*, **223**, 73-103.
4. http://www.chem.leeds.ac.uk/luk/.
5. http://www.criver.com.
6. Matthews, E.J., Contrera, J.F. (1998). A New Highly Specific Method for Predicting the Carcinogenic Potential of Pharmaceuticals in Rodents Using Enhanced *MCASEQSAR-ES* Software. *Regulatory Toxicity & Pharmacology*, **28**, 242-264.
7. http://www.ap-algorithms.
8. http://www.accelrys.com.
9. Ashby *et al.* (1989).

Appendix K
MEMBERS OF THE ROYAL COMMISSION

CHAIRMAN
Sir Tom Blundell FRS FMedSci

Sir William Dunn Professor and Head of Department of Biochemistry, University Cambridge and Professorial Fellow, Sidney Sussex College

Chief Executive, Biotechnology and Biological Sciences Research Council 1994-96

Director General, Agricultural and Food Research Council 1991-94

Member, Advisory Council on Science and Technology 1988-90

Honorary Director, Imperial Cancer Research Fund Unit in Structural Biology, Birkbeck College, University of London 1989-96

Professor of Crystallography, Birkbeck College, University of London 1976-90

MEMBERS
Professor Roland Clift OBE MA PhD FREng FIChemE Hon FCIWEM FRSA

Distinguished Professor of Environmental Technology and Director, Centre for Environmental Strategy, University of Surrey

Visiting Professor, Chalmers University of Technology, Göteborg, Sweden

Member, UK Ecolabelling Board 1992-99

Chairman, Clean Technology Management Committee, Science and Engineering Research Council 1990-94

Professor Paul Ekins

Professor of Sustainable Development, University of Westminster

Head, Environment Group, Policy Studies Institute

Associate Director, Forum for the Future

Senior Consultant, Cambridge Econometrics

Specialist Advisor, House of Commons Environmental Audit Committee

Member, Government-Industry Forum on Non-Food Uses of Crops

Member, Environmental Advisory Group, OFGEM

Trustee and Special Adviser, Right Livelihood Awards Foundation

John Flemming CBE MA FBA

Warden, Wadham College, Oxford

Chairman, Management Committee, National Institute of Economic and Social Research 1996-2002

Treasurer, British Academy 1995-2002

Chairman Finance Committee, Brunel University 1994-2002

Director, Brunner Investment Trust since 1997

Chairman, Hansard Society/Economic Policy Forum Commission on the Regulation of Privatised Utilities 1995-97

Chairman, National Academies Policy Advisory Group, Working Party on Energy and the Environment 1993-95

Chief Economist, European Bank for Reconstruction and Development 1991-93

Chief Economist, Bank of England 1980-91

Member, Advisory Board on Research Councils 1977-90

Sir Brian Follett FRS

Chair, Arts and Humanities Research Board

Professor, Department of Zoology, University of Oxford

Chair, Inquiry into Infectious Diseases of Livestock 2001-02 (for government under auspices of the Royal Society)

Chair, Review into Research Library Provision 2002-2003 (for UK universities under auspices of the Funding Councils and the British Library)

Vice-Chancellor, University of Warwick, 1993-2001

Professor of Zoology and Head of Biological Sciences, University of Bristol 1978-93

Vice-President and Biological Secretary, The Royal Society 1987-93

Dr Ian Graham-Bryce CBE DPhil FRSC FRSE

President, Scottish Association for Marine Science

Chairman, East Malling Trust for Horticultural Research

Principal and Vice-Chancellor, University of Dundee 1994-2000

Convener, Committee of Scottish Higher Education Principals 1998-2000

President, British Crop Protection Council 1998-2000

Member, Natural Environmental Research Council 1989-96

Head, Environmental Affairs Division, Shell International 1986-94

President, Association of Applied Biologists 1988-89

Director, East Malling Research Station 1979-86

President, Society of Chemical Industry 1982-84

Professor Stephen Holgate MD DSc FRCP FMedSci FRSA

Medical Research Council Clinical Professor of Immunopharmacology, University of Southampton

Member of the Polish Academy of Arts and Sciences

Honorary Consultant Physician, Southampton University Hospital and the Royal Bournemouth Hospital Trusts

Former Adviser, House of Lords Select Committee on Science and Technology

Chairman of Expert Panel on Air Quality Standards

Seat on various Department of Health Advisory Committees

Professor Brian Hoskins CBE FRS

Royal Society Research Professor 2001- and Professor of Meteorology, University of Reading

President, Royal Meteorological Society 1998-2000

President, International Association of Meteorology and Atmospheric Sciences 1991-95
Chair, Royal Society Global Environmental Research Committee

Chair, Meteorological Office Science Advisory Committee and Member of the

Meteorological Office Board

Vice-Chair, Joint Scientific Committee for the World Climate Research Programme

Member, Scientific Review Committees for Hadley Centre and European Centre for Medium Range Weather Forecasts (Chair 1985-88)

Foreign Associate, US National Academy of Sciences

Foreign Member, Chinese Academy of Sciences

Professor Richard Macrory Barrister CBE MA*

Professor of Environmental Law, University College London

Board Member, Environment Agency

Former Specialist Adviser, House of Commons Select Committee on the Environment, Transport and Regional Affairs

First Chairman, UK Environmental Law Association 1986-88

Editor-in-Chief, *Journal of Environmental Law*

Chairman, Merchant Ivory Productions Ltd

Honorary Vice-President, National Society for Clean Air and Environmental Protection

Former Chairman, Steering Committee, European Environmental Advisory Councils

Mrs Cheryl Miller CBE BA FRSA#

Chief Executive, East Sussex County Council

Member, Advisory Council to the South East England Development Agency

Junior Vice-President, Society of Local Authority Chief Executives

Past Chairman, Association of County Chief Executives

Dr Susan Owens OBE AcSS FRSA

Reader in Environment and Policy, University of Cambridge, Department of Geography, and Fellow of Newnham College

Member, Defra's Horizon Scanning Sub-Group 2003

Member, Countryside Commission 1996-99

Member, UK Round Table on Sustainable Development 1995-98

Member, Deputy Prime Minister's Panel during preparation of 1998 Transport White Paper 1997-98

Member, Foresight Agriculture, Natural Resources and Environment Panel, Office of Science and Technology 1994-96

Professor Jane Plant CBE FRSA FRSE FIMM CEng FGS

Chief Scientist, British Geological Survey (Natural Environment Research Council)

Professor, Geochemistry, Imperial College, London

Visiting Professor, University of Liverpool and University of Nottingham

Council Member, House of Commons Parliamentary and Scientific Committee

Chairman, Advisory Committee on Hazardous Substances

Member, Chemical Stakeholder Forum

President, Institute of Materials, Minerals and Mining
(formerly Institution of Mining and Metallurgy)

Councillor, International Union of Geosciences

John Speirs CBE MA MBA FRSA

President , National Society for Clean Air and Environmental Protection

Director, The Carbon Trust

Member, Management Committee of the Prince of Wales's Business and Environment Programme

Member, Advisory Committee, Kleinwort Benson Equity Partners

Managing Director, Norsk Hydro (UK) Ltd 1981-2001

Past President, the Aluminium Federation

Member, Science and Engineering Research Council 1993-1994

Member, HMG's Advisory Committee on Business and the Environment 1991-1995

Chairman, Merton, Sutton and Wandsworth Family Health Services Authority 1989-1995

Divisional Director, The National Enterprise Board 1976-1981

Professor Janet Sprent OBE DSc FRSE FRSA FLS

Honorary Research Professor, Scottish Crop Research Institute

Emeritus Professor of Plant Biology, University of Dundee

Board Member, Scottish Natural Heritage

Member SHEFC 1992-1996

Member NERC Council 1991-1995

Governor, Macaulay Land Use Research Institute 1990-2000; Chairman 1995-2000

Honorary Member, British Ecological Society

* *Professor Macrory leaves the Commission on completion of the Chemicals Study.*
\# *Mrs Miller left the Commission in April 2003.*

INDEX

Note: This index appears in word-by-word order, with terms which are defined in the text denoted by ***bold italics*** in the index.

Printed in the UK for The Stationery Office Limited
on behalf of the Controller of Her Majesty's Stationery Office
06/03, C143237
Printed on recycled paper containing 75% post consumer waste and 25% ECF